the food maze
and how it conceals the truth about real food

robert elliott

real life books

ISBN 978-0-9558425-0-4

First published 2008
The Real Life Book Company Limited,
Hoarwithy,
Herefordshire, HR2 6QP.
Telephone 01432 840353
www.reallifepublishing.co.uk

Cover design and Printed by
Orphans Press
Leominster, Herefordshire
United Kingdom
01568 612460

Printed on paper from sustainable sources

About the author

Robert Elliott is a chef and the co-owner of Aspen House, a highly acclaimed award-winning B&B, which he runs with his partner, nutritionist Sally Dean. Their ethos is centred on real food, to the exclusion of all processed alternatives. All food for themselves and for their guests is bought in season from local farmers, growers, producers and independent shops, effectively within a 10-mile radius.

Dedication

To my sons, George and Edward,
because I worry about the health of the younger generation.

ACKNOWLEDGEMENTS

As with all such projects, the list of people to whom I would like to extend my gratitude is a long one, so I have restricted it to the following:

To Sally, for inspiration, support, enthusiasm, patience, critical appraisal and good editing, as well as introducing me to the principles of good nutrition and bearing the weight of the B&B chores while I was busy writing.

To my mother, Jadwiga, for teaching me to appreciate real food, and to my brother Chris, for teaching me to think.

To my sons, George and Ed, for keeping their faith in me and treating me as a friend.

To Brian and Ella Dean (Sally's parents), for their encouragement and support when we moved to Aspen House; without that there would have been no book.

To Michael Ridley, for his positive commentary, his appreciation of my previous scribblings and for his critical appraisal of the manuscript for this book.

To Robert Dean, for welcoming me as a brother when I had no place to go and helping to give me the confidence to pick myself up and give life one more try.

To Jayne West and Corrina Norton, for helping me to understand so much more about how to keep the body healthy.

To Steve Pike, Peter Norton, Shaun Greetham, Russell Hurley, Mervyn and Virginia Morgan for their positive feedback on the manuscript.

To Linda Moss, for keeping me motivated when clouds of misgivings darkened the sunshine of my confidence.

To Walter Yellowlees, for inspirational informal chats, a lifetime of knowledge and a great deal of humanity.

To Cameron and Moira Thompson, for painting a picture of possibilities.

To Jenny Beard and Fiona Richmond, for taking me seriously.

To Robin Francis, for his open-mindedness, enthusiasm and sound accounting advice.

To Richard and Gill Fothergill, for introducing us to the works of Sally Fallon.

To all of our guests who have stayed at Aspen House and with whom we have had so many conversations about real food.

To all at Orphans Press, but especially Helen Bowden, Steve Bowgen, Ed Jeavons, Duncan Betts and Gary Nozedar – and a special thank you to Kate Bowden.

To Christine Farrell, Alison Davison, Arthur Cunynghame, Kevin Roche and Roni Jay, for their help and guidance in getting this idea to germinate and grow into a book.

"If mankind cannot devise and enforce ways of dealing with the earth, which will preserve the source of life, we must look forward to a time – remote it may be, yet clearly discernible – when our kind, having wasted its great inheritance, will fade from the earth because of the ruin it has accomplished."

Prof N S Shaler, Harvard University, 1896

"The world is not to be put in order, the world is in order. It is for us to put ourselves in unison with this order."

Henry Miller

CONTENTS

INTRODUCTION

I am not a scientist or a doctor or even a nutritionist. I do not have a PhD after my name. I am no more than an ordinary mortal trying to make sense of things in an increasingly complicated world. What I lack in paper qualifications, however, I make up for in common sense, the wisdom of experience, an insatiable curiosity and a desire for the truth.

Born into a world where food was a central theme of family life, I have seen that world change for the worse. The drive for agricultural production following the Second World War and the almost idolatrous pursuit of the concept of cheap food has precipitated consequences unimagined fifty years ago. Without a doubt, we have cheap food in abundance, but at what price? It seems to me that we are now standing on the chasm's edge, staring into the black void of failing health and social disintegration. And all for the sake of a good meal.

That might sound like a simplistic comment, but I have come to understand the damage that has been done to our food over the last fifty years, and the damage that has been done to us and our environment as a consequence. We will never be told the truth about this because too many big businesses have grown rich on supplying us with industrialised foodstuffs and the products of intensive agriculture. In addition, too many successive governments have been subjected to powerful lobbying to keep these businesses in the manner to which they have become accustomed, sustained by cheap oil, favourable trade legislation and government subsidies.

During the years of rationing after World War II, it was deemed imperative to find a way for Britain to get back to some semblance of self-sufficiency. Increased agricultural production was vitally necessary, and opportunities were there for chemical companies like ICI to suggest new ways of growing that would give us cheap food in abundance. With results that initially looked astonishing, the use of synthetic nitrogen fertilisers soon caught on. Before too long, however, it was found that other chemicals, in the form of pesticides, herbicides and fungicides had also to be used to achieve the desired results. Fifty years on, and it is now becoming increasingly apparent that the regime of chemical agriculture has in effect rendered our soils lifeless in terms of microbial activity, mineral content and nutritional value. As Lady Eve Balfour, one of the founders of the Soil Association, pointed out, if we deplete our soils and persist with intensive agriculture, we will lose the vitality of the soil. Growing crops and raising animals on such soil renders them nutritionally deficient. We end up eating both the crops and the animals, thus causing damage to our own health. She lived by the maxim, "Healthy soil, healthy plants, healthy people."

Lady Balfour co-founded the Soil Association in 1946, three years after she had published what is seen by many as the seminal work on organic farming, *The Living Soil*. She was hugely influential within limited circles, and her work is still recognised today, but not by the agri-business corporations. Organic sustainable farming is not for them because it is insufficiently profitable in the short term. So for the last fifty years or so, big business has continued to pump chemicals into the soil and over crops. Residues from these chemicals end up in the crops, the adulterated synthetic feed that is given to animals and in the animals themselves. Crops are no longer grown simply to feed the population, but grown as commodity cash crops, which are sent straight to the food factories to re-emerge as processed foodstuffs destined for the shelves of supermarkets.

Real food has all but disappeared. For every food that I enjoyed without fear or question as a child, there is now an industrialised equivalent which has taken its place. From the bread, milk and cereals we eat at breakfast to the snacks we might indulge in during the day, to the meals we prepare at home in the evening, much is now suspect. The same suspicions hang over all the global fast-food chains, and even over the plethora of cafés and other eating houses that have mushroomed in every city. Produced and processed by large scale operations, even our staples, such as wheat, dairy products, fruit, vegetables and meat cannot be trusted.

Much has been written by eminent authors over the years about the dangers of industrialising our food and the extent to which it is being carried out. Anything I say on the subject will already have been said by someone else, and probably far more eloquently. So why am I bothering to write this book? During the course of running a food-conscious B&B with my partner, Sally, we have had many conversations with our guests about the food issues that concern us, and it is blindingly obvious that there is a lot of confusion out there, despite all of the information in circulation. This book is my attempt to dispel at least some of that confusion, to guide the reader through the maze and to show how it has now grown so complex that it conceals the truth about real food. By unlocking the secrets that the maze tries to hide, a clear picture emerges of how the world really looks. Thus we are then able to see what we must do to live in harmony with it.

At this point – my own version of a TV programme warning: 'the following pages contain scenes of an anti-corporate nature that some readers might find alarming.' However, the fact is that global corporations run our world. In particular, supermarkets now control the supply and sale of around 80% of the food we eat, and it is impossible to examine the state of food today without talking about them. So, no apologies for discussing their influence on the situation. In any case, my words in this book should precipitate a reaction in those who read them, otherwise why write them? Emotional involvement in the subject of food is essential if we are to regain all that lost ground.

I am not another faddist, and I don't subscribe to this diet or that diet. I do not have any particular dietary preferences, in that I am not a vegetarian or a vegan. Each of us is entitled to make a choice when it comes to eating, and I choose to remain what I believe I was made to be – an omnivore. This literally means I will 'eat anything'. Okay, I may not have developed a taste for some things that are considered a delicacy in certain parts of China or South-East Asia, but I survive quite well on a varied diet, which includes fish, meat, fruit, vegetables and dairy products as well as grains, pulses, nuts and seeds.

By being omnivorous, the species *homo sapiens* has given itself an excellent chance of survival. We have in fact become the dominant species on this planet, and our position is unassailable. Our omnivorous diet has meant that we have been able to adapt to any conditions regarding the availability of food. Unlike the poor panda, which will eat only bamboo shoots, we are so eclectic in our eating habits that, if push came to shove, we could end up eating either the bamboo shoots or the panda, or both.

Adaptability of this order has kept us going as a species. But more than that, it has enabled us to keep going even on a diet that has been depleted of nutritional value. It says something for the tenacity of life that many people on this earth today eat nothing but low grade food, are beset with the problems that this precipitates, such as diabetes, heart disease and obesity, and yet somehow still survive. Often their quality of life is poor, and their bodily systems are being supported by medical drugs and, in some cases, more invasive treatments such as chemotherapy or surgery, but they do survive.

A medical profession that is committed to our modern drug culture will insist that people are in fact living longer today than ever before. My immediate response is, "But how are they living?" My grandfather 'lived until he died'. In other words, he lived without resorting to visits to his GP, without medication and drugs, and with all his physical and mental faculties intact. At the age of 94, his innings came to an end, and he passed away peacefully in his sleep having lived a full and meaningful life for the best part of a century.

His diet was simple but varied. He ate bread, meat, fish (when he could get it) eggs, cereals, fruit, vegetables and dairy products, including cheese. The key issue here is that what he ate for most of his life was real. Some of it he produced himself and the rest was bought from people known personally to him. He didn't indulge in fancy chocolate bars or savoury snacks made from processed cornstarch, sugar, synthetic flavourings and industrialised vegetable oil. That doesn't mean that he never ate chocolate or sweets. He did, but such things were an infrequent treat. He simply didn't feel the need for them, preferring an apple from the garden for a quick snack.

His meals were cooked from scratch using fresh ingredients. A high proportion of his diet was saturated fat, in that he loved his roast meats, butter and fatty home-cured bacon. Plus of course, my grandmother used lard and suet in her pastry cooking. She avoided margarine, believing its taste to be inferior to butter. Modern cooking oils were still virtually unheard of, and sugar was used only in cakes and jam making. My father also grew up in this tradition and, by the time I was born, cooking and eating like this was still the central pillar of the family's understanding of food and its place within the family structure.

I am part of the so-called 'baby boomer' generation and thus I went through a rebellious age when I stood in opposition to authority, disagreeing in principle with much of what was told me by my parents, my employer, the government of the day and the law of the land. But the one subject that never became contentious was food. Family meals were important. So important, in fact, that they were used as an excuse by me to air the 'issue of the day'. The dining table became our forum, and sitting around the table before, during or after a meal gave us all the opportunity to discuss whatever matters came to mind.

We discussed politics, religion, war, sex, drugs and rock 'n' roll. But never food, unless it was to pass comment on a particularly succulent leg of pork or how tasty those wild mushrooms were that we had gathered that afternoon. Food was food. It was the bedrock of life. My two grandmothers knew how to cook, and so did my mother. So food was something we enjoyed, and we looked forward to each meal, with virtually no snacking between them, having no hunger gap to fill.

Imperceptibly, however, food was changing. Industry and factory production were taking over agriculture, animal farming and horticulture. Food was being compromised, adulterated, synthesised, depleted of nutrients and tainted with toxic chemicals. All of this was happening insidiously. It was taking us unawares. With the rise of industrial food manufacturers, our choice seemed to grow, and many variations on a theme began to appear in the burgeoning convenience store. But it was illusory, almost a case of 'water, water every where, nor any drop to drink,' as our choice of nutritionally depleted factory foods grew in the wake of competition between rival manufacturers. Convenience stores mushroomed into supermarkets, and we were faced with a bewildering and deceptive choice of similar 'foods', whilst our choices of real food were suppressed.

Whilst this change was going on, I was practising a culinary tradition learned from my mother, blissfully unaware that our food was under threat. When I left home to go to university, my eating habits changed. I no longer had access to vegetables from the garden and so I began buying from shops whose owners were not known to me. At the time, this was not an issue. I was merely buying what I needed from wherever I could find it. I was still mostly cooking everything from scratch and I still loved food. So long as I was able to buy fresh meat and vegetables, I thought I was doing the right thing.

Twenty-five years after I left university, however, I began to feel unfit and unwell too much of the time. No one was able to find anything wrong with me, but I was morbidly tired, terminally listless, unable to concentrate, sleeping badly and constantly reaching for a packet of Nurofen to ease my bad headaches. Unable to obtain a convincing diagnosis from the doctor, I myself began to speculate on what might be causing me to feel so bad. My only conclusion was that I was suffering from stress. It was the mid nineties and the UK was still effectively in the grip of a recession that had virtually closed down some industries, undermined an overheated housing market and precipitated thousands of repossessions.

I had been a victim of all this, having lost my job in the building industry and then my home, with insufficient means of meeting the ever-increasing monthly mortgage payments. I was at an age when I was virtually unemployable in any meaningful career, and my marriage was breaking up. It was not difficult, therefore, to conclude that it was stress that was causing me to be Tired All The Time, to quote an expression that was being bandied about during those years.

Not for a minute did I think that it was my eating habits that were causing any of this. Why should it? I was still cooking from scratch, using fresh vegetables, fruit and meat, so how could that be a problem? In common with most people I knew at the time, I was living in a town dominated by supermarkets, and I was too busy to think about the fact that most of the little independent shops had vanished. So, just like everyone else, I would happily trawl through the aisles of my local supermarket and take home the bounty in plastic bags. Because most of what I was buying was fresh produce, I almost felt smug. I certainly experienced a glow of satisfaction that I was still cooking from scratch whilst others were buying into the ready meal revolution. Little did I know that my fresh produce was itself nutritionally depleted and contaminated with toxic residues.

By the time I woke up to this reality, I was being tested for food intolerances, as my level of listlessness and lethargy had become a matter of some concern. The tests showed that I was intolerant to wheat, dairy products, sugar, coffee and a few other lesser items on my normal shopping list, such as lettuce, oranges and mushrooms. Whilst the last three left me slightly baffled, it came as no surprise that I had become intolerant to wheat and dairy products. There was, at the time, increasing mention of this phenomenon in the media, so I felt that I was merely the victim of something that was affecting many others, much like 'flu or the common cold. I asked no questions as to why this might be, I just went along with what I was being told and avoided certain things as best as I could.

The symptoms receded, and I thought I was getting better, but then some of the symptoms would return and I would have to be tested again. Gradually it became clear that my intolerance was not simply to specific foods, but to foods that had undergone some sort of processing. The first clue to this was the discovery that, whilst being given the OK to eat peanuts, I was found to be intolerant to peanut butter. I had also replaced dairy butter with Pure spread, on the grounds that it was 'dairy free', but had never been tested on it. The peanut butter incident prompted me to ask to be tested on the Pure spread. I was diagnosed as intolerant to it. Testing was subsequently carried out on a number of other products where a combination of ingredients was being used, notably the inclusion of 'vegetable oil' and certain common additives (stabilisers, emulsifiers, etc). I showed intolerance to all of them.

It was becoming increasingly difficult to avoid the conclusion that it was 'processed' food that was upsetting me, rather than simply the main culprits such as wheat and dairy products. This theory was examined one day when I was tested against two different types of milk. On the one hand, we had organic semi-skimmed milk from a supermarket, and on the other, unpasteurised raw milk from a Jersey cow. The result was spectacular – intolerant to the organic semi-skimmed but invigorated by the raw milk.

From then on, I deliberately set out to eliminate anything processed from my diet. As I progressed towards this goal, I became stronger. My listlessness and lethargy fell away. I was no longer tired all the time. My diet went through a transformation as I avoided anything that I was not 100% confident about in terms of ingredients or provenance. Out went all the proprietary brand names whose products were mass produced in giant factories. In came home-made alternatives. Out went processed sunflower oil and in came cold-pressed extra virgin olive oil. All processed 'margarine' spreads, such as Olivio, Pure and Flora were banned forever. In their place I used either olive oil, coconut oil or organic farmhouse butter.

Today, I eat much as my grandparents would have eaten, because it appears that in order to eat real food we have to undergo this kind of culinary reversion to get back to a time before our food was industrialised. The problem with industrialising food is that the nutrition is killed off. Even simple processing will do this up to a point. For instance, peeling and then boiling carrots will deplete the nutritional value by an alarming amount. In the food factories, the equivalent of peeling and boiling might happen as a preliminary process and then the vegetables might be subjected to further processing before they become part of a ready meal or a soup. Chemicals, such as stabilisers, emulsifiers, preservatives or other additives in the form of flavour enhancers or colours may then be added to the 'brew' before it finally comes off the end of the production line ready for packaging and distribution. And all of this on top of the fact that mass-produced basic ingredients such as cereals, vegetables, fruit and meat are already tainted at source by chemicals of one description or another. Is it any wonder that we have a problem with industrialised food?

To me, as an ordinary mortal who loves his food, it seems clear that the products of factory farming, agri-business and the high-volume food industry are nutritionally worthless. Further, it is also clear, to me at least, that those who attempt to survive on these kinds of foodstuffs will ultimately fall into ill-health. I have already visited that dark place where health is failing and there is no obvious diagnosis to be made, but by moving away from processed foods and eating real food instead, I have made a complete recovery.

Though overweight by around 25% when I was at my lowest ebb, that weight fell off as soon as I began eating real food again. It has stayed off now for the last seven years, stabilising around the weight I was when I was 20. I no longer need to check if I am overweight – my clothes tell me that my weight hardly varies. Yet I eat what I like. This does not mean that I binge on snacks or pig out on huge helpings at every meal. By eating real food packed with nutrition, I eat when I am hungry. Generally, this means three meals a day. I really enjoy my breakfast, something light in the middle of the day and then something more substantial in the evening. Between these meals, I have no hunger pangs or cravings for sugary snacks.

I am fit and well. My blood pressure, pulse rate and all the other basic indicators of health are normal (actually, they are more akin to someone half my age). I have no need to visit my GP and even less need of anything that he might normally prescribe to anyone else of my age. Call it anecdotal, but I am absolutely positive that this is the result of eliminating processed food from my diet and making sure that what I eat is fresh, locally sourced and seasonal, that it is produced by people who practise the principles of organic growing and caring husbandry and that contamination of my food by toxic chemicals is kept to a minimum. In other words, I make sure I eat real food.

There are those who think that I have compromised myself in some way by shunning the supermarket, paying more for basics like bread and milk and spending more time looking for the right food. The way I see it, however, is that I have liberated myself, and gained an understanding of how I fit into the natural order of things. Though it may seem as if I pay more for my food, my overall shopping bill has been much reduced. On top of that, I am back in charge of what I eat, and what I eat has been produced without exploitation of natural resources. The benefits of feeling in prime condition far outweigh any perceived benefits of cutting my shopping bill to the minimum (a myth, as I say) and filling my fridge with alien foods.

On top of everything, there is a massive pay-off. Shopping in this way is helping to support sustainable farming systems that represent the only viable option we have in redressing the devastating ecological imbalance caused by Man's interference in natural rhythms. Simplistic as it sounds, growing and eating real food will go a long way to saving our planet, and the most exciting thing of all is that each one of us can make a contribution and each one of us can start today.

As for the other criticisms of this philosophy, the time issue is one that many people cite. To me, it is a question of priorities, but I certainly cannot impose my own priorities on anyone else. It is up to each of us to search our souls and decide what is most important to us. Speaking personally, I find that taking the time to buy my food from a number of sources rather than just one has turned out to be far more rewarding and far less onerous than I had imagined. Just for example, it has put me in touch with real people who care about what they do. I hope that what I have written in the following chapters will help you to understand why our food choices are so important, not just for our own health but for the health of the planet. I also hope to dispel any myths and fears about shopping in a way that is no longer the norm, and show you that the necessary changes can be made, whether you live in the heart of the country or indeed in the centre of a city. There is no reason to suppose that, if one lives in a city, the sourcing of real food becomes aspirational rather than practical. It is easier than you think.

What I have set out in these pages is not the whole case for real food. Others before me, erudite, academic and highly intellectual, have done this most effectively. However, although it may not be within my capacity to act as principal counsel for the defence, this book represents my own personal eye witness account. I believe that my testimony contributes to making this an unassailable case for the consumption of real food.

By returning to the values of good nutrition, not only do we improve our own health but also we revitalise our ailing soils and thereby make a serious contribution to the recovery of a planet damaged by exploitation. Though such a change in our attitude to food may seem nothing more than a personal choice, it is far more than that. In a world that runs its economy on the availability of cheap oil, much of what we have come to see as our secure and affluent way of life will shudder to a halt as oil production declines and the price goes up. On 9th September 2000, we had a glimpse of what could be in store for us, when a group of protesting lorry drivers set up a road block at Shell's petrol refinery near Ellesmere Port in Cheshire. Within days, supermarkets were running out of food and chaos threatened.

The blockade was not just about the actions of a few maverick lorry drivers complaining about the price of fuel. Such incidents act as a barometer of our oil-dependent society, and we should always heed the barometer, for it warns us of impending storms. We need to change what we do very quickly in order to prepare for the very different kind of society that will evolve once oil becomes prohibitively expensive. This may seem like an enormous and insurmountable problem, but the key to the solution is to change the way we eat. By moving away from the globalised, supermarket-driven, processed food economy and seeking real food, produced locally, organically and in season, we give ourselves a chance.

In retrieving responsibility for the sourcing of our own food, we become more aware of our relationship with the earth, what we have been doing to it and how we can put ourselves back in tune with it. A return to real food is a return to the fundamental principles of natural balance. It is essential to our ultimate survival. But first of all, we need to be able to find our way through the food maze and discover the truth about real food. Once we see the truth, the maze will hold no power over us, and we can take our first steps towards living in symbiotic harmony with this Garden of Eden that is our only home.

part one

LOST IN THE MAZE

An observation on industrialised food,
the confusion surrounding it,
and the loss of real food

FIRST IMPRESSIONS

When I was in my teens, my father bought a house in the country. Born and brought up in the Forest of Dean, the son of a farmer, he had decided that farming was not for him, thus breaking a family tradition that went back to at least the middle of the sixteenth century. Laudable as such dedication to agriculture might appear, my forebears were no more than small-time tenant farmers. They made a living, but no money. My father needed something different, so he enrolled at the Dean School of Forestry, hoping that this would open new doors.

It did. He found himself working in the primeval forests of Uganda. The outdoor life he was born to came with this job. He thrived, but he was on a limited contract. Retiring at 45 on an index-linked pension, he came back to England with the responsibility of a wife and two young sons. Through interminable job searches (even then, no one wanted to employ anyone over 45) he eventually located a good position with the old Midlands Electricity Board, working as a line surveyor and wayleave officer. Again, it was the perfect job. He was outside most of the time and spending a good proportion of his working day chatting to farmers on whose land the MEB wanted to erect electricity poles and, in some cases, pylons. He would sip tea with them and, occasionally, he would help them to do a comparative taste test of selected single malt whiskies.

Aware of the need to be close to his work and schools for his sons, the first house my father bought in England was in Worcester. 'The last house in the city' he called it, in acknowledgement of its position at the end of a street of typical 1930s properties that ended abruptly at the top of a hill. Beyond our house were open fields and grazing animals and, for my father, this was the perfect compromise between accessibility to amenities and the need to live in the country.

Once this purchase had been made, it gave my grandparents the opportunity to retire from farming and come to live with us. Grandpa was nearly 90 when this decision was taken, demonstrating quite clearly how farming was a way of life rather than a mere job. Sadly, for so many farmers today, this is no longer the case. Losing that sense of belonging to the land that my grandfather had, too many farmers in this new century are just 'doing a job' that involves no more than growing cash crops for the food industry. In so many places, the soul has gone out of farming, crushed by the boot of profiteering, a subject which we will look at more closely in the ensuing chapters.

Though our house in Worcester overlooked farmland, it hardly compared with the spirit of the old homestead set high on the hill overlooking the 'big bend' in the River Severn at Newnham. With panoramic views across eastern Gloucestershire and the Bristol Channel sweeping away to the south, the old farmhouse stood like a sentinel over lands unchanged for hundreds of years. There were still fields up there that showed the undulating evidence of the old feudal strip farming system.

Man and boy, my grandfather had lived the life of a 19th century farmer. He was as close to nature as the birds and animals that shared the land with him. Moving to Worcester, albeit to the last house in the city, unsettled him on a number of levels. Ever cheerful, he made the best of everything, so he never said anything to anyone about his feeling of estrangement, but his joy was unmistakable when my father decided to move to the country.

My grandparents had always looked like fish out of water in this suburban situation. Shortly after the move to Worcester and the celebration of their golden wedding anniversary in the same year, Granny fell victim to senile dementia and it became impossible for my mother to give her the professional care she needed. A reluctant decision was taken to move her to a place where 24-hour qualified care was available. Grandpa was thus left with nothing but his old collie, Bosun, to remind him of his life as a farmer and a countryman.

If he missed the natural life he had left for a concrete pavement and street lights, he never said so. Neither did he say anything when he saw the neighbouring fields being besieged by bulldozers one day. Within the week, there was noise, bustle and site traffic everywhere. Fences and hedges were uprooted and the topsoil was stripped. Another farm had been lost as the farmer, fighting against a new system that was curtailing his ability to make a living, sold his soul to the devil of development.

Almost like mushrooms coming up overnight, houses appeared where there used to be fields. Trotshill Farm had turned into Warndon Estate, with Lake District street names like Windermere Drive, Coniston Close and Ambleside Drive. The decision to move was taken without too much hesitation.

A suitable place was found in the quaintly named village of Drakes Broughton. Though situated on the main road through the village, this new house was surrounded by market garden land. For my father, this and the fact that we were in Green Belt territory, was what most influenced his decision. Whilst still needing to be close to his work and our schools, he wanted to get back to the land, and a quarter of an acre of prime ground, nowhere near any other buildings, was just what he was looking for. The fact that this plot was a ploughed field deterred him not a jot. When we had come to view the house, it had been surrounded by a strip of very tired lawn supporting several gnarled plum trees that were well past their best. The owner, possibly ashamed by this obvious neglect, decided he should smarten the place up in case we changed our minds, so he ploughed up everything except the plum trees and a square of grass by the back door.

My father always rose to a challenge. After all, he had been a forester in Uganda and had literally been in places where 'no white man has been before'. Before that, he had been a gunner in the Royal

Artillery, as well as a PT and unarmed combat instructor. My father, to my teenage eyes, was the original superhero. As far as I was concerned, nothing was beyond him. And he didn't let me down, setting out the basic plan for his garden meticulously, working out from the house one section at a time. The transformation took place remarkably quickly.

Sticking to the first principle of land surveying, 'Always work from the whole to the part', my father sorted out the boundary to the property, deciding where he was going to put a quick-growing coniferous hedge and where it might be more appropriate to have native species like beech and hawthorn. From there, he roughly marked out flower beds, lawns and a vegetable plot.

With wisdom handed down from Grandpa, who was there every day to guide the hand that dug and hoed, reinforced by his former need to organise frequent safaris into the Ugandan bush and the food supplies that went with that, the first thing my father did was to mark out and dig the vegetable plot. Indeed, back in the early sixties, it would have been the first thing that anyone would have done in his situation. In England at that time, growing and eating your own vegetables was seen to be, not just normal behaviour, but infinitely preferable to buying vegetables from the greengrocer. Not that any of us had anything against greengrocers. We bought vegetables from the greengrocer, but only if and when home-grown supplies were exhausted. But nothing tasted as good as vegetables harvested from the garden and served up at table an hour later.

Surrounded as we were by prime horticultural land, the soil in our garden was black, crumbly and highly fertile. My father, whom my brother and I in our increasing admiration and affection for him, had christened Pop, after a character in the Beezer comic, soon had this soil weed-free and broken down to a fine tilth. Neatly set out rows, bearing short hazel wand markers at each end, began to appear each evening as he worked in the garden after coming home from work. He seemed to labour unceasingly, and always under the watchful eye of Grandpa, whose own garden back at the old farmhouse had been so productive that Granny rarely found herself looking for vegetables in Newnham.

For me, something magical was going on. Living out in the countryside, I found that I was able to exercise my own choice as to how I occupied my time. So I could live the slow life in the country or I could dabble in the fast life of the city, where most of my school friends lived. From this rural retreat, I was able to view from a distance the frenetic mayhem that followed the explosion onto the music scene of the likes of The Beatles, The Rolling Stones and The Who. I discovered that it was possible to be part of this new teen scene whilst still observing it from afar, or at least backing off when I felt threatened by it.

Thus, while my friends in Worcester became almost trapped into becoming those dedicated followers of fashion during the first awakenings of what has since become full-blown consumerism, I was able to choose which parts of this revolution I was prepared to support. If there was a party going on and I felt like going to it, then arrangements would be made. Otherwise, I was quite content to stay at home and help Pop, although it must be said that my help often consisted of mentally urging him on whilst charging around the garden with my younger brother.

In less boisterous moments, I could be found in the kitchen, helping my Mum with the cooking. Or even doing the cooking for her, so that she could go out into the garden and get some sun. My interest in food meant an interest in the kitchen garden too. Although Pop was doing most of the work, I did learn to appreciate something of what it takes to keep a vegetable plot seasonally productive throughout the year. What really hit the spot, however, was the introduction of chickens.

Grandpa had kept chickens. He also had ducks and a duck pond, a horse, a couple of collies and a few pigs, the number of the latter depending on how many piglets or weaners were running around at any given time. Eggs from the hens appeared at the breakfast table or went into Granny's egg custard tarts. It was no surprise, therefore, that my father also kept chickens in Uganda. Our brief sojourn in Worcester saw us buying our eggs from the grocer or the butcher, but once Pop had got to grips with the layout of his new country garden, he decided there was room to simply fence off an area for the chickens, thus keeping them off his nascent flower borders.

My brother, Chris, and I were taken into his confidence and told that keeping chickens would have to be a joint effort. I was keen, and my youger brother, recently seduced by the whole romantic notion of an idyllic life in the country, was more than happy to offer his services. So a henhouse was acquired, the area was cordoned off with a wooden framework covered in chicken wire and some young pullets were bought from a farmer in the next village.

The first eggs were small, but with yolks of unbelievable colour. Though I had always eaten eggs and enjoyed them, there was something deeply significant and almost mystical about this first batch. Carrying them triumphantly from the nest box to the kitchen, my brother's excitement was palpable. There were only four eggs, so we decided we should have them boiled for tea, one each and two for Pop. As we started to tap at the shells with our teaspoons as a preamble to peeling them, Pop gently pointed out that, with eggs this fresh, it was easier to cut a slice off the top. Slicing into mine, I just cut the top of the yolk, which glowed a deep seductive orange in a white disc that looked crumbly rather than shiny.

Chris and I dipped our toasted bread soldiers into the middle. What came out was thick and unctuous, almost like orange honey. It clung to the end of the bread fingers on the way to hungry mouths and it tasted like heaven. It was a defining moment in my understanding of food. This bounty of nature, reluctantly given up by our young hens, tasted to me like a rare delicacy. Though still a teenager (and given that teenagers at the time were getting some pretty bad press for their lack of sense and sensitivity) I felt gratitude to our hens for laying such wondrous eggs.

Before long, fourteen eggs a day were being liberated from the henhouse. We were treating the hens as pets and pampering them with all sorts of goodies – potato peelings, cabbage leaves, turnips, bacon rinds. You name it, they ate it. And the eggs they laid were consistently the best I had ever tasted, even to this day. Around six eggs a day were being consumed by Pop, Chris and me at breakfast time My mother, in the true spirit of her Polish motherland, used quite a few of the eggs in salad dishes or in making rich baked cheesecakes, using fresh curd cheese and sour cream that she bought from the Polish deli in Worcester. Beyond this quantity, any surplus eggs were consumed by me and my brother almost surreptitiously. If our hens had given them up to us, we felt that the least we could do was to eat them. Eventually of course, when the daily quantity moved towards two dozen, and we were about pigged out on boiled eggs, fried eggs, scrambled eggs, egg salads, eggs in cheese sauce and Mum's cheesecake, our friends became grateful recipients of the surplus of this glorious bounty, and never an egg was wasted.

Our house in the country opened my mind. Until then, I was quite happy to eat food that appeared on the table in front of me, but I had no relationship with it, no understanding of how it came to be there. Even with a burgeoning interest in cooking, that clarity of comprehension regarding the source of the ingredients that were being prepared was not there. By collecting eggs from the nest boxes and becoming involved in the sowing and harvesting of vegetables, I developed a respect for food. Prior to our arrival at this house in the country, though I had known something of the time it took to prepare Sunday lunch for the family, I had a limited appreciation of the effort involved in producing the vegetables that accompanied the roast. Pop's efforts in the garden changed all that. At the same time I began to understand something about the roast itself.

One of my school friends, Tony, was the son of a village butcher. Weekend and holiday visits to his house opened my eyes to the life of a butcher, and I came to see Tony's jovial father as a gentle protector of animals rather than a hacker of meat. He would buy animals from market at least a few days before he needed them, and in the interim they would quietly graze in the field behind his shop until their time was up, when they were dispatched quickly, cleanly and without trauma. Tony's father was highly skilled in his transformation of carcases into attractive joints of meat. Again, nothing was wasted. All the meat found its way through the shop into the kitchens of his customers. Anything he couldn't use, such as skins and hooves, could be used by others, such as the tanneries and glue factories in Worcester.

By the time I went to university, the foundations to my understanding of food production had been laid, and onto them had been built an appreciation of what food really is. After the vegetables from our garden and the eggs from our chickens, I found it hard to subsist in a city. I longed for the weekends when I could go home for some real food.

But I survived and, as the years rolled on, I got married, had two sons and notched up four career changes and five house moves before I decided I was in the wrong life. As the clock ticked away the final hours of the 20th Century, I was, without knowing it at that time, looking at a new life where food would become my central focus. All the things that I had learned from my father and grandfather would help me to focus on what real food is and to understand how, in a few generations, it has been surreptitiously removed from our dining tables and replaced with inferior imitations.

CULTURE SHOCK

Fast forward to the present, and I have a new life. For the last five years or so I have been living with Sally, the person I was always destined to meet. We live in what used to be the main homestead of a traditional mixed farm. It was sold because the next generation could see no way of making a living from the land. We love the house, but we are aware of its three-hundred year history as a farmhouse and the fact that it has long since ceased to function in that capacity. Today, the rural economy is losing its farmhouses at an alarming rate, sold off for redevelopment as more and more farmers go to the wall. This is one more symptom of the malaise that grips our society today.

At the risk of sounding crass, Sally and I appear to be soul mates or, at the very least, two people who seem to tick in the same rhythm. This old house, built in 1726 out of the local red sandstone, has become the symbolic heart of our philosophy on food. We run it as a B&B where the emphasis is on real food, and we pride ourselves on being able to quote the provenance of the fresh produce we use, while the more exotic ingredients, such as tea, coffee, spices, nuts, beans, pulses and the like we buy as far as possible under organic and fair-trade labels from independent shops we trust.

It is a Sunday morning, a bright spring day and we are cooking breakfast for our guests on the last morning of their stay. Separating four rashers of home-cured bacon from the pack, I place them in the grill pan and slip it under the grill. The bacon is from diminutive black Berkshire pigs, lovingly reared by the famous Mr Tudge (Gordon, to those who wish to command his attention) on the natural pasture of his farm in north Herefordshire. The rashers are small and the meat is rather dark, in contrast to the pale pink pork products in plastic packs generally found elsewhere.

The bacon begins to sizzle alongside the sausages already browned on one side. The sausages too are from Mr Tudge. They contain no additives, no cheap preservatives and no industrial rusk – just meat, breadcrumbs and a little curing salt. It is all you need in a good breakfast sausage. That, and the knowledge that the man that sold it would never cheat you.

Bacon like this has all the smell and taste of a time that for many is fast becoming a nostalgia trip. But not here in our kitchen, the engine room of our business. This place, just a few miles up river from Ross-on-Wye, is our sanctuary. Here we celebrate real food and share that celebration with those who come to stay. Our philosophy is not just to guarantee the provenance of all our ingredients, but to ensure that all the food we serve is bursting with vitality. It must be the freshest, most nutritious food we can find. This morning, Mr Tudge's bacon and sausage will be served with orange-yolked eggs laid in pale olive shells by Cream Legbar hens from our poultry-mad friend just down the road.

Our eggs are not branded with a silly little lion stamp. We have no use for specious guarantees of this kind. If certain government departments feel that they must stamp eggs with a symbol of authority, then we feel there must be something to hide. For us, it is more important to know the person who keeps the hens. We see how the hens roam free all day long, scratching for grubs around the yard and amongst the grassy tussocks under the farmyard wall. These hens do what hens were born to do in a completely natural and unhindered way. Though there are those that would argue against me, I can tell you that eggs from hens like these are full of flavour, bright in colour and firm in texture. Putting food like this on a plate requires nothing more than a basic command of culinary skills and an appreciation of how real food should taste. After that, the ingredients speak for themselves. Using the best ingredients we can find makes life simple and satisfying, turning what is so often derogatorily called a fry-up into a meal to savour.

As ever, the plates come back empty from the dining room – practically licked clean. Our guests are now toasting some of Sally's home made bread in anticipation of spreading it with organic farmhouse butter and our home-made marmalades and preserves. Not everyone toasts the bread. Some prefer to have it as it is, saying that nothing beats the flavour of real bread. We agree.

A buzz of conversation generally fills the dining room as guests quiz Sally on the arcane art of making a jam that actually tastes of fruit or the techniques used in baking the perfect loaf. She is happy to oblige and tells them all about sourcing fruit directly from orchards and hedgerows and avoiding the use of white refined sugar. She talks about the organic flour from Bacheldre Watermill, ground slowly between stones in the traditional way, and the organic butter made on a local farm using the milk of pasture-fed cows.

Unfortunately, we cannot speak directly to the people who pick coffee beans or tea leaves (although there is now a commercial tea plantation at Tregothnan in Cornwall) but organic and Fair Trade is the next best thing. For those who prefer to have milk in their tea, the milk we serve comes from one of two small herds, either from a Jersey herd grazing the rich green pastureland of Grosmont, near Abergavenny or, for the true taste of real unpasteurised milk, from a herd in the Forest of Dean. Luckily, neither of them is too far from us. It should stand as a matter of national disgrace that the availability of unpasteurised milk is now limited to a tiny handful of accredited herds in England and Wales – there are none at all in Scotland, as far as we know – but we are grateful that we have access to this one. There were, until relatively recently, two herds in Herefordshire, but both farmers have now pulled out of dairy farming. A sad loss.

Though our guests this morning have taken the relaxed approach to breakfast and have allowed themselves enough time to savour the flavours on offer, before long our dining room duties are over and we can sit down to our own breakfast. This being Sunday, it is the one day of the week that we allow ourselves to slip into the idea of a gentle start to the day by indulging in a cooked breakfast ourselves. We are generally too busy for such self-indulgence but, we tell ourselves, we have to sample Mr Tudge's bacon and sausage once in a while just to make sure the standard remains high.

On this particular Sunday, we are heading off for a few days. A gap in the diary has left us with an opportunity to visit some people in Perthshire in Scotland whose observations on health and nutrition appear to dovetail neatly with our own philosophy on real food. Although it is Sunday, we expect the traffic to be heavy and anticipate a long drive to our first scheduled stop, so a good breakfast is what we need before we go. Everything for the journey has been packed, so we can afford to be leisurely.

As I cut into the bright runny yolk of one of my eggs and dip a small slice of sausage into it, I know that it does not get better than this. Breakfast, like any other meal, is foolproof if you use the best ingredients, by which I do not mean the most expensive. Just the best. This is simple fare, but it is the very simplicity that hits the spot. The look of this food, the aroma that drifts from the plate, the colour of the egg yolks and the sheer pleasure of these tastes in your mouth bring a sensuousness to the meal that is almost erotic. Like the elusive pleasure of real sex, this feels indulgent, almost naughty. How such a plate of food ever came to be reduced to the status of 'fry-up' says so much about how the importance of food has slipped down the charts from its rightful Number One slot. It also says so much more about how our misunderstanding of food has allowed this to happen. It is just a simple meal, our Sunday breakfast. Given the right ingredients, however, and someone to whom cooking is a pleasure, this simple meal becomes a symphony of taste, a sublime experience.

As we mop up the last morsels on our plates, my thoughts turn to all the children who are growing up in this new world of ours, youngsters who know nothing of cooking and, by definition, nothing of food. To them, food comes in the shape of a frozen pizza or a black plastic tray of something gloopy with a computer-enhanced photo on the packaging that tries to depict the contents as appetising. Beyond this, so many young people have simply become habitual grazers, snacking on cheap chocolate and crisps doused in chemical flavourings. It is so sad. Lost boys and girls, beguiled by high pressure advertising into a predilection for nutritionally empty 'foodstuffs'.

Already we are a couple of generations away from a time when sweets were a weekly treat, bought with pocket money that was no more than a few coins. A far cry from the 14-stone 8-year old recently featured in one of TV's shock-horror documentaries. She was spending all of her £10 a week pocket money on huge bars of Galaxy chocolate.

Alarming as this is, the interview with the girl's mother was downright terrifying. Perfectly illustrated in this interview was the fact that the mother lacked basic food knowledge and possessed no more than a rudimentary grasp of kitchen skills. Her generation would have been subjected to trendy new school curricula that would have dismissed the usefulness of Domestic Science in favour of the far more exciting Food Technology. According to the school gurus that set up these changes, learning to cook is far less useful than learning about different types of plastic packaging. Who wants cooks anyway? Industry wants people who understand what's going down the conveyor belts of food processing plants.

These thoughts are with us as we do a last minute check and make sure that everything we need is in the car. Sally has offered to take the first stint at the wheel, so I assume the role of navigator, not that I am called upon to use those particular skills to get us onto the country's main arterial road system – the southern end of the M50 is only five miles away. Normally, we would shun the motorway in favour of a leisurely cruise along the quieter roads, but having to look after our guests this morning has meant a midday start. Aberfeldy is our destination, and we intend to get as far as Stirling for a stopover, so time is a consideration. Relying on the fact that the volume of traffic should be sufficiently low on a Sunday to get us past Birmingham in good time, we have opted for the motorway this time. There will be plenty of time for the slow road once we get past Stirling.

Leaving the lane that takes us from our house towards Ross, we join the A40 at the roundabout. We wait there while two trucks, one from Asda and one from Tesco, go by. Sunday morning, and you still cannot get away from them. Life today has no breaks, and one day is like any other. With all supermarkets open seven days a week, and many of the bigger stores also open 24 hours a day, life for some of their customers has become little more than a non-stop shopping opportunity, serviced by an endless procession of large trucks.

The dominance of supermarkets in food retailing has come about partly because they were able to push for longer opening times. The small independent greengrocer cannot consider longer hours. To start with, he has a life beyond his shop, so a normal working day plus at least one day a week off is what he needs. Supermarkets are different. They can employ people to work in their stores any time of day or night. Just one of the many advantages that these giants have over ordinary shopkeepers. So here we are today, waiting for two supermarket delivery lorries to go by before we can join the road. According to the Institute of Science in Society, in a report in September 2005, food transport accounted for an estimated 30 billion vehicle kilometres back in 2002, since which time it has grown by a significant proportion. This does not include the number of other vehicles involved in the transportation of ancillary food industry products, such as packaging, boxes and other containers. Altogether, keeping the supermarkets in business accounts for one-third of all the freight on our roads which, amongst all the other considerations, impinges significantly on our total energy costs.

Today, as we pull onto the M50, I am thoughtful. My mind is playing with the reality that such a high proportion of the 40-tonners are ferrying food up and down the motorways, from producers, growers and 'food factories' to central distribution depots and then out again to all points of the compass, in many cases back to the areas they came from. There was a time, not so very long ago, when this did not happen, a time when goods carried by long distance hauliers were generally factory goods. Fresh local produce was mostly distributed and sold within its own local area. Almost within a generation, however, this country has sustained a culture shock of dramatic proportions, the effects of which have changed the way we look at everything. It is interesting to examine how this situation came about.

Since the end of World War II, the Britain that our grandfathers knew has virtually disappeared, undergoing a rapid transformation from the moment hostilities ceased. The euphoria of victory was dampened by hunger and, in government circles, by the fact that Britain now owed a huge sum of money to the US (finally paid off in 2006) and would have to dance to this particular piper's tune. Food rationing, begun in 1940, shortly after the outbreak of war, would continue until 1954. Fourteen years is a long time to live without enough of the finer things in life, such as eggs, butter, cheese and meat, even though vegetables were readily available. Following government exhortation for everyone to 'dig for victory', vegetables were being grown in allotments and gardens everywhere. Even lawns and flowerbeds were dug up and turned into vegetable plots. It is estimated that 1.4 million Britons had a working allotment by the time the war ended.

At that time, it was simply an accepted fact of life that the vegetable plot was an essential part of any garden. Even a small plot would deliver up a surprisingly large quantity of first class produce. There is, after all, no contest in terms of flavour and freshness. Even buying from the local greengrocer was second best. Having your own vegetable plot meant that you could just go out and dig what you wanted, when you wanted it. You didn't have to think about buying a pound of carrots or five pounds of potatoes – you simply harvested what was required for the next meal.

Being part of the culture, fruit and vegetable growing became instinctive for many, and those skilled in the art of horticulture passed on their wisdom and knowledge to others. Whilst still being that 'nation of shopkeepers' that Napoleon so derided 130 years previously, we were also a nation of gardeners. Growing your own means cooking your own too. So vegetables from the garden ended up in the kitchen alongside the meat, eggs, cheese and butter.

Britain was taking self-sufficiency seriously, and food was an important element in the make-up of society. We grew, we cooked and we ate. Meals were taken at set times and the family all sat together at the table to eat them. However, there was revolution in the air, and it was being generated by insidious new influences from a very different culture.

Our American allies, from that faraway country to whom we were now beholden through the grip of financial indebtedness, did not think like us. It might be historically accurate to say that they used to think like us, but that was back in the 17th Century, when the country was under colonial rule by an acquisitive empire-building super-power that did not stop until half the world, as depicted in old school atlases, was coloured pink. Breaking free of the grip of colonial rule in 1776, America went on to develop its own culture, similar but quite different from that of its old rulers.

Joining us in battle in World War II, and in the subsequent joint victory celebrations, the smartly dressed members of the American armed forces were affectionately dubbed as 'overpaid, over-sexed and over here'. Their charm, charismatic sense of informality and eccentric turn of phrase secretly captivated us. Though the more formal amongst the British were not easily persuaded that the Americans were anything but loud, ill-mannered and vulgar, the 'ordinary Joes', as our new trans-Atlantic friends might have described them, were more than ready to taste their culture, initially through music, Shakespeare's so-called 'food of love'. It was a love affair that had started at the end of the previous global conflict, as American troops added their numbers to the Allied forces literally bogged down in the killing fields of France.

American Jazz, the music that was introduced by them, soon found new audiences on this side of the Atlantic too. Captivated by these new sounds, we Brits listened and danced, as the music changed from Dixieland to Swing between the wars. The era of the big swing bands took us through the years of World War II, with Glenn Miller, amongst many others, becoming a cult hero, especially after his death. Shortly after rationing was lifted and Britain officially ended its era of austerity, American music had evolved into something which has since become an iconic symbol of a new generation – Rock 'n' Roll.

In the vanguard of this new sound were the likes of Bill Haley & The Comets. It is said that he appealed to a younger generation, but in reality popular music had always appealed to a younger generation. The flappers of the '20s were as young and carefree as Bill Haley's audiences. But then, in the mid-'50s, onto the stage stepped someone who did more than simply appeal to a younger generation, he was of that generation himself – Elvis Presley, the boy from Tupelo, Mississippi. He was only 19 when he recorded his first hit. Two years later, he was essentially the symbol of the new generation. It would probably not be an exaggeration to say that 'Youth Culture' as a serious social force started with Elvis in 1956.

This recognition of youth effectively as a separate branch of society had a profound effect on our way of life. The teenager now became someone with his own culture, his own ideals, aspirations and rules of behaviour. Teenagers made their own decisions about what music they listened to, what clothes they wore and what they liked to eat and drink. On a collision course with a society trained to respect authority, teenagers rebelled against such received wisdom in their search for their own voice.

Never slow to spot a marketing opportunity, the big American corporations, perhaps with a zeal picked up from their former masters and the first global corporation, the East India Company, began to aim their persuasive ad campaigns at these new free-thinkers, pandering to their desire to break away from the authority that would have them conform to pre-ordained rules of social interaction. Cultural changes in the United States were easily exported to Britain. In both countries, a new world was created for teenagers, in which they could happily live with like-minded people of the same age. Their music, clothes, food and drink became specialised and available in purpose built retail outlets, such as the 'record store' or the 'coffee bar'.

It was in the United States that the cult of the teenager first took hold and then established itself through the help of a corporate marketing strategy that was keen to take advantage of this powerful new force. Hollywood got in on the act, seeking out and establishing teen idol movie stars like James Dean and Marlon Brando. The new culture was branded and sold as a symbol of the new Free World, in direct contrast to the drab existence and lifeless oppression of the increasingly powerful Soviet empire. Those who saw themselves as the winners in a global war that had divided the world into two opposing forces embraced this new culture with as much defiance as the Communist dictators despised it.

Easily persuaded to emulate the other players that were part of the winning team in 1945, Britain was not backward in adopting all things American. The untimely death of James Dean had spawned a new 'live fast, die young' attitude amongst the burgeoning baby-boomer population, in Britain as well as in the USA. Always ready to respond to the market, the corporations were happy to fuel this fire by promoting a fast lifestyle. Everything from domestic appliances to cars and from fashion to food was designed to be quicker, easier, cheaper and more disposable.

Beholden as we were to our new benefactors, every new trend that took hold in the States seeded itself in British culture not long afterwards, and since the late '50s we have gradually become more Americanised. The music revolution in the '60s helped to fuse the thinking of teenagers on both sides of the Atlantic, making the upward rise of youth culture more rapid. With the ever-increasing speed of life, fast living was fuelled by fast food. American corporations like MacDonald's, Burger King and Pizza Hut moved into town, opening outlets as fast as they could. At the same time, the 'convenience store' arrived, aimed at the easy target of cash-strapped housewives. Almost imperceptibly, this mutated into the supermarket, with British companies like Sainsbury's understanding what could be gained from imitating the profiteering ways of their more successful American counterparts.

A quarter of a century after rationing ended in Britain, Margaret Thatcher came to power and vowed to shake Britain up and make it the land of free enterprise. Her counterpart in the US, Ronald Reagan, was in complete agreement with her reliance on Free Trade and a market-driven economy. Between them, they removed many of the barriers that had kept the giant corporations confined behind monopoly laws, and capitalism moved into a new era. Another quarter of a century has passed since then and the world is unrecognisable from the world that existed 50 years ago.

Halfway through the 20th Century, my grandfather could still relate to life in Britain. With one foot in the 19th Century and the other in 'modern times', he simply acknowledged that much had changed, but the cornerstones of life in general, and therefore of his own life in particular, were still in place. His pace of living was still relatively slow, he had his family close to him and he felt protected. Meals were still enjoyed at the table 'en famille', and were cooked at home from fresh ingredients either harvested from the garden or bought from small independent shops. My grandfather died in 1966 at the age of 94. In the 40 years since then, that kind of life has in many places vanished like morning mist, its place taken by what amounts to a monstrous parody of the real thing.

Society has become fragmented as this parody is played out on the social stage. Too many older people are no longer close to their families and no longer feel protected. And those family meals, so lovingly prepared from fresh ingredients? They have been replaced with something quick and easy, a meal in a packet that cooks in seconds in the microwave. Housekeeping is no longer seen as the lynchpin that holds a family together through the creation of a secure and happy home. It is seen as a drudge that no self-respecting person should have to do.

The family meal has all but disappeared in some sectors of society. All too often these days, meals are not shared. Each member of what used to be the family unit merely comes and goes at different times. Even children still at school are quite likely to come home to an empty house and have to cater for themselves. Some even leave from an empty house to go to school each morning. The cultural tsunami that raced across the Atlantic has swamped our previous way of life. Its shock waves have long since died down, but in its wake lies what I and many others now see as a devastated culture, where fundamental foodstuffs have become cash crops, mere commodities, and the value of real food has been diminished to nothing more than a competition between giant retailers to drive prices ever lower.

THE ANSWER LIES IN THE SOIL

Drive along any road today between two urban centres and you will see our glorious countryside, that wonderful patchwork of different coloured fields that epitomises the rural scene. Such a scene makes us feel content, along with all those other images we have that illustrate it, such as grazing animals, happy farmers in Barbours and flat caps bouncing along in tractors, and fields of waving corn turning golden in the summer sun. Hurrah for a life in the country, and a ramble in the new-mown hay! What an idyllic picture this paints, but perhaps we should take a closer look at the brushstrokes. All may be not as it seems.

As we travel north on our way to Scotland, agricultural land flanks the motorway practically without a break between Ross and the outskirts of Birmingham. I remember some of these fields when we first moved to Worcester. Traditional pasture fields for the most part, these were places where mushrooms could be found in abundance in the autumn. Not any more. The pastures have been ploughed up and what has taken their place leaves me feeling uneasy. As we pass them now on this high speed highway, it is spring, and many of the fields are in transition between the harvesting of the last crop and the sowing of the next one. Early wheat and potatoes that were sown some months ago are already putting on growth and turning the fields from dull brown to green. The oilseed rape is in full flower and startlingly bright patches of yellow seem to jump out of the picture, that bigger canvas of rolling patchwork fields. The brilliance of their colour makes these flowers look almost unnatural.

Take a closer look. What else do you see in these bright yellow fields? The answer is 'nothing'. Nothing, that is, except the parallel evenly spaced lines where a tractor has been up and down the field. To those who know little of farming practices, this fact would not excite comment. To me, Sally and others like us who have come to understand these things, the tramlines in fields mean only one thing – chemical farming. This is why they are so indelibly traced in each field. The tractor carrying the spraying equipment is guided along these tramlines as it sprays, thus minimising the amount of ground lost to the tractor's passage. Fields are entered maybe half a dozen times during the course of a growing season in order to spray the crops with various pesticides, herbicides, fungicides and growth promoters.

Nothing grows in these fields except the crop in question. No weeds are allowed to survive in this unnatural monoculture where profit margins are tight. The farmer can't afford to give over any of his field to anything except the cash crop from which he wants and needs the highest possible yield. It is of course a fundamental matter of agricultural (and horticultural) principle to maximise yields from crops, but to do this in an artificial way ultimately makes no sense. In the years following World War II, it was government policy to go for growth in farming, but the desperation of years of rationing must have clouded the vision of government decision makers as they held open the door to the chemical companies. The result, after fifty-odd years of chemical abuse, is that the land is dying. It is dispiriting to think that all this might have been avoided. In the 1930s and '40s, many influential people, including Lady Eve Balfour (see Chapter 15) were already predicting that it would be a disaster to go down the chemical farming route. Their warnings were ignored. Sadly, 'twas ever thus. How many prophets have gone unheeded over the centuries?

Since joining forces with Europe, the Common Agricultural Policy that has ruled us all for far too long has made matters considerably worse. Many clear-sighted individuals have been saying over a long period of time that intensive farming is not sustainable, but their comments inevitably fall on deaf ears. When intensive farming produces multi-million pound profits for the agri-chemical companies, it is hardly surprising that no one is listening. However, despite the might of these industries and their lobbyists, there are still noises off.

One of those comes from the European Commission Joint Research Centre, which published the first Soil Atlas of Europe in 2005. The depressing and alarmingly clear message in this document is that we are in serious trouble already and that it will get worse unless we change our ways. European agriculture is under threat, with 16% of agricultural land already useless through degradation brought on by intensive exploitation of the soil – that is to say, through the use of chemical fertilisers and pesticides, erosion, loss of organic content, pollution from industry, loss of biodiversity, an increase in salinity and the negative effects of climate change, such as flash flooding, earthquakes and landslides. In southern Europe, nearly 75% of the land has such a low level of organic matter that the situation is causing huge concern. But it is not just a southern European problem. It is in our own backyard. In England and Wales, the percentage of land now considered to be on the danger list regarding low organic content rose from 35% to 42% in the fifteen years between 1980 and 1995, brought on by an ever-increasing use of chemical fertilisers and pesticides.

In a past so dim and distant that you would have to be of a certain age to remember it, there was a radio comedy programme called Beyond Our Ken. One of the stars of the show was Kenneth Williams, and one of his characters was a gardener called Arthur Fallowfield, whose response (in a mock country accent) to any question was, "The answer lies in the soil." In 1962, this had the audience helpless with laughter, but out there in the world of farming, while Kenneth Williams was making us laugh with his parody of an old-fashioned son of the soil, the new sons of the soil were busy poisoning it with the help of government money. And all the while they thought they were helping to make Britain self-sufficient.

So what is so very wrong with using a bit of artificial fertiliser to help your wheat grow strong? Well, as with so many aspects of life where profiteering is the driving force, it is the scale of the operation that leads to disaster. If it was just a 'bit of fertiliser', it may never have caused a problem. My father used to do just this when he felt that his naturally composted organic manure needed a helping hand, but it was such a rare event as to be hardly worth mentioning. With farming, however, it became a complete new credo. The Gospel According to Agri-business.

Perhaps we should analyse the problem in more detail. As a good starting point, let's look at wheat. There is something symbolic about wheat. It is a grain that is as old as farming itself. References to wheat appear in the Bible and other ancient texts. It is a staple of life and in Britain today, despite a huge choice of other foods, we still manage to get through about five million tons of the stuff every year, in bread, cereals, cakes, biscuits, pasta and pizzas. Much can be said about the decline in nutritional value of wheat grain once it has been processed into flour, but for now we will concentrate on how the wheat is actually grown today.

Anyone looking at a field ready to be sown with wheat could be forgiven for thinking that the soil looks very much like subsoil simply broken down into a reasonable tilth. It looks like subsoil because that is very nearly what it is. The fine soil rich in organic matter that one would expect to see is virtually a thing of the past in many areas of the country. With most of this organic content gone, microbial and insect activity has practically ceased. The soil is clinically dead, though it can be resuscitated by injecting it with synthetic nitrogen fertilisers. Once this is done, the wheat can be sown. What happens after that has been detailed by Graham Harvey in *We Want Real Food*.

In the autumn, when the plants are still small, it is time for their first dose of overground chemical spray. This is a cocktail of weedkillers (isoproturon and pendimehalin) mixed with a pyrethroid insecticide, Lambdacyhalothrin. As stem growth comes on in the following spring, a new cocktail is sprayed onto the growing plants. This time it is a mixture of two fungicides, propiconazole and Chlorothalonil, to prevent attack from fungal diseases. To this mixture is added a plant growth hormone called Chlormequat, euphemistically called a 'growth regulator' by the chemical companies that sell it.

The plants grow taller as the spring progresses, and another fungicide mixture is applied, containing the chemicals Azoxystrobin, tetraconazole and another dose of Chlorothalonil. Once again, growth hormones are added to the mix, Trinexapacethyl, Chlormequat again, choline chloride and iazaquin. With the onset of rapid stem growth, a mix of three more fungicides is applied: tebuconazole, Azoxystrobin again and a third dose of Chlorothalonil. A final does of fungicide, metconazole, is applied as the flag leaf emerges.

Although five separate sprayings, involving thirteen different chemicals, may seem a little heavy-handed, it becomes necessary for plants growing on synthetic nitrogen fertiliser. The plants are in effect being over-stimulated by the fertiliser to produce lush green foliage. It looks good and 'healthy' but is in fact susceptible to disease, hence the need to 'protect' it with fungal sprays and to help it along with a few growth promoters. Hard work and huge expense (about £100 per acre at 2006 prices) for the farmer, but lots of celebrating in the boardrooms of the win-win agri-chemical companies.

Following Graham Harvey's lead, I have set all this out in detail because I think it is important to realise just how much our crops are sprayed with chemicals. I have used wheat as an example, but a similar regime of crop spraying is going on with other cereal crops, oilseed rape, lettuces, potatoes and most other vegetables grown on a commercial scale, to say nothing of soft fruit and tree fruit. Those companies whose profits and contented shareholders depend on continuing sales of these chemicals will tell us that none of this is a problem, that the applications of chemicals is not injurious to health and that we have never enjoyed such abundant harvests of good quality crops. Logic, however, tells us a different story. It tells us that the use of chemicals is relatively new, that we seemed to be able to grow perfectly good crops before the advent of chemical agriculture and that such a high level of chemical application just cannot be good for us.

Although it is rarely mentioned that chemical agriculture is killing our soil, it is accepted that residues from pesticides (commonly used as a generic term for all agri-chemicals) occur in our food. We even have an official government watchdog, the UK Pesticide Residues Committee, to monitor the situation. Tests that were carried out in 2003 on 72 samples of bread found that 56 of them were contaminated. The four most common contaminants were Chlormequat (growth hormone) glyphosate (a weedkiller) and two insecticides, pirimphos-methyl and malathion.

Predictably, the Pesticide Residues Committee, whilst accepting the existence of these chemicals, concluded that 'there was no concern for human health'. The companies that manufacture these products describe them as 'largely benign' or of 'low toxicity'. Other studies by other independent bodies do not agree. In California, for example, studies carried out on occupational risks demonstrated that glyphosate weedkillers were the third most common cause of pesticide illness among agricultural workers. With symptoms ranging from skin irritation, headache and nausea to more serious conditions such as heart palpitations, peeling skin, blurred vision and constricted breathing, glyphosate is demonstrably toxic to humans. Malathion is much the same in terms of the symptoms it generates, and might even be worse. The US Environmental Protection Agency has gone as far as to say that there is 'suggestive evidence' that malathion causes cancer.

Similar conclusions were reached in Canada by the Ontario College of Family Physicians, a voluntary non-profit making association of doctors. Their studies found 'positive associations' between pesticides and a number of cancers, including those of the brain, kidney, pancreas and prostate. It was further suggested that pesticide exposure can be linked to general damage of the nervous system. Accepting that 'many of the health problems linked with pesticide use are serious and difficult to treat', Dr Margaret Sandborn, one of the authors of the report, advocates a reduction of exposure to pesticides as a necessary first step.

Studies by bodies such as the Pesticide Residues Committee are unfortunately no more than that – just studies. It is in the nature of such investigative work to remain empirical in assessment and theoretical in application. Thus a chemical pesticide might be studied in isolation, possibly in a clinical laboratory using lab rats, and the results of the testing published as a theoretical risk assessment. What the tests don't tell us is what harmful effects we might be suffering from an ingestion of small quantities of chemical residues each time we eat. Even more significantly, we are not told what detrimental effects on health occur as a result of consuming a 'chemical cocktail' on a daily basis. Those institutions that do research into pesticides and their effect on human development accept that it would be impossible to test all pesticides in all possible combinations. Their advice, quite sensibly, is to err on the side of caution. My advice, as a know-nothing layman, would be to avoid chemical ingestion altogether.

And what of the studies on the pesticides themselves, before they are released for sale? John Humphrys, in his book, *The Great Food Gamble*, has some pertinent comments to make on this. He quotes Janie Axelrad, a toxicologist who worked for a number of years testing new compounds for chemical and pharmaceutical companies. She became so disenchanted with the methods employed for research and testing that she left the industry to carry out her own research on the effects of pesticides on humans.

For her, one of the big problems was the lab rat. Animals used in laboratory testing are effectively identical. Just suppose for a moment that real people were used in the testing of a new chemical product. Is it likely that they would all be of similar age, and that they would have been fed a perfectly balanced diet all their lives in order to keep them at optimum weight? What about if none of them was allowed to drink anything but water and what if they were kept in a climatically controlled sterile atmosphere for the whole time? On top of that, what if our test cases were all albino and related to each other? Would any results produced from such a test have any meaning or relevance to the population at large?

Janie Axelrad believes that data from standardised groups like this are worthless because they fail to take into account the problems caused by individuality. She is appalled that the protocols for toxicity testing have remained unchanged since mandatory testing was first introduced in the late eighties. She suggests that 'animal toxicity tests have evolved to produce results that are easy for scientists to interpret and reproduce.' The same species of animal are used for lab tests because there is a huge amount of background data available on them. The animals are housed together, in controlled conditions of air, humidity and temperature, and are kept free from disease so as not to influence test results. They are rationed with a feed designed to be perfectly balanced, allowed only water to drink, are the same age and weight range and come from the same breeders. And albinos are used in order to eliminate the possibility of pigment influencing the results.

As Janie Axelrad says, 'this totally unrealistic situation ensures that extrapolation to the human population is fundamentally impossible.' Human beings are all uniquely individual in terms of physiology, psychology, race, age, food consumption and environmental influences. How can any laboratory test cover all of these differences? In short, it can't. On top of that, the animals being tested are not human beings. Whatever the genetic similarities are between lab rats and human beings, logic again steps in and tells me that the similarities are not close enough and that results produced in such tests will not be effectively applicable to a large cross-section of the human population. Laboratory testing is carried out in order to assure us that new chemicals released onto the marketplace are safe for human beings. If you wish to believe everything you are told about these chemicals, and especially those used in the food industry, that is of course your prerogative. Personally, I remain hugely sceptical.

Subscribing to the Chinese philosophy that 'the master teaches the pupil, the pupil learns and then the pupil teaches the master', I believe that our formative years are spent learning the basic skills we need to survive in the world, and once we stand on our own feet it is up to us to work everything out. At that point, we should be in a position to be able to challenge received authority for, without that challenge, no changes would ever be made in society. If we are being grown-up about life, therefore, we should indeed challenge anything that looks spurious, specious or just downright odd.

My own philosophy is to question everything anyway, because so many people and organisations are working to a concealed agenda. It is often revealing to get behind the public message to see what the real motivation is. I cannot watch an advert on TV without questioning the statements and claims being made. Once you begin to do this, you also quickly realise that the main purpose of any ad, especially an expensive one on prime time TV, is to sell you something, irrespective of whether or not you want it and regardless of the fact that it may not be good for you. But more on that later.

For now, we just need to be aware that the high-powered sellers of agri-chemicals are all giant corporations and, as such, subscribe to only one mission statement: minimise costs, maximise profits, keep the shareholders sweet. Yes, I have said it before and, yes, I will say it again before the end of the book, but it is important to understand the motivation behind a corporation, and the behaviour they are capable of in order to achieve their goals. They would rather not spend vast sums of money on testing pesticides. They do this only if legislation and regulation forces them to. If they can get away without testing, they will. Currently, there are approximately 80,000 man-made chemicals on the market, and roughly 29,000 of them have not undergone adequate tests. Does that alarm you? It certainly alarms me.

The whole subject of pesticides and how they adversely affect our health is a huge one. It is beyond the scope of this book to cover it in sufficient detail, but there are some excellent publications available that go into the whole question very thoroughly, notably *The Detox Diet* by Paula Baillie-Hamilton. On the internet, the website www.pesticidescampaign.co.uk is run by Georgina Downs, someone who has endured ill-health as a result of pesticide contamination. The site represents her personal story. Suffering for years from the toxic effects of pesticides being sprayed on the fields next to her home, she has become a passionate, eloquent, tireless campaigner for the abolition of these dangerous chemicals. Please visit her site and see for yourself just how bad it really is out there.

As for the Kenneth Williams character, Arthur Fallowfield, and his assertion that the answer lies in the soil, how true that has turned out to be. How little did we appreciate that this comic character really did have his finger on the pulse. The old proverb, 'many a true word is spoken in jest', like all proverbs, proves itself right on the money yet again.

LEANING ON THE STAFF OF LIFE

By the time we reach Birmingham, the traffic on the motorway has increased to alarming levels, considering that this is not a weekday. We think about getting off and looking for an alternative route, but the thought is soon put to flight by the voice of reason.

To fight our way from somewhere south of Birmingham in search of an easy route through to the M6 north of Walsall makes about as much sense as building a raft to cross a river within sight of the bridge. Driving on the motorway can be mind-numbingly tedious, but motorways are relatively direct routes and, despite volume of traffic and potential restrictions to flow such as lane closures, they can still be the quickest route between two points, so long as the traffic is actually moving. On this Sunday, traffic was slow approaching Birmingham, but it was moving, so we kept going. The commercial traffic we had noticed as we joined the M50 outside Ross had of course increased by the time we hit the M5 at Strensham, and now that we were heading through Birmingham to join the M6, the 40-tonners were much in evidence, each displaying their message to the world on their cabs and trailer awnings.

"Rathbone's Quality Bread," proclaimed one. What should we make of this? Presumably, the lorry was carrying bread made by a company called Rathbone, and presumably the bread might be worth buying and eating – it is after all described as 'quality' bread. But how often have you seen that word 'quality' applied to something that quite obviously isn't. It is reminiscent of the pub that has a blackboard propped up against the door jamb carrying the message 'good food'. Most of us know that 'good' in this context is a seriously overworked word. To many people, the first reaction, on seeing such an advertisement, is to drive on to another pub and look for a more persuasive and convincing message. And so it is with the word 'quality'.

Other than the fact that 'quality' is probably not an accurate description of what is in the back of this particular lorry, the whole message, 'Rathbone's Quality Bread' tells us nothing. Nothing about the company, nothing about its size or its place in the great scheme of corporate things. More disturbingly, it doesn't actually tell us anything about the real quality of its bread. Anyone driving along the motorway and seeing this truck would not give it a second glance or a second thought. But spending a little time in getting behind the declaration that this lorry is carrying Rathbone's quality bread is a revealing exercise.

We find that Rathbone is a multi-million-pound big player, and part of an even bigger company. Around February 2006, it was seeking to expand its operation and was looking to acquire a site for a new factory that was expected to turn out 6000 loaves an hour. *Six thousand loaves an hour*, dropping off the conveyor belt in some huge factory. These expansion plans came shortly after its takeover in administration (April 2005) by Morrisons supermarket group, who paid £15.5m for the collapsed baking firm in order to expand its own manufacturing operations. So now we begin to see a different picture from the one which is being painted by those three innocent words on the side of this 40-tonne truck. Now we see a vehicle that is part of the huge supermarket operation in this country, a vehicle that carries pallets full of industrialised, pappy, nutritionally depleted cotton wool bread. So what does it actually mean when we see 'quality bread' written on the side of a big truck? Absolutely nothing. Those three words are at the very least misleading, and at worst actually disinformative. To anyone who had the time and patience to take it on, there might even be a legal argument that 'quality' in this instance is against the Trades Descriptions Act.

Man, it has been said, shall not live by bread alone. But, in many parts of the world, he has had a pretty good attempt at doing so. Bread (or, more precisely, products made from wheat flour) certainly represents a dietary staple in the culinary traditions of many countries. The grinding of wheat grains into flour, and the making of a dough by adding water or other wetting agent, is a practice that has been going on for thousands of years, probably to the first days of farming 10,000 years ago. There is certainly evidence that bread was made by the ancient Egyptians in 8000BC.

With the phrase 'Rathbone's Quality Bread' still in my head, it is interesting to note that the baking industry does appear to be open to abuse, and research reveals a long history of nefarious practices amongst millers and bakers. By the Middle Ages in England, it was common for each 'manor' to have a bakery, virtually a public facility open to villagers who brought their own home-made dough to be baked in these ovens. Bakers invented some devious ways of stealing a little dough from each person, thus accumulating enough dough to make bread which they then sold as their own. Not only were they stealing dough from others, but also, in selling bread, they would often cut corners on weight and quality. A favourite trick was to bake each loaf with a little lump of something heavy in the middle.

Such chicanery, which records suggest had been going on since at least the Norman Conquest, led to the introduction of legislation in the form of the *Assize of Bread and Ale* in the mid-13th century. Designed to standardise quality, measurement and pricing for bakers and brewers, it was the first law in Britain to regulate the production and sale of food. The response from the aggrieved bakers in the nascent baking industry was to sell thirteen loaves for the price of twelve (hence the baker's dozen) so as to be sure that they would not be seen as cheats involved in short-changing their customers. Even before the Norman Conquest, cheating bakers were nothing new. Roman bakers were at it a thousand years before that, being accused of adding 'white earth' (chalk or magnesia) to their loaves.

But all this is as nothing compared to the kind of underhand practices that proliferated in the food industry once the Industrial

Revolution had built up a head of steam. Mass production and distribution of food provided ample opportunity for a bit of swindling on the side. Cheating and the adulteration of foodstuffs began to happen on something of a grand scale, affecting many of the basic foods of the day such as bread, beer, wine, tea, confectionery and condiments. So rife was this adulteration that, in the early nineteenth century, it had become a serious cause for concern. A man by the name of Frederick Accum, erstwhile assistant to one of the celebrities of the day, Humphrey Davy, decided it was time to tell the world. In 1820, he published *A Treatise on Adulterations of Food and Culinary Poisons*, highlighting the bad practices in some detail.

Some of what was going on was toxic by nature, some was just simple cheating, like recycling used tea leaves, or watering down beer and milk. In the case of bread, it was a case of undesirable additives. A substance called alum (potassium aluminium sulphate) was routinely added to bread to whiten cheap flour and bulk it out. A report from 1848, entitled *A Treatise on the Falsifications of Foods* found this to be a universal practice. Although alum is not necessarily dangerous, it is still responsible for some unpleasant side effects as it has a negative effect on digestion.

The Industrial Revolution opened the door to such malpractice quite simply by creating a situation whereby the pursuit of wealth became a goal in itself. Thus any manufacturing process or sales opportunity became the means by which wealth was created. The speed and level of industrialisation separated producers from their customers in a way that had not occurred hitherto. Traditionally, millers, bakers, brewers and farmers worked very much at a local level, where their customers were known to them. Thus cheating would have been a mug's game – cheat on the man from the same village and all your other customers will soon know about it, and that's your business down the pan. It's just not worth the risk. But if you are baking bread, adding alum to it and then sending your loaves in bulk into the expanding cities via a wholesaler, who is going to know it was you who added the unwanted ingredient?

The nineteenth century also saw the introduction of what we now call free trade (i.e. free from the constrictions that make trade fair). The way was made easier for big businesses to thrive, and silly little rules like those laid down in the 13th century under the *Assize of Bread and Ale* were abolished. No longer regulated, the baking industry was open to free competition, resulting in a huge influx of people who saw baking as their opportunity to get rich quick. As we all know, it doesn't work like that. All that happens is that you get too many people trying to get their hands on their slice of the action, producing aggressively competitive factions desperately undercutting each other to get a bigger market share for themselves.

And what happens to the product in a situation like this? Obviously, it becomes of secondary importance. The quality of the product and the satisfaction of the customer comes further down the list than the desire to turn a profit. By 1850, in this newly liberated free market, there were reputed to be 50,000 bakers competing for the market, and 75% of them were underselling in order to stay in the game. To undersell, i.e. to sell below the cost of production, requires some creative thinking. This mainly involved defrauding the customer, by selling a product which has been debased with cheap ingredients, and getting your workforce to work more hours than you are paying them for. Such was the situation in 1850, and so it is in 2007, although 150 years of this kind of behaviour has produced a very complicated and involved relationship between manufacturer, worker and customer. But the underlying principle remains much the same, and profit still comes before all other considerations.

So, to recap, we see that the industry which produces most of the bread sold in the UK today is run by big business, which has its roots in the Industrial Revolution. Big business, then as now, is geared towards profitability, allowing every cost-cutting measure there is to be applied to its factory systems in order to maximise profits. The potential corruption in the baking industry (as in every other major industry), once controlled by legislation, has been let loose by a relaxation of restrictive statutes. So far removed are we, the consumers, from the primary producers, the manufacturers and the wholesalers that they have absolutely no connection with us and therefore no conscience about whether or not our food has become nutritionally degraded. Far from having a conscience, many of those involved in the modern day food supply chain will go to great lengths, via their marketing, to persuade us that their debased and nutritionally imperfect products are actually full of health-giving properties and therefore essential to our wellbeing.

Bread, that so-called staff of life, is a typical example of this kind of disinformative advertising. But surely, you protest, bread is bread, so whatever kind of advertising is used we are still just eating something that is essential to our daily diet and has been produced in the same way since the year dot? Well, no, bread is not just bread and it has not been produced in the same way ever since the first loaf was made. Everything has changed since Man first experimented with grinding up grains of wheat between two stones to make flour. At a fundamental level, it is clear that the grain itself has changed. The wheat grown today is essentially a different species from that grown even as recently as forty or fifty years ago.

I remember helping with the harvest as a child, in the capacity of interested bystander. I remember what a wheat field looked like then, splashed with colour from the corn marigolds, corncockles, blue cornflowers and bright red poppies, adding highlights to the tall pale gold wheat waving in the breeze. My grandfather was still farming at that time but, being close to retirement, he was really just tinkering. However, his neighbour, a much younger man, was very much the active farmer operating a traditional mixed farm. In common with other farmers in the area, he grew a few acres of wheat and, once the crop had ripened, he would join forces with the others in order to get the harvest in. It was a time of great community spirit. Everyone joined in and the farmers shared their machinery, one combine harvester being used on several adjoining farms.

I was fascinated by the whole process. On the one hand, I was awed by the noise and clatter of the machines as the combines chewed up swathe after swathe of golden wheat and, on the other hand I was excited by the hares, rabbits, harvest mice and voles that ran from the blades of the harvester. In my childlike way, I felt deeply sorry for the fact that their homes had been destroyed by those nasty men and their noisy machines. But how different it is today. Now you would be lucky ever to see a hare or a harvest mouse, let alone have to worry about the destruction of their nests. What reason would they have to build homes or seek cover in a field of poisonous plants growing on dead soil?

Monoculture has no room for sentiment, and therefore no room for wildlife and native plants. Monoculture is about efficiency. Monoculture subscribes to the mantra 'farming is a business just like any other'. And monoculture in the wheat industry has produced new kinds of wheat – short-stemmed, chemical-dependent, heavy croppers with big ears. These short-stemmed varieties, developed around fifty years ago, are less likely to fall over in the wind and rain. Thus they are receptive to higher doses of growth-promoting nitrogen fertilisers without risk of damage. The chemical fertiliser generates good yields, but the grain is effectively 'forced', so the nutritional value is compromised. Further damage is done through the overuse of pesticides.

Agriculture of this kind was perfected in America, following the exploitation and subsequent collapse of that carefully balanced and highly fertile grassland ecosystem known as The Prairies. Growing wheat on vast tracts of virgin land is easy. All you do is rip up the ancient turf, sow your seed into soil that has lain undisturbed for a thousand years, sit back and watch the bumper crops grow into bumper harvests. Repeat ad infinitum, flood the world's grain markets with your surplus (and put a lot of small farmers out of business while you are at it) and count your money. This kind of intensive exploitation has a very short life, however. In only a few decades, the vast fertile prairies of America had literally turned to dust and blown away on the wind.

Enter the scientists, charged with finding a way to grow crops again. The answer is what we see today in the semi-dwarf varieties mentioned above. It is not simply a question of new hybrid varieties, however. It is more about chemical agriculture, a deeply destructive and exploitative industry, as harmful as the extractive industries, such as mining, in its degradation of ecosystems and the natural environment. It is the kind of agriculture that is unsustainable on at least two counts: it is killing the fertility of the earth's soils, and it cannot be made to work at all without massive financial assistance from government subsidies. Yet this American model of agriculture, mocking as it does the kind of agriculture that was successful for the 10,000 years since Man started farming, has been 'sold' to the rest of the world by those pharmaceutical companies that were accumulating massive profits from the sale of the chemicals that underpin it.

Those harvests that I witnessed as a child now form in my mind a picture of the past, faded into pale grainy muted colours like a Lartigue autochrome. Consigned to history by the invasion of chemically-dependent, profit-fuelled 'big wheat' companies, modern wheat production is all about creating a surplus and driving down prices. It is not a world in which the traditional farmer can survive. In this world only the biggest, most ruthless competitors can stay in the game, growing nutritionally degraded grains.

As if this were not enough to contend with, there is one more trans-Atlantic legacy that has severely compromised the vitality of this, our most basic staple food. At the time the North American prairies were being ripped up for the cultivation of wheat, changes were taking place in the milling industry. A group of commercial flour millers based in Minnesota were looking to make improvements to handle the increasing quantities of grain more efficiently. They started by installing a new French device known as the purifier, which extracted a higher proportion of flour, separating it from the coarser parts of the grain. Then, from an idea first designed by a Swiss engineer called Helfenburger, came an invention first used in Hungary as long ago as 1874.

This was the high-speed roller mill. It would hardly be an exaggeration to say that this was the kiss of death for the humble grain of wheat. Traditionally, flour was produced using millstones to grind the grains. Milling between two stones is a gentle process and flour produced in this way retains most of the goodness of the grain. Being relatively slow and small-scale (a traditional stone mill produces something like 250 kilos of flour an hour) milling was very much a local enterprise supplying equally small-scale bakeries. The steel roller mill changed all that. It made milling a factory system capable of producing *twenty tonnes* of white flour every hour – ideal for the burgeoning wheat and flour industry in America. With exports of wheat from America arriving on our shores, new steel roller mills were constructed at our ports so that the wheat could be processed into flour on arrival. Many small-scale rural millers and bakers were forced out of business by the increasing dominance of these giant factories, supplying white flour to new style 'plant bakers' involved in the large-scale production of white bread.

Milling on an industrial scale was obviously beneficial to those companies that had invested in the industry, but it was not beneficial to the grain itself. There are three main constituent parts to a grain of wheat: the outer layer (the fibrous bran), the germ (the part of the grain that will germinate into a new plant) and the endosperm (the white inner part of the grain). Nutrients are contained in all three of these. The bran contains protein, fat and minerals as well as fibre. As you might expect, the germ, being the literal heart of the grain, has most of the oils, vitamins and mineral and a little protein. The endosperm is mostly carbohydrate, although it too has a little protein. The most nutritious part, as we can see, is the germ, one of the most important sources in our diet of essential fatty acids, vital for brain, nerve and tissue function. Where traditional milling retains all of this goodness, industrial milling dumps it, along with everything else except the starchy white endosperm.

So ferocious is the expulsion of minerals and vitamins during the production of white flour that as long ago as 1919 it became a matter of serious concern that consumption of white flour products (mainly bread) would leave humans undernourished. The uneven battle between heavily financed profiteering companies and the relatively impecunious government of the day, in its role as custodian of public health, ensured that another 21 years would pass before the government decided to do anything about the situation. It was proudly announced in Parliament in 1940 that vitamin B1 was to be added to bread for the sake of the nation's health. Today, vitamins B1 and B3 are put back, as well as calcium and iron, but not in the original proportions. Calcium (derived from chalk) is replaced at four times the original level, but iron and the two vitamins go back in at the minimum allowable levels.

In the same way that it has been said that a democracy gets the politicians it deserves, it could be argued that a free market gets the products it deserves. How these things start, of course, is another question altogether, but in the brave new world of the Industrial Revolution, the idea that white bread was superior to any other type of bread had taken hold in the public imagination (and is still very much with us today). The factory millers and plant bakers would have argued then, as they still do today, that they are merely fulfilling a demand.

My suspicious mind tells me that, if a steel roller mill produces mountains of white flour, then the marketing boys are hardly likely to sell the idea that wholemeal flour is a better deal. Suspicion tells me that white flour and white bread would have been hyped up as the new clean food on which to build empires and go forward into a new century, and that old-fashioned breads of the wholemeal variety would have been ridiculed as being hopelessly out of step with the New Age of Enterprise, a relic of those dusty old country millers and village bakers. Any marketing message that is effectively constructed and persuasive enough can create mass hysteria in a very short time, and so it was with the image of white bread. The soft and springy white loaf might well have looked squeaky clean compared to the coarser loaves that preceded it, but its uniform lines disguised some fatal flaws. As we have seen, flour from a roller mill is practically devoid of nutrients, with only the starchy endosperm of the grain making it through the rollers and sieves. The bran and wheatgerm are lost along with most of the vitamins, minerals and essential fatty acids.

Okay, legislation says that the plant bakers are obliged to replace the lost nutrients, but I am sure common sense, that facility that has been bludgeoned into submission by the increasingly heavy scientific approach to life, will tell you that the product will be inferior despite these additions. To look at this trade-off in more detail, the main minerals lost through the milling process are zinc, calcium, potassium, selenium, copper, iron, manganese, magnesium and phosphorus. Vitamins removed include the all-important B vitamins, niacin, riboflavin, thiamine and pyridoxine. By way of a return gesture, the millers put back two minerals (calcium and iron) and two vitamins (thiamine and niacin) all of which are synthetically produced and in different proportions from those found in nature. Fair exchange? I don't think so.

In assessing the implications of removing nutrients and replacing them with a synthetic alternative, Sally Fallon, nutritionist and author of *Nourishing Traditions*, points out that far from being a like for like replacement, such 'fortification' of bread and wheat products is potentially harmful. Synthetic vitamins and minerals are not the same as the real thing and there is evidence to suggest that the excess of iron that is caused by using it as an additive in this way may cause tissue damage. As for vitamins, adding thiamine (B1) and niacin (B3) without the other B vitamins leads to imbalances in numerous processes within the body that involve B vitamin pathways.

One could argue that all of this is debateable, that there is no really hard evidence that synthetic nutrients are any worse than natural ones. However, common sense again tells us that a synthetic version of something as delicate as this will not be as good as the original. To start with, the original will be perfectly balanced, and we can see that the artificial replacement is not. Investigating more closely what goes into our modern day loaf and how it is produced in a plant bakery will paint a clearer picture.

That tireless investigative journalist, Felicity Lawrence, has described an experience in her book, *Not on the Label*, which few of us are likely to have – a visit to a plant bakery to see a white sliced loaf being made. The factory, owned by one of the giants of the baking industry, British Bakeries, is the production base for brands such as Hovis Great White, Mother's Pride and Nimble, as well as supermarket own-brand loaves for Tesco, Sainsbury's, Morrisons and M&S. Ten thousand loaves an hour, a quarter of a million loaves a day, come off its production line. 1.5 million loaves every week, all bagged up in plastic ready for distribution. This process is so far removed from traditional bread making that it would be obvious to even the casual observer that, on this industrial scale, it has very little to do with real bread.

A visit from Mr Spock of the Starship Enterprise might provoke a comment to his commanding officer that, "It's bread, Jim, but not as we know it." The degraded flour produced in giant roller mills from chemically adulterated wheat undergoes yet more processing once it reaches the factory. Up until the 1960s, mass production bread was still made along vaguely traditional lines in that the dough was still given time to rise and prove. All that changed as a result of work carried out by researchers at the British Baking Industries Research Association at Chorleywood. Here they found a way of dispensing with all that time and energy. Air and water were incorporated into the dough by mixing it energetically at high speed. Twice the normal quantity of yeast was needed in order to make the bread rise at all, chemical oxidants had to be added to introduce the gas and hydrogenated fat to provide structure. Labour costs were reduced, time was saved and, because this process absorbed more water, higher yields were achieved. This type of bread production, the Chorleywood Bread Process, or CBP, has become the standard for the industry.

The CBP method has also made it possible to use cheaper varieties of wheat. At one time, EU-subsidised British wheat, although cheaper, was considered too soft for factory processing, but CBP has perfected a way of extracting the gluten from the flour and then replacing it with gluten from other sources. Thus another cost saving has been introduced to the process.

Until the late '80s, wholemeal bread was safe from the CBP system, but new legislation at that time sanctioned the use of flour 'improvers' for wholemeal bread as well as white, so now wholemeal bread too is subject to the CBP. Flour improvers or flour treatment agents appear in the list of ingredients on a standard factory loaf, but this tells you very little about what these additives are. Legislation requires a manufacturer to declare the use of these improvers as an ingredient, but there is no requirement to declare the ingredients within any improver. At the plant bakery, to quote from *Not on the Label*, deliveries from ingredient manufacturers will arrive displaying information such as 'pumpable fats in returnable bulk tanks' with 'high slip point fat for use in CBP . . . to provide increased volume, texture and improved fresh keeping . . .made with hydrogenated oil, water and emulsifiers E471, E475, E476'.

Factory bread also has a high salt content. In fact it is officially a high-salt food according to government health guidelines. It needs its salt, however, because the flavours that normally develop in a traditional loaf during fermentation have no time to develop in the CBP loaf. Also present are mass-produced customised enzymes to help speed up biological reactions in the process. These are, as often as not, produced by genetically modified organisms but, as enzymes are destroyed in the baking process, they do not have to be declared. And finally, when these factory produced loaves are ready for the supermarket shelves, they are sprayed with anti-fungal agents, generally sorbate or calcium propionate, to give them a longer shelf life.

British Bakeries is a subsidiary of the even larger global player, Rank Hovis McDougall (RHM). RHM and its great rival, Allied Bakeries, control between them the production of nearly 70% of the bread sold in the UK. British Bakeries itself, as mentioned above, sells brands like Hovis, Mother's Pride and Nimble, as well as supplying burger buns to McDonald's and pizza dough to Pizza Hut. Allied Bakeries supplies Kingsmill, Sunblest and Allinson brands. Both companies supply partly-baked products to the supermarket in-store bakeries. Thus the impression given to its customers by any in-store bakery that they are buying freshly baked traditionally made bread is an illusion. Most of this bread is made via the same CBP system, sent out to the supermarkets as pre-baked loaves and simply finished off in the in-store bakery.

Only 2% of UK bread is now made in a traditional fashion by independent bakers and, argues Felicity Lawrence, even this figure is misleading because only a small number of independents genuinely bake from scratch. Many of them are buying in the same factory 'premixes' of flour and additives that are used in the supermarket bakeries. It is a sad indictment of our baking industry that there are only about 3,500 independent bakers now left in the UK, and that so much of what is available, including the output of some of these independents, is of such inferior quality in terms of its ingredients that it is actually damaging to our health. Plus, this factory bread is not satisfying, as real bread is. As for the taste, those brought up on a diet of white sliced CBP bread have no conception of what 'bread' actually tastes like. Give them a slice of naturally leavened sourdough, and their noses will wrinkle in disgust.

Of course, bread is not the only product to come from wheat grains. The flour itself is sold in vast quantities via the supermarket shelves, and most of it is coming from the giant roller mills. So those of us who are really zealous in our attempts to bypass the industrial bread process by making our own at home (a breadmaker is a great investment) need to be careful when it comes to choosing flour. The basic message is to avoid all of the normal brand names, such as McDougalls, Hovis, Homepride and especially any supermarket own-brands. Instead, look out for stone ground flours from small independent mills such as Bacheldre, Shipton Mill or Doves Farm. You may have to seek out your local independent shops for these, although Doves Farm is fairly easy to find even in the bigger shops.

The caveat here is that the more readily available a product is, the greater the danger of its being compromised in some way. Thus Doves Farm, in its ubiquity and the resulting volume of production, might be considered to be too mass-produced. If you take a look at their website, you will see that they make all the right noises about their raw materials and organic methods of production, but they also admit t using roller mills. For us, that is a bit of a disappointment, so we make sure we buy flour from traditional millers instead, but we would readily admit that Doves Farm is still infinitely superior to anything that comes from the industrial mills.

Mainstream branded breakfast cereals also account for a large proportion of the world's wheat production, and the market is dominated by big players. No surprise there. Cereal Partners UK, for instance is a partnership between two huge global corporations, Nestlé and General Mills, and owns brands such as Shredded Wheat, Shreddies and Cheerios. Weetabix is the top selling cereal in the UK, followed by six Kellogg's brands (Special K, Corn Flakes, Crunchy Nut Cornflakes, Frosties, Rice Krispies and Coco Pops). The last three in the cereal top ten are Nestlé Shredded Wheat, Nestlé Shreddies and Alpen, another Weetabix product.

The breakfast cereal market is worth billions and is dominated by these huge companies. They deal in enormous quantities of grains and are thus supplied from some of the most intensive cereal producing areas of the world. The wheat-based cereals use the same pesticide-laced, nutritionally degraded grains that end up in our bread and are all processed before being packaged and distributed. You might think you are doing yourself a big favour by tucking into your Weetabix in the morning, and all of the company's marketing would certainly support your view. More accurately, however, the company's marketing has probably sold you that view in the first place. By selling Weetabix on the precept that it is simple, unprocessed wheat flakes with no additives, its makers are persuading us that this particular cereal is the 'healthy option' compared to, say, Coco Pops, which somehow look manufactured. And, yes, I have been there and done that. My two boys were crazy about Coco Pops until their mid teens, and then seemed open to persuasion, at which point I stepped in and introduced them to Weetabix. Since then, of course, I have found out so much more about the process that creates this healthy looking cereal, and I feel deeply resentful that I was deceived into believing that I was doing my sons a favour by suggesting Weetabix as an option.

This type of cereal is made by pressure-cooking whole wheat grains with water, sugar and salt before the grains are rolled out very thinly and pressed into biscuits. This process begins to break down the raw starches in the grain and so it is absorbed more readily by the body, producing a high glycaemic index score of around 75, which compares unfavourably with the 45 scored by unprocessed grains such as oatmeal and sugar-free mueslis. Shredded Wheat and Shreddies, those other two highly popular 'healthy' 'whole grain' alternatives fare little better. They too have to undergo the same pressure cooking, after which they are passed through rollers to squeeze them into strands and build them up in layers. These are then cut into squares and baked until dry and crisp.

With other types of breakfast cereal, e.g. puffed cereals, flakes and cereals made from extruded shapes, the processing is even more severe. That well known urban myth that suggests that there is more nutrition in a cereal box than there is in the flakes within it may not be all that far from the truth. In this chapter, however, I am primarily concerned with wheat and the products that come from it, so I will resist the temptation to explore the systems used in producing these other cereals. Suffice it to say that all proprietary manufactured cereals are being sold to us under false claims about their health-giving properties. If you value your health at all, they are best avoided. Transfer your allegiance to simple, organic whole grain cereals, such as porridge oats or muesli, and buy from wholefood shops if you can. If you can't, and you feel committed to the local supermarket (in the short term!), then look out for the new ethical brands such as Dorset Cereals. They will cost more money than the cheap-n-cheerful standard manufactured cereals, but they will do you good.

Besides the fact that wheat-based breakfast cereals are made from degraded grains that are then nutritionally compromised even further during the manufacturing process, we also have to contend with at least one unwelcome side-effect. That is to say, once the grains are heated to high temperatures, a compound called acrylamide is produced. Acrylamide is known to have caused cancer in animals and is described as a 'probable human carcinogen' by the Food Standards Agency. Sally Fallon, in *Nourishing Traditions*, argues that some breakfast cereals are 'actually quite toxic and have caused rapid death in test animals'. She also points out that studies have shown that 'extruded whole grain preparations can have even more adverse effects on the blood sugar than refined sugar and white flour.' In the words of Homer Simpson, "It just gets worse and worse!"

In exploring the nature of food today, I certainly have no wish to be alarmist or hysterical. I admit only to the desire to get at the truth. In common with a rapidly growing number of people, I have in the past been told that I am intolerant to wheat. An insignificant ailment by some standards, this so-called 'intolerance' (along with an intolerance to dairy products) is now so endemic that it could be classified as one of the 'diseases of civilisation'. When I was told that I had become a victim of this disorder, I found it hard to accept. I am no fan of white sliced bread, and I considered that my diet was reasonably healthy. Once I started asking questions and searching for information, however, I realised how much bread (other than white sliced) I was actually consuming, as well as cakes, biscuits and pizzas, to say nothing of the flour I was using at home during my normal culinary adventures in my kitchen.

As I began to find out more about how our wheat is grown and how our flour is made, so I also came to realise that I had been consuming a lot of degraded wheat products without realising how nutritionally poor they were. When I think of all those tomato sandwiches that I used to snack on! I used to be quite proud of myself making a tomato sandwich (with what I thought was quality bread) to satisfy a little hunger pang, instead of reaching for a packet of crisps or a chocolate bar. But now I know that the bread in those sandwiches, although not white sliced, was still a factory product using poor quality ingredients, and the same goes for all the other wheat-based products.

It is the lack of awareness that upsets me the most. The fact that I was unaware of the content of what I was eating. But then, I was a victim of marketing and advertising hype, just like anyone else. If we are sold a story that is convincing enough, it is easy to accept what we are being told. Thus it is easy to assume that those lovely fresh rolls piled loose in a willow basket just next to the in-store bakery are so much better for you than the Kingsmill loaf lurking sullenly in its plastic wrapper. The feel-good factor swamps you with self-satisfaction as you get out the loaf in your kitchen, knowing that you have to slice it with an actual knife. Like going back to the good ol' days, with Granny carving paper-thin slices off the end of a farmhouse loaf on her well-scrubbed kitchen table. Like millions of others, I had no idea that my 'freshly baked' loaf was nearly as bad as the glutinous cotton wool impostors filling the supermarket shelves.

But I know now. I understand how the staff of life has been leaned on so heavily that it has snapped and is no longer able to support us. I know what goes into our factory bread, white sliced or otherwise. With that knowledge comes an understanding of the prevalence of that new phenomenon, wheat intolerance. A genuine intolerance to wheat probably does manifest itself in a small number of people, but not the huge number that is currently deemed to be suffering from this new ailment. I believe that many of these people are actually suffering from an intolerance to gluten, to yeast or to the toxins present in bread and wheat products. We will look at this in more detail in a later chapter.

THE MILK OF HUMAN BLANDNESS

Sally and I don't like motorways. For us, they are symbolic of the superfast world in which we are all expected to live, despite the fact that some of us may want to live at a different pace. Bizarrely enough, most motorways these days are not even fast any more, just a quick route to stress.

On this Sunday, travelling north, we have managed to get past Birmingham without too much difficulty, but we both know that at this time of day on any given day during the week it would be a different story. At home, we hear the traffic reports on the radio each evening describing the horrendous queues that build up in certain parts of the country every rush hour, morning and evening. The same names get mentioned regularly – Thelwall Viaduct, M56, M62, M6 southbound to Birmingham, M42 around Redditch, M40 between Oxford and London and the M25 anywhere around its circumference. What is this all about, we wonder? Why does anyone need to live like this? The madness of our modern world, where everyone seems to be spinning in a centrifuge, leaves us gasping.

Okay, I can see the fingers pointing as I write, "Huh! You're just a grumpy old git – forgotten how to enjoy yourself, that's all it is." Well, no. Sorry to disappoint anyone, but I have *remembered* how to enjoy myself, not forgotten. I have stepped off the carousel, and I see it for what it is – just another theme park ride. It's great to go to a theme park once in a while, but do I really want to live on one of the rides? No thanks. Especially the one called 'Life Today' – scarier than anything at Alton Towers.

This is the one that you can't get off unless you jump, and if you don't jump you could be on it for the rest of your days. Anyone can get on, however. There is no height or age restriction. All that is required is a belief in the system and an ability to confuse want with need. The glossy promotional literature for this ride shows you all the prizes that you can win if you stay on – houses, cars, exotic holidays, and enough consumer goods to drain your bank account several times over. But beware. Consider the possibility that you are being sold a dream which cannot become reality, some intangible rainbow, at the end of which life is somehow supposed to come right. Also consider this well-known aphorism, "Life is something that passes you by while you are busy doing something else."

I used to build motorways. Well, more accurately, I was involved in the process of building them. As a trained land surveyor, it was my job to tell others where to put the motorways by setting out line and level control. I am no longer involved with motorway construction. I gave it up after only a few years, because I could see that ripping up so many acres of valuable farmland merely to accommodate more vehicles was never going to be a solution to our congestion problems. As it happens, my attitude at that time has been vindicated, and there are now many people who are also saying that laying down more roads does nothing for our transport problem. How can it, when we are creating a net annual increase of around half a million vehicles on our roads? But that's a different debate.

It was not just motorways that I was involved with, but by-pass roads too, plus housing developments, industrial estates and anything that required the use of a theodolite and level. Sometimes I would get a contract to do some pure surveying work, recording all the detail in a particular area and creating a map from it. That was brilliant fun, and it did not despoil the countryside, so I could cope with it. At those times when I became the true surveyor, I understood what an absolutely monumental task was taken on by the Ordnance Survey in creating a detailed small-scale map of Britain. But that was the Victorians for you – nothing daunted them. As with much of what the Victorians achieved, the scale of the work is incomprehensible. All of those mountains in Scotland, every loch and burn, every contour, and all done with the most cumbersome of equipment.

In this new world of ours, we get annoyed if our satellite navigation equipment goes on the blink or takes us to the wrong destination. Victorian surveyors had no aerial photography to help them get the picture right. Their equipment was archaic and primitive by comparison with modern computerised GPS theodolites, and yet they achieved more than we could ever dream of today. Where the Victorians learned to be the masters of the tools at their disposal, we so often are victims of the tools we have invented. The world of technology moves too fast for most of us to keep up, but do we really care? We just throw our hands up in despair and walk away from it. Plus there's always retail therapy if the weight of the world gets a bit heavy. Yet, despite this strange detachment many of us feel, we still believe we have progressed since Victorian days. We believe that we are progressing all the time. Even the '80s now look like the dark ages by some people's standards. But I wonder whether we really have progressed, when it seems to me that we have lost our souls and made a Faustian pact with Consumerism.

We love the things money can buy. But what did we spend our money on before all these things were available? Why is it that we now find so many things indispensable ("Well, I simply can't live without my iPod.")? At the risk of generalising, the answer is that we have been persuaded by the sellers of these things that they will change our lives for the better. It seems that we will go to extraordinary lengths, and unbelievable expense in some cases, to buy these new 'essentials'.

At the same time it seems we no longer want to spend money on food. Each supermarket chain has been telling us for a few decades now that we really don't need to spend a lot on food, but that message is not what it seems. It is delivered through a self-serving 'shop-with-us' strapline. Any given supermarket chain wants you to shop in their stores, and one of the main tools in their armoury of persuasion is to tell you that you will save money by being loyal to them. The trouble is, they all do it. In this race to the bottom, prices tumble as each 'brand' tries to outdo the others, resulting in nothing but negative effects. Rock-bottom pricing means compromise somewhere, whether it is the price that is being paid to suppliers, the cost of ingredients, the provenance of ingredients or the actual quality of the food on offer.

Unfortunately, the sales pitch on cheap food has been misunderstood. Or it may be that the supermarkets have been wily in disguising the fact that they are actually engaged in an interminable price war with each other. Through clever spin, we have been sold the idea that the supermarkets have only our interests at heart, and that they cut their prices purely because of 'consumer demand'. Cutting prices to steal customers from our rivals across town? Don't be silly – what a crazy idea!

There is now a common belief that buying, say, a litre of milk for around 62p constitutes some kind of basic human right. In demanding that right, many people tacitly accept the malpractices that take place in our dairy industry in order to supply milk at such a low retail price whilst still making a good profit for the supermarket. Some people even understand that dairy farmers are going out of business because supermarkets have forced on them a price that is below their production costs. Yet the belief in cheap food is so strong that it is not difficult to find people who will complain that, even at 62p, milk is still too expensive. This despite the fact that the dairy farmer who sells it might be poorer than the consumer who buys it.

Sally and I pay £1 per litre for real unpasteurised milk which we buy direct from the farmer. He has a small herd of 30 cows feeding on rich pasture land. The milk is as good as it gets, and we believe that we are getting a bargain at £1 a litre. The two of us have come to understand the true price of real food, but the information necessary to arrive at this understanding is hard to find. It takes time and effort to uncover what we need to know. Most people do not have the time to spare, and it is so easy to be misled by those who control the retailing of our food.

These thoughts are with me as we travel between Birmingham and the next mighty metropolis, Greater Manchester. My first experience of travelling this far north was as a boy of thirteen. There were no motorways then, apart from the London to Birmingham stretch of the M1. We travelled on ordinary A-class roads to visit friends who lived in Bury, then a town in its own right. Now all those towns around Manchester have joined up, stretching from Rochdale to Wilmslow and from Urmston to Stalybridge. Worse than that, it is only five minutes on the motorway from Stalybridge to Huddersfield and the Leeds conurbation.

However, as we head along the M6 towards all this, we manage to catch a few glimpses of real countryside, with fields and black-and-white cows. As if in homage to this rural scene, a southbound 40-tonner comes into view sporting a black and white livery just like one of these cows. The truck also carries the easy-on-the-eye green oval logo of Robert Wiseman. Just another truck on the motorway – who would give it a second glance? Maybe a small child in the back of a car might just spot it and say, "Oooh look Mummy, the lorry's dressed like a cow!" This quirky paint job is no doubt designed to evoke this kind of positive response, and there is no doubt about the fact that it is noticeable. But that is as far as it goes with most people. Like the Rathbone's truck, it tells you very little about the company.

Get into the website, however, and a very different picture emerges. The first thing that hits you on the home page is the corporate look. Dominating the page is the succinct mission statement, "Robert Wiseman Dairies procures, processes and delivers liquid milk to customers throughout Great Britain." By way of emphasis, the statement appears twice. Other than that, the clean lines of the page design let you know immediately that you are dealing with an organisation whose preoccupation is with efficiency and, by implication, profitability. Nothing wrong with that, of course. We all need to be efficient, whether we are running a business or not and, if we are running a business, profitability is essential. Without it, insolvency looms. Yet I get an uncomfortable feeling looking at this page. Could it be because the company's current share price is prominently displayed? Perhaps it is because the buttons on the toolbar appear to be too cold to belong to a company dealing with food: Corporate Profile, Investor Centre, Media Centre, Corporate Responsibility, Careers and Contact Us. Nothing about milk.

By way of digression, I must define what I mean by 'corporate' and 'the corporation'. Every legally defined company, even if it is a virtual one man band, is 'incorporated' in law, and therefore can be defined as a corporation. But there is a big difference between John Jones Ltd. and the kind of global organisations that run our modern world. That difference is that the big corporations are shareholder-driven, whereas the small private company, even though it will have share capital, is more often than not run on private funds. For the purposes of this book, 'the corporation' and its corporate activities refer to the big players who rely for their existence and growth on shareholder investment – corporations such as Robert Wiseman Dairies, who we can now get back to.

On the Robert Wiseman website, two brief but descriptive paragraphs about what the company does are full of Bizspeak, with phrases like 'processing dairies', 'product' and 'a strong and diverse customer base'. Recently, we are told, the company has 'expanded its business with the multiples so that, now, the Company is a major supplier to many of the sector's leading players'. All very laudable, but also very corporate. The multiples? The sector's leading players? More business euphemisms for 'global supermarkets'.

The company has come a long way since Robert Wiseman Senior started up in 1947, delivering milk in cans and bottles with his horse and cart. In the late 1970s, the company really began to grow via acquisitions. It now operates five dairies in Scotland and England, the largest of which is at Droitwich in Worcestershire. Here they process 500 million litres per annum. Much of their production goes straight into the supermarkets. Their web pages on corporate strategy are all about being bigger than anyone else – but this is the raison d'être of all corporations. It is symptomatic of what is wrong with our food supply systems.

Robert Wiseman Dairies plc is a success story – on the stock exchange at least. It is the result of one man's desire to ensure that his family business remained alive, and one must admire the tenacity and drive of the company's founder and his sons in moving the business from a horse and cart milk round to one that sells well over a billion litres a year. However, as much as I recognise this achievement in company growth, I take issue with how this has become possible.

I cannot see anything positive in the way farming has been industrialised, nor can I admire the acquiescence of all our governments since World War II in the concept of 'farming is a business like any other'. Such a concept has produced rich companies like Robert Wiseman Dairies but it has severely compromised the quality of what is farmed and made it impossible for all but the most determined or foolhardy of farmers to stay in business themselves. While Robert Wiseman continues to attract keen investors willing to back a company determined to be the 'supplier of choice' in a ruthless marketplace, three dairy farmers a day are going out of business because that same ruthless marketplace has driven down the price they are paid from 24.5p per litre in 1995 to 18p now, despite the fact that all costs of production continue to rise. A price of 18p a litre is below production costs. In that same period of time, supermarkets have managed to increase their margins from 3p to 16p per litre. Tesco buys 60% of its milk from Robert Wiseman, a company turning over £600 million per annum, with an operating profit of £35.7m. A mere 5.95% net profit and only 2.3p per litre – but that's volume sales for you. So everyone is getting a slice of the cake except the farmers who produce the milk.

Business sector gurus dispel this as just another manifestation of market forces. But real people are losing their livelihoods, and real people like me sense that there is something seriously wrong with all of this. Those farmers who manage to stay in business are doing so by the skin of their teeth, many of them in debt to the banks. In some cases, the indebtedness is such as to demonstrate total unviability of the operation, but the banks are curbing their instinct to foreclose, because of the damaging effect on land values, something that ultimately hurts the banks themselves. This is the emotive side of the issue, and much has been said about it, in political, economic and human terms. The debate continues, of course. Important as this may be, there is more that is fundamentally wrong with the dairy industry than this debate indicates. A brief look at its development over the last half a century will help us focus on these flaws.

The austerity of the war years and the rationing that continued until 1954 generated a zealous drive for self-sufficiency in the UK. A new kind of farming, nowadays inexplicably called 'conventional', was born in the wake of wartime food shortages. This was farming with chemicals, and its effects can be seen in the vast prairie lands of southern England, where hundreds of miles of hedgerows have been ripped out over the last fifty years to accommodate this new idea of growing crops on an industrial scale. What is less obvious is how this drive towards intensive farming has affected the dairy industry.

We are all used to seeing those familiar black-and-white cows contentedly grazing in the fields, and for many of us this is almost the last link with our childhood recollections of what farming was all about. It is difficult to relate to a thousand acres of wheat, but a black-and-white cow, or any cow for that matter, in a green field can still touch our souls. The imagery is used emotively and effectively by everyone from Robert Wiseman Dairies to the manufacturers of BabyBel cheese and all those whose business it is to promote dairy products. Cows have such an accessible image that it has even appeared in the world of popular music – Pink Floyd once used a picture of a cow on the cover of an album, *Atom Heart Mother*, released in1970. Cows are real in a way that a field of wheat can never be. We see cows out there in the fields, and to us they look perfectly normal and just as they always have done. Maybe this is why very few people question anything to do with the production of milk.

The drive for self-sufficiency after World War II increased the powers of the Milk Marketing Board, originally set up in 1933 to regulate the supply of milk in the UK. Incentives to increase yields were introduced. Forty years later, in 1973, when Britain joined the then European Economic Community, more intensive methods of dairy farming were introduced, following further incentives via the Common Agricultural Policy (CAP). The CAP was effectively subsidising farmers into intensive over-production, resulting in the infamous butter mountains and milk lakes. The effect this had on the quality of milk has been disastrous, though played down to the point of silence.

I know what a glass of milk tastes like, and I know that standard supermarket milk is nothing like it. Milk features in one of my most vivid childhood memories, when I would walk down the lane from my Grandpa's farm to the neighbour's farm, where I would 'help' Pip Robertson and his father milk their small herd. I suspect that my help generally consisted of getting in the way and asking too many questions. However, once milking was done, my reward was to be given a drink of this gorgeous, aromatic, warm and creamy liquid. Not quite straight from the cow, the Robertsons having progressed to what was then a modern milking shed, but it was fresh, it was real and it was a taste that I am sad to say my own children have never experienced.

Unaware of the politics of milk production at the time, I cannot tell you anything about the regulations that the Robertsons were tied to, but I can tell you that the day's production was put into aluminium churns and left for collection by the milk lorry. Its destination would have been some central dairy. This was in the late '50s, and already milk production was well on its way to industrialisation. On the plus side, the milk left in those churns for collection was of the highest quality, in common with much of Britain's milk production at that time. But dairy farmers were under pressure to increase their yields, and bad practices began to creep into the industry.

Cows are herbivores, which means that they like to eat grass. If the cows across the road from our house this week are anything to go by, they are also partial to a flower or two. Our neighbour's young heifers have been out in the meadow these last two days chewing the heads off all the buttercups. In an ideal world, this is exactly what they should be doing at this time of year – grazing flower-rich spring growth traditional pasture. Sadly, it is no longer an ideal world and the sight of cows doing what comes naturally is becoming rarer. All too often, even the grass they eat is the herbivore's equivalent of junk food, but more on that later.

From the archaeological record, it is clear that Man's involvement with the herding, domesticating and milking of certain wild animals is a tradition that goes back at least as far as the dawn of agriculture, if not beyond. It would appear that the value of milk as an important food source was recognised at least 10,000 years ago. According to Joann Grohman in *Keeping a Family Cow*, there is evidence that as long ago as 30,000 years "people in the High Sinai were confining and breeding antelope with the aid of fences". During our long history of shepherding around the world, we have tried milking a variety of animals, including sheep, goats, donkeys, horses, buffalo, camels, llamas, yaks, reindeer and other antelopes. But the one animal that stands out from all the rest is the cow, widely used around the world as a source of meat and milk. Milk and other dairy foods, such as yoghurt, cheese and butter, have a long tradition of consumption in nearly every human culture, with the interesting exception of East and South East Asia.

Considered by many cultures over many thousands of years to be the perfect food, milk certainly lives up to its reputation when it comes to nutritional value, but it must be heavily stressed at this point that I am referring to traditional *real* milk, that is to say fresh milk from animals that have grazed on rich healthy pasture, milk that has not been contaminated by chemicals and has not been pasteurised, homogenised or adulterated in any other way.

In this condition, milk is a supremely simple whole food. Within that creamy liquid, however, there is a complexity of nutrients that adds tremendous value to this simple food. Milk from traditional grass-fed cows is full of enzymes and micro-organisms and rich in fat-soluble vitamins A, D, E and K. Vitamins A and E are powerful antioxidants, protecting us from pollutants and free radicals, and therefore good anti-cancer agents. Vitamin D is essential for strong bones and teeth and Vitamin K is essential in blood clotting.

Also present in real milk are essential fatty acids, particularly the one that most people have now heard of, Omega-3. Less well known is the unique and highly beneficial conjugated linoleic acid (CLA) a powerful anti-cancer agent. CLA is present in large amounts in milk from cows grazing on traditional pasture, and is concentrated in cream and the butter made from it. The more complex the pasture, i.e. the greater the presence within the pasture of native species such as plantain, self-heal, red clover and bird's foot trefoil, the higher the level of CLA. The further away we get from this type of pasture, the lower the levels of not only CLA but also all other nutrients.

Much has been written about the benefits of milk, and just as much has been written condemning milk as a modern-day demon. But, as Nina Planck says in her book, *Real Food*, "all milk is not created equal". In trying to understand the arguments for and against milk, it is essential to establish what kind of milk is being talked about – is it real, unpasteurised milk from grass-fed small herds, or is it industrialised milk from intensively reared milkers living on an unnatural diet?

Going back to the end of World War II, dairy farming was still fairly traditional. Dairy cattle grazed on pasture land in herds that were generally small and manageable. Although the milk from these herds was being processed under the supervision of the Milk Marketing Board, the milk itself was generally of good quality. Nowadays we would call it organic, but of course back in the 1950s, and even into the 1960s, there was no need for the term because farming was predominantly 'organic' by default anyway.

Dramatic changes have taken place since then. Principally, yields have gone up. From an average yield of around 3000 litres per cow per year in the '50s, it is now around 6500 litres on average, but yields of 10,000 litres are not unheard of in some high-production herds. In order to achieve these yields, most of the old specialist dairy breeds suited to local conditions have disappeared, their places taken by custom-built hybrid Holstein-Friesians, the ubiquitous black-and-white breed that now accounts for 90% of the EU's dairy herd. Because a cow is able to transfer only a fixed amount of vitamins to her milk, the first thing that happens with higher yields is that the vitamin content is diluted. Then we have the problem of how these monster milkers are bred and what they are eating.

Modern hybrids have been selectively bred from animals with overactive pituitary glands. The pituitary glands secrete hormones that stimulate the production of milk. Unfortunately, they also secrete growth hormones, which inevitably turn up in the milk. According to a study carried out in 1997, high levels of pituitary hormones have been linked to the formation of tumours that lead to breast cancer. Another knock-on effect is that these 'high-performance animals', as Graham Harvey calls them in *We Want Real Food*, cannot sustain themselves on grass alone. They need high-performance, energy-rich protein supplements to keep them going.

One cheap and plentiful energy source is from cereals such as wheat, maize and barley. Grain like this comes from the industrialised cereal fields discussed in the previous chapter, so they are already nutritionally depleted and contaminated with pesticides. Other 'foods', such as potato waste and bread discarded by the bread factories, may also turn up in the diet of these Holstein milk machines. Extra protein comes from soya bean, groundnut or rapeseed meal, most of which is once again contaminated with pesticides. In their zeal to get extra protein into their cows, dairy farmers until recently also indulged in the utter madness of feeding their cows animal products in the form of meat and bone meal. Many people seemed surprised when dairy cows began to stagger and collapse, mortally afflicted with bovine spongiform encephalopathy (BSE) or 'mad cow disease', as it was more popularly known, but what can we expect when we turn herbivores into cannibalistic carnivores? We live in an insane world in which abnormal foods are creating abnormal cows producing abnormal quantities of abnormal milk.

It has been said that, in metabolic terms, the amount of work an average modern dairy cow has to do in her short life is the equivalent of a human being having to jog for six hours a day every day until they drop. Anyone having to do that would not last too long, and neither does the dairy cow, usually sent to slaughter at five years old, after only three years of milking – a short life in a potential maximum of 25 years. Traditional dairy breeds could be expected to produce milk naturally for about ten years. It seems to me that our modern dairy industry is rife with malpractice on a number of counts, not least of which is the inhumane exploitation of animals.

This level of overwork, as well as the ingestion of an unnatural diet, leads to many other problems. Put simply, modern dairy cows are sick. Unsurprisingly, forcing grass eaters to consume large quantities of starchy grains, soya bean protein and possibly fish- and meat-based supplements causes digestive problems. The cow's rumen, the first stomach in its digestive tract and designed to break down the cellulose in grass, becomes over-acidic with too much starch. To counteract this, the rumen microbes produce extra lactic acid. This can be absorbed into the cow's bloodstream, disrupting normal metabolism. Excess acid also kills the normal micro-organisms present in the rumen, leaving the way clear for pathogenic microbes to multiply. These include the *E.coli* 0157 strain, which can be seriously harmful, possibly even fatal, to humans.

Lameness, another side effect of over-acidity in the rumen, is also endemic in our dairy herds. Over-acidity produces toxins and histamines in the blood, which then permanently damage the blood vessels to the foot. Much of the cows' time in the milk shed is also spent with their back legs standing in the dung slurry, causing their hooves to soften and crack and allow infection to enter.

Sick cows are less able to defend themselves against any invasion of pathogens, and the intensive nature of their lives as milkers leaves them prone to the udder infection, mastitis. It is estimated that 40% of our national dairy herd suffers from some form of mastitis. However, a study by Bristol University published in 2005 suggests that the figure may be nearer 70%. As the cow's body attempts to fight off the bacterial invasion that is causing the mastitis, pus is produced and is secreted into the milk we end up drinking. The disease is treated by injecting antibiotics into the udders, and these too can end up in our milk.

In fifty years, dairy farming has gone from the natural process that I witnessed as a child to pure industrialisation. Dairy cows today are no more than cogs in a factory production system of conveyor belt commodity goods, in this case milk. By the time this milk reaches the retail outlets, most of it is nothing more than a contaminated, nutritionally depleted, substandard non-food. Those that would argue against this are those who stand to gain most from maintaining the status quo. The scientists and technologists certainly know that all is not well, and they are kept busy inventing new ways to keep every dairy cow on target whilst at the same time bolstering this inferior milk with artificial versions of the nutrients that have been lost.

Dairy cows no longer solely eat grass and herbs, the food nature intended and for which their digestive systems are specifically designed. They now eat what the lab boys call Total Mixed Rations (TMR). This includes some grass-based feed, mostly silage, in order to keep some semblance of natural digestion in the cow's system, but the rest is made up of the energy-rich cereals and high-protein feeds needed for higher milk yields. Into the mix also goes an artificial mineral supplement to make up for those absent in these industrial grains.

In terms of human nutrition, one major preoccupation these days is with the diminished levels of Omega-3 in our diet, a high proportion of which would have come from the milk of pasture-fed cows. To get over the deficit, the scientists and dairy technologists have come up with the idea of adding fish oil to TMR. This is their answer to the problem of the bigger, more intensive herds hardly setting foot in a pasture meadow these days, and thus having little or no chance of eating the food that would give us Omega-3 in our milk. Increasingly, these herds are kept indoors for months at a time, living in pens in huge warehouse barns where they can be fed a controlled diet.

Further strain is put on natural dairy farming by the demand for a continuous supply to the processing plants. Fifty years ago, on traditional dairy farms, cows calved in the spring. Thus a cow's lactation peak coincided with the new growth of rich spring grass. Milk was rich and nutritious, and the surplus was available to turn into butter and cheese. With factory production, however, emphasis is on plant efficiency. The plant must be kept operating at optimum levels throughout the year, otherwise the company loses money. This puts pressure on the farmer to keep the milk flowing even in the winter months, and that is when more reliance is put on grains, silage and soya bean protein feeds.

As with many of the principles of intensive farming, we have taken our lead from the United States. The principle of housing dairy cows indoors for most of the year is a matter of fact across the Atlantic. Here dairy cattle are penned all year round in warehouses that will accommodate hundreds of cows at a time, under daylong artificial light if necessary (another way of increasing the yield). At milking time, the cows merely walk from their individual pens to the milking station. It is all about maximising output and minimising labour costs. To me it is a nightmare scenario of barbaric animal exploitation.

Some intensive dairy herds are occasionally let out to graze, but traditional grazing lands, like the arable fields for intensive crop production, have fallen foul of the chemical companies. Back in the days when I would watch Pip Robertson milk his small herd, the land upon which his cows grazed was rich with wildflower species such as clover, various vetches, other native wild flowers and herbs and different species of native grass. Variety, after all, is the spice of life, and this applies to dairy cows too. Once the intensive farming lobby was on the march, however, this all changed. The chemical fertiliser companies believe in monoculture for all crops – it is so much easier to design fertilisers and pesticides to control them. As chemical farming took hold, so our farmers were persuaded, with the help of successive British governments, that perennial ryegrass was the thing to sow on temporary grass leys. So out went all the mixed pasture and in came one strain of grass and nothing else. I am no dairy cow, but it strikes me that this must have produced an intensely boring feeding experience for our national dairy herd. But in terms of milk yield, ryegrass growing on chemical nitrogen fertiliser puts on more growth than traditional species, so the theory is that the farmer can feed more cattle on less land. Ryegrass could also be turned into silage, so farmers were also talked out of their traditional practice of maintaining hay meadows which were cut once a year for winter fodder. Making silage with intensively grown ryegrass meant increasing the output of grassland.

Like the wheat and other cereal crops, however, perennial ryegrass grown as a monoculture suffers from the same depletion of vitamins, minerals and nutrients. The cows eat this silage through the winter, but as they are not getting the nutrition they need from it, the milk they give is also nutritionally depleted. The equation is simple: poor food in = poor milk out. We feed our dairy herds on nutritionally deficient and chemically polluted grass, we supplement the grass with equally poor quality cereal crops that dairy cows have difficulty in digesting, adding soya bean protein and possibly even animal protein, ignoring the fact that cows are herbivores, and then we drink the milk that comes from these overworked milk machines – but not before the huge processing dairies get their hands on it.

To those who profit most from the dairy industry, namely the supermarkets, milk is not seen as a food but as just another commodity. And those who serve the supermarkets, namely the industrial dairies, are happy to go along with this idea, in exchange for just enough of a profit margin to make volume production their only viable option. Before the milk reaches the supermarket shelves, it must be processed and packaged to suit its commodity status.

The first process it undergoes is pasteurisation. Named after the French scientist, Louis Pasteur, who completed his first test of this new heat sterilisation treatment in 1862, this process generally involves heating the milk to 72°C for two 15-second periods. The story goes that Pasteur originally intended the process to improve the keeping qualities of certain liquids, such as milk, and that is still the principal purpose for its use today. We are, however, sold the 'health' message too, and we are told that pasteurisation is designed to kill off harmful pathogens, such as *salmonella*, *E.coli* and *campylobacter*. Unfortunately, pasteurisation also kills off vitamins, enzymes and beneficial bacteria such as *Lactobacillus acidophilus*, as well as adversely affecting taste and texture. Arguments for and against pasteurisation continue, but no spokesperson from the pro-pasteurisation camp has yet been able to deny that the process kills off much of the goodness in milk as well as some pathogens.

Furthermore, and somewhat disturbingly, it could well be that Pasteur was wrong. There are many who believe that Pasteur plagiarised most of his work from a contemporary of his, Antoine Béchamp and, in doing so, fatally misinterpreted Béchamp's work. Both men studied disease, but their views were diametrically opposed. Béchamp believed in pleomorphism (plural lives) and Pasteur believed in monomorphism. Thus Béchamp's theory was that the cells of our bodies carry the potential for disease, and benign germs within our cells morph into something lethal if a suitable change occurs in their environment. Pasteur on the other hand believed that a specific germ maintained only one form throughout its lifecycle. In establishing his Germ Theory, Pasteur expounded the idea that germs invade our bodies and cause disease, completely missing the point that Béchamp was making, i.e. germs within the body mutate into more harmful forms as a result of cells made 'sick' through poor nutrition or some other agency. Another player in this game was Robert Koch, a German industrial chemist, who saw in Pasteur's theories an opportunity to manufacture chemical combatants against invasive germs. The medical profession at the time responded favourably to Koch's 'magic bullets', chemicals designed to kill specific germs, and the world turned its back on Béchamp and his theory that if we keep ourselves healthy, our immune systems will repel disease. It can be argued that, as a result of this, all medical practice is fatally flawed, but it is not an argument I wish to enter at this stage. However, one fact that is inescapable is that pasteurisation of milk is now seen as normal practice.

Pasteurisation of milk as a policy was considered during the first quarter of the 20th century in response to increased public concern about the cleanness of milk. Industrialisation was still gathering pace at that time, and the drift from country to town created a new demand from the growing urban populations for goods and food. With regards to the supply of milk, this encouraged zealous entrepreneurs to set up new urban dairies. Their standards of cleanliness, however, were somewhat lacking, as were their scruples when it came to what they fed their cows. Waste products from breweries were a favourite due to cheapness and plentiful supply. The quality of milk deteriorated to such an extent that something had to be done, and pasteurisation was deemed to be the answer. It seems, however, that the finger of blame was pointed in the wrong direction. According to Nina Planck, in 1908, whilst the matter of public health was being discussed, a panel of 'experts' appointed by President Theodore Roosevelt claimed that raw unpasteurised milk was responsible for food-borne illnesses. Like many panels of experts, they completely missed the point. Let's face it, if there was a diametric difference of opinion between the two people credited with investigating such illnesses, any given panel of experts would have only a 50-50 chance of coming up with the right answer. In this case, they got it wrong, and the damage was done. This kiss of death instantly demonised real milk.

Though there is much evidence today that raw milk from traditionally farmed pasture-fed cows is a thoroughly nutritious food full of vitamins, minerals and beneficial micro-organisms, the demon is still out there, prowling the media. My suspicion is that governments and those with a financial interest in milk as a commodity just cannot be bothered with real milk because it now represents such a tiny percentage of all milk production, and to become involved in the distribution of it to what is in effect a minority is not what giant processors and retailers are about. Quite simply, anything of limited sales potential just does not make it onto the supermarket shelves. When it comes to milk, because it is an industrial food, the simplest answer is to treat it all the same and pasteurise the lot. In any case, milk that is processed through the intensive dairy system is in such poor condition that it really needs to be pasteurised to give the general public any chance of not being adversely affected by it. But it seems a bizarre irony that, in the few places where raw milk can be purchased legally, the containers it is sold in have to carry a government health warning!

A farmer wishing to sell unpasteurised milk has to go through a detailed and rigorous procedure in order to get certification. He would probably find it easier to smuggle drugs into North Korea. He is required to have a herd of traditional pasture-fed cows and work to the highest standards of environmental care and animal husbandry. His cows must be fit, healthy and free from all the aliments suffered by the overworked Holstein milk machines. His dairy must be scrupulously clean and he must sell his milk at the peak of freshness. Yet on every container he must put a label that says, "This milk has not been heat treated and therefore may contain organisms harmful to health." And so the myth continues, and meanwhile the intensive dairy farmers carry on supplying the market with a poor quality, potentially toxic non-food masquerading as milk which is then processed out of all recognition and sold to us as a 'healthy' product. It is indeed a supreme irony.

This, however, is not the full story. Cream is a value-added product in its own right, so this is removed from the milk, effectively creating a situation whereby the milk can be sold twice. To disguise the fact that the cream has been removed, the remaining milk is homogenised. This means that it is passed through some high pressure equipment that, to quote from the sales catalogue of one firm that makes it, 'creates conditions of high turbulence and shear, combined with compression, acceleration, pressure drop and impact, causing disintegration of particles and dispersion throughout the product'. This is milk we are talking about – nature's original food. But it has been reduced to nothing more than an engineering problem, illustrating perfectly how our food has been adulterated. So, the process of homogenisation means that the milk is fired through tiny holes in the homogenising gun, which causes the fat particles to break up into globules so small that they cannot reform, and thus become part of the liquid within which they are suspended. And when the plastic milk containers are lined up in the chiller cabinet of your local supermarket, they appear to be completely filled with a white liquid which displays no signs at all of the fact that milk should have a head of cream on it. The exception to this rule, and the only one that looks anything at all like milk, is organic whole milk that has not been homogenised. Even this, however, is virtually a specialist product and available only in limited quantities in certain outlets. And it is still pasteurised!

Having undergone all of this, the nutritionally deficient commodity milk that arrives in our shops (it is hardly ever delivered by the milkman anymore) is now deemed, by those authorities that believe they are qualified to make such decisions, to be fit for human consumption. I disagree. In fact, I would go as far as to say that I believe it is harmful. Before we look into my reasons for this, we should look at what else is being said about milk.

Firstly, milk is condemned by diet gurus. They say that the cream in milk is mostly saturated fat and that saturated fat is bad for us. American scientists, trying to establish a cause for the rising incidence of heart disease through the 1950s and 1960s, concluded that animal fats and cholesterol-rich foods raise blood cholesterol, which furs up the arteries, restricts the flow of blood and causes heart attacks. Thus the reputation of saturated animal fats, including cream, butter, eggs and meat fat, was cast into the outer darkness. Despite the fact that so much more has since been discovered about the way cholesterol behaves, and these discoveries have largely dismissed the arguments against saturated fats, the myth persists, as such myths have a habit of doing. You have only to look at what has happened to the reputation of real milk (or mutton, to quote another example) to know that this is true.

Latest research reveals that saturated fats are in fact essential to human nutrition, playing a role in protecting the immune system, fighting pathogens and contributing to the normal function of vital organs, including the heart, kidneys and lungs. This represents another vindication of the benefits of real milk, but access to this valuable food is practically denied us because it is not a sellable product line for the giant processors and retailers. Let's face it, they would prefer not to stock whole milk of any description, let alone *raw* whole milk. Whole milk is less profitable, so the big players try to dissuade us from buying it by reciting redundant dogma along the lines of: whole milk bad; skimmed milk good. This perfectly suits an industry geared to removing the cream from the milk and selling it to us at a premium price. Even some of the facts about the composition of milk have been deliberately skewed in order to kill the demand for whole milk. We all know that advertisers are legally obliged to tell the truth, but there is nothing to stop them telling you just those bits of truth they want to highlight, or to use a half-truth as part of a bigger message.

Take the fat content of milk, for instance. On average, in whole milk, this is between three and four grams per hundred. With Jersey and Guernsey cows, this may go up to 5.5%. Skimmed milk is generally less than 1%, while semi-skimmed is 2%. Most of the buying public, having been persuaded that whole milk is a serious no-no because of its 'very high fat content', opt for semi-skimmed as a reasonable compromise between this 'dangerous' fatty whole milk and the completely tasteless skimmed version. The media message has sunk in, and it is reinforced every day in the supermarkets and health and lifestyle magazines. So often is the same message repeated that no one has to bother to think anymore. Bombarded by health messages, we now live in a mindless daze. But much can be discovered by just stopping to think for a moment and by asking questions.

For instance, what's the difference between whole milk and semi-skimmed? Answer – about 2% fat. So that makes skimmed milk a low-fat food then? Well, that's what the big processors and retailers would have us believe. But milk is nearly 90% water, so the rest of it, 10%, contains everything else, including the carbohydrates, proteins and fats. Out of every 100 grams of whole milk, 10 grams is the nutrient portion, and 40% of this is fat. Semi-skimmed milk is just skimmed milk that has had half the normal amount of cream put back. So this means that semi-skimmed milk is around 95% water and 5% nutrients. The proportion of fats is again around 40%. So semi-skimmed, the UK's favourite, is technically no more a 'low-fat' food than whole milk. The nutritionists' definition of a 'low-fat' food is based on the number of calories by weight that a food delivers. In the case of whole milk or semi-skimmed, the fat provides around 60% of the calories, and the nutritionists say that this figure should be 30% or less to define a food as 'low-fat'. This sounds a bit like one of those American short-change scams (works best with dollars, because all the notes are the same size and colour) where someone buys something for 50 cents and manages to come away from the shop with the change plus a $10 bill. But that's consmanship for you, and the milk scam is just that – a con.

Then there is the fat itself. The story is that whole milk has far too much saturated fat in it to make it healthy, and we are sold the idea that 4% fat is enough to set the alarm bells going. Two things to consider here – most whole milk sold in this country is only 3.65% fat, and not all of this 3.65% is saturated. In an average sample of milk, the saturated fat is around 1.9%, the rest being made up of monounsaturated fats and a small amount of polyunsaturated fats. There is enough evidence now to show that saturated fats are an essential part of a normal diet, but even for those people who still believe the opposite, surely a figure of only 1.9% saturated fat is a cause, not for fear, but for jubilation.

Milk is not condemned solely by the diet gurus and by those who live in fear of it because of what they have been told about saturated fats. There is a growing movement against milk and dairy products of any description, as a result of the increasing incidence of intolerance to milk and all its derivatives. Medical journals, lifestyle magazines, the mainstream press and certain publications by the Vegetarian and Vegan Foundation have all run articles condemning milk and dairy products. Cases are cited of babies and children with milk allergies.

As an aside, I have observed in these publications that there is widespread confusion about the difference between 'allergy' and 'intolerance'. Just for the record, an allergy is a hypersensitive reaction to a particular food that can, in some cases, be life-threatening, and which afflicts a relatively small number of people; a food intolerance results from the inability of the body's immune system to combat something perceived as invasive. With reference to the articles written on the subject, practically without exception the milk to which they refer is pasteurised. No differentiation is made between real milk and commercially produced commodity milk, and there appears to be an assumption that all milk is the same.

Raw unpasteurised milk is not the same as pasteurised milk, and raw milk from traditionally reared grass-fed contented cows is a world away from pasteurised, homogenised, semi-skimmed, commodity 'milk' from over-fed, over-milked, indoor-reared Holstein milk machines living short, brutish lives. I make no apology for the emotive language, because it is important to distinguish between real milk and what is generally being sold to us as milk.

Real milk, as discussed by, amongst others, Pat Hagan in the Daily Mail on 7th August 2006, is full of health-giving properties. Far from making anyone allergic to dairy products, it is more likely to help in controlling, reducing or even eliminating other allergies. The article cites examples of how feeding untreated milk to children can reduce their risk of suffering allergy-related conditions such as eczema and hayfever.

It is just one hundred years since someone in New York attempted to blame untreated milk for society's ills, and the arguments, for and against, just will not go away. Much has been written about the health-giving properties of real milk, and many highly qualified and learned individuals since 1907 have stated a positive case for its consumption. Although more references will be made to this further on in the text, it is beyond the scope of this book to examine in detail the works of Dr Charles Sandford Porter, Dr J R Crewe and the famous Cleveland dentist, Weston A Price, all of whom have set out very detailed arguments in support of real milk. However, for those of you who wish to investigate this further, there are two websites which will give you instant access to much valuable information. The first is that of the Weston A Price Foundation, www.westonaprice.org and the second is a site which details many aspects of real food in general, www.seedsofhealth.co.uk. The latter is in need of updating, but the information on it is still relevant and important.

As we see, untreated milk has suffered from a bad, if somewhat misguided, press. Bad news, as we all know, travels fast and just refuses to go away, and so, amongst the misconceptions surrounding real milk, there is the belief that 'you get brucellosis from drinking unpasteurised milk.' In an article on the *Seeds of Health* website, entitled The Case for Untreated Milk, written by Dr B M Pickard, this point is taken up and put into context. From the article it can be seen that brucellosis is simply one of a list of food-borne infections which may or may not be contracted from raw milk, that its incidence is rare and that it is quite likely to be caught by the vet treating the sick animal as it is by someone drinking the milk from that animal. The article is useful in the way it deals dispassionately with the whole question of food-borne illnesses, and is far more factual (as well as highly annotated with relevant references) than your average urban myth.

In searching for the reasons for the growing intolerance to dairy products, I think it is fair to say that they are unlikely to be found by looking at unpasteurised milk. Speaking as one who has undergone rigorous testing for food intolerance, I can quote directly from my own experience. In one session, I was tested on organic semi-skimmed milk from a local dairy (but a relatively big one) and on unpasteurised milk from a farmer who used to supply us at that time with milk from a small herd of grass-fed Jerseys. The results were dramatic. Whilst failing miserably on the organic semi-skimmed commodity milk, I was 'as strong as an ox' on the unpasteurised version.

Each of us is entitled to our own opinion on anything and everything, and these writings may be considered to be no more than my opinion. No doubt if I were sitting across the table from a spokesman for the dairy industry or the chairman of Robert Wiseman plc, I would be shouted down for uttering such heretical opinions. Nonetheless, I believe in the efficacy of the testing, and for me it was all the proof I personally needed that commodity milk is harmful to our systems. I believe that this is where the root of the problem is with regard to our society's increasing intolerance to dairy products. I further believe that such intolerance is limited to the products of our industrialised dairy system and would not manifest itself if the milk we were using was pure, clean, real and untreated.

I am not alone. Much research has been done over the years, and many books and articles have been written in which the conclusions are much the same as my own. There is a great deal of understanding about what kind of damage is done to milk as a result of the way it is produced and processed for sale and I am certainly not the first person to say so. To quote from Nina Planck, for example, "Pasteurisation inactivates the enzymes required to absorb the nutrients in milk: lipase (to digest fats); lactase (to digest lactose); and phosphatase (to absorb calcium)." She goes on to say, "Pasteurisation also creates oxidised cholesterol, alters milk proteins and damages Omega-3 fats."

Despite much advertising propaganda to the contrary, it appears that by simply pasteurising our milk, we are in fact impairing the ability of our bodies to absorb any goodness that the milk contains, including the calcium, the presence of which is one of the cornerstones of the sales pitch. This would be the case even for good milk from pasture-fed cows. If in fact the milk comes from intensively reared cows, then we are effectively lost before we start. The combination of pesticide-infected feed, too much soya bean protein in the diet, growth hormones and antibiotics (as well as pus cells from the mastitis that the antibiotics are there to fix) the pasteurisation, homogenisation and even the packaging of milk in plastic containers creates a cocktail of harmful ingredients that our immune systems cannot easily deal with. It should not take a genius to work out why an intolerance to 'dairy products' is on the increase. However, in order to recognise what it is that so many people are intolerant to these days, it is essential to understand the difference between real dairy products and the cheap industrialised imitation.

Unless one takes the trouble to read, question and investigate, it would not come to light in the normal course of events that the milk we buy from the supermarkets is nothing like the milk our grandparents consumed. Thus, when milk is talked about, by farmers, retailers, governments, scientists, teachers, The Vegetarian and Vegan Foundation (VVF), or even round-the-world yachtswoman, Tracy

Edwards (who loves the stuff, allegedly) the milk in question is that which is generally available – commodity milk. Within the list above, there are opinions that are diametrically opposite. The VVF, for example, say that all dairy products are deadly, whereas Tracy Edwards says she drinks a pint of milk every day. No doubt, if she were questioned further, she would claim that milk keeps her healthy, at which members of the VVF would no doubt shake their heads in disbelief. The fact is, we are all different and we all have different immune systems. Mine, for instance, is prone to attack, making me somewhat sensitive to bad foods. Sally, by contrast, has a very strong immune system that she has no doubt inherited from her mother. She has been able to maintain a healthy body despite a diet that formerly contained some 'foods' that she would studiously avoid today.

It is this difference in all of us, this unique individuality, which makes any discussion on food difficult in terms of reaching a consensus on any given topic. It would be so much simpler if we all reacted positively to, say, unpasteurised milk and all became ill on commodity milk. But we don't. Some of us practically exist on a junk food diet with no visible ill effects, and others, careful to maintain an organic wholefood diet, get sick or die too young. It is all a matter of an individual's constitution and history of food consumption. We need look no further than a typical modern refugee camp, archive photographs of British soldiers in Burmese prison camps or those haunting images from Auschwitz, to realise that, even under the same extreme conditions of life and diet, some wither quickly whilst others seem almost indestructible.

This does make it difficult to spot the differences between real milk and commodity milk, between real bread and processed bread, but that is exactly why the differences should be highlighted. It is important to know what we are persuaded to eat by slick sales pitches and glib advertising. It is equally important to know that there is an alternative, however hard that may be to find. With just a little knowledge, we can get behind the advertising and not be taken in by gimmicks such as the visually appealing black-and-white livery of Robert Wiseman's trucks.

EVERY LITTLE HURTS

We manage to get past the Manchester motorway system without any trouble. Traffic is heavy but moving at a reasonable pace. We feel we are on the way now. North of Preston, the scenery changes and the countryside really begins to open up, giving a sense of space after the industrial Midlands and the great Mancunian sprawl. This northern half of Lancashire is a lovely part of the county, such a welcome after the claustrophobia of conurbation and well worth a closer look, but it will have to wait for another time. As that thought goes through my head, I realise that it occurs every time I am on the M6, because invariably on any trip north of Manchester I am heading for Scotland, thus denying myself the pleasure of exploring England's north-west corner.

Two Asda forty-tonners, separated by a van, a smaller lorry and two cars, come towards us on the southbound side. It seems only moments since we overtook a Morrisons truck, tattooed with huge strawberries indicating, bafflingly, More Reasons for shopping there. And at regular intervals the inevitable Tesco trucks of course, each one reassuring us of Tesco's concern for our wellbeing by displaying the declaration, 'You shop, we drop', or the company strapline, 'every little helps'. With Tesco now controlling 30% of the total grocery market in the UK, not everyone agrees with this three-word summary of how the company promotes its customer care. Take for instance the new campaign group by the name of Tescopoly. Using Tesco's avuncular but specious little assurance, they have turned Tesco's famous strapline into their very own, 'every little hurts'. Tescopoly, www.tescopoly.org, sets out to stand in the way of these juggernaut retailers and slow them down long enough for government and a hitherto unsuspecting public to take notice of the negative impact of their presence in the retail marketplace.

The big four, Tesco, Asda, Morrisons and Sainsbury's, are fighting like pit bull terriers for an ever-bigger slice of the retail cake, using their most effective weapon, price. Like a razor-sharp Samurai sword, there are a number of basic moves that can be employed to harm an opponent, one of the most aggressive being the loss-leader cut. Though somewhat crude, it is a very effective move that involves slashing the price of basic commodities to a point where they are being sold for less money than it costs to buy in. The theory is that, because of the demand for basic commodities, customers will flock to the store with the lowest prices on these items and then, because it is convenient to not go anywhere else, will buy the rest of the weekly shopping while they are there.

All's fair in love and war and business, it is said, and anyone is entitled to employ whatever means are at his or her disposal to attract customers and generate profit. But when companies reach the size of these giant retailers, a whole new set of rules applies. In any discussion on food, and the divide that now exists between real food and its industrialised imitations, we cannot avoid talking about supermarkets. Their very size means that they wield extraordinary power (who else but a company the size of Tesco can make a decision to buy up 800 retail units with the stroke of a pen, in order to move into and throttle the corner shop market?) and every decision they make has far-reaching effects not generally understood by those who shop in these huge emporia.

Take the above-mentioned loss-leader pricing policy, for example. To the average shopper pushing a trolley up and down the aisles, milk or bread at so many pence less in one store than another is seen as a good thing. It represents a saving, because the customer has a pretty good idea of what these staple commodities should cost, even though that idea has actually been fixed in the customer's mind by the retailers themselves. It is interesting to note at this stage that these basic commodity items are generally found at the far end of the supermarket. Thus the customer enters the store through the fruit and veg section (feel-good factor, plus basic items in the shopping trolley) and then has to trundle through all the other aisles to get to the bread and milk. Just an accident of store design? Not a bit of it. A deliberate ploy to get customers to traverse the whole store before getting to the items on which they are clued up on price.

The customer is happy with the price on these items, and of course the store is happy too, because the customer is buying other things along the way – other things about which the customer has only a limited amount of price awareness. Thus it is easy to rack up the price on other items to cover the absence of profits on the loss leaders. However, cutting the price on these staples or, as they are called in the trade, 'known value items', or KVI, is a constant skirmish, a running battle between the big players in their war over market share. They all cut their KVI prices all the time. Each one wants to be seen as offering the best 'value for money' to its customers. For the suppliers, though, it's a different story, as we shall see.

Call them supermarkets, call them retailers, call them chain stores, it does not alter the nature of these wolves in sheep's clothing. They are corporations at heart and, as Joel Bakan points out in his comprehensive dissertation, *The Corporation*, their whole raison d'être is to make money. There is an argument that supports the theory that any organisation must make a profit, but this principle of 'expand or die' becomes distorted when the organisation in question is a corporation goaded into increasingly self-interested behaviour by the baying pack of shareholders snapping at its heels. This is an alarming scenario in any sector of society, but particularly disturbing when the corporations we are talking about are those which supply our food.

Read the blurb on the cover of Bakan's book and you will see that he believes that the activities of all corporations represent little more than 'the pathological pursuit of profit and power'. Not that this is a side of them that they like us to see. Understanding fully that their customers invariably make comparisons and judgements in human terms, corporations like to promote themselves in human terms too. Thus their corporate identity is branded in such a way as to appear, not only unique in terms of their competitors, but also friendly, attractive and, in the case of the supermarkets, family-orientated. Asda, part of the Wal-Mart family . . .

But don't be fooled. Every corporation is programmed to 'take over the world'. Globalisation cannot occur without a corporate mentality. Unlike the growers, producers, and independent shop owners with whom Sally and I deal every day, the corporation has no concept of 'enough'. Our small suppliers understand that they are 'in competition' with others supplying the same products, but they also understand that there is room for everyone. Of course they must make a profit on their commercial activities, but their main aim is to make a living and have a life. They do not want to grow beyond that point, and they are quite happy to share the cake as long as they get their slice.

This is not the way of the corporation. The corporation wants all the cake, and then it wants to own the person that made the cake, and then it wants to buy up the people that supply the ingredients to the person that made the cake. After that, like some kind of psychotic Terminator robot, it is searching for any other cake makers or sellers that it can swallow up. When it runs out of cakes, it will turn its attention to other commodities. And, with no concept of 'enough', it can never be satisfied.

Such is the modern corporation. Finally released from the chains of restrictive legislation in the 1980s, it has grown into the monster that cautious legislators always feared. Laws designed to curb the enthusiasm of companies whose only goal is to monopolise were scrapped in favour of a belief in the free market, championed in the UK by Margaret Thatcher and in the USA by Ronald Reagan. Persuading themselves, their governments and an ever-gullible public that their actions would result in a settling down of trade into some kind of noble equilibrium, they have left us the legacy of globalisation, and a handful of dominant corporations that effectively do rule the world. Everyone, including once-powerful governments, dances to their tune.

There is a multi-billion dollar marketing industry out there that is trying to convince us that this is a Good Thing and that corporations are there only for us and that they respond only to the demands of their customers. As plausible and sincere as this might seem, it is simply not true. We, the customers, are no more than resources to be used, in the same way that suppliers are used, in the single-minded pursuit of profits and satisfied shareholders. Just watch how the giant High Street retailers react to a drop in turnover. More importantly, watch how their shareholders react, and the panic that is caused in corporate boardrooms. However blithely Mr Johnson, CEO of S C Johnson (the company that swamps our homes with artificial chemical smells), might come across in the TV adverts for his 'family' business, and despite the fact that it is still a family-owned company, it is nonetheless a typically acquisitive global corporation, turning over $6.5 billion through 70 worldwide bases and sales in 110 countries. I am not picking on S C Johnson specifically, merely using the company as an excellent example of the family-friendly imagery that dominates the TV adverts whilst disguising the corporate heart beating beneath this smooth skin of benign 'family values'.

Another example, to pick one at random, is Marks & Spencers. Loss of market share forced it to look closely at its board of directors and its marketing strategy. A reshuffle at board level and a new marketing campaign, and M&S is back on track, regaining some of the market share it lost, with a catchy new strapline, 'your M&S'. It is not *your* M&S, any more than it is *mine* – unless you or I are shareholders. It's more a case of the company having to do something to persuade more people to enter its stores and spend money that they were previously spending in other stores, and what better way to do that than to persuade you that M&S really is there for you? The reality is the other way around. You are there for M&S. Their job is to get you through their doors and up to the tills with your money, so that the stores can report back to the board and the shareholders that turnover has gone up and that this will translate into an increase on the bottom line. This is not just profit, this is corporate profit . . .

It is much the same with our food retailers, the Big Four. They smile sweetly and tell us how well they are looking after us, but by some perverse twist they manage to keep the advantage for themselves and their shareholders. Take Tesco's Computers for Schools promotion, for instance. It is now entering its sixteenth year of promotion, and is described on www.tescocorporate.com (the site the company likes its shareholders to look at) as 'another result for Tesco'. Well, of course it is. What a brilliant wheeze. Whoever thought that one up must surely have earned a decent bonus by now. The scheme is absolutely foolproof – get your customers to plug into a righteous community project which involved them spending oodles of money in your store, then give them the little carrot you have been dangling in front of them. All that is required after that is to get your accountants to tot up your profit for you. Easy.

The whole idea, a bit like the loyalty card bonus scheme, hinges on handing out vouchers to Tesco shoppers that can be saved up and exchanged for computer equipment for local schools. It is a stunningly brilliant way of attracting praise and admiration for Tesco's social awareness and community responsibility whilst at the same time making money like there's no tomorrow. In 2001, nine years into the annual scheme, *Which?* magazine decided to investigate and came up with some 'inconvenient truths', as they might be called today. By their calculations, 4,490 vouchers would be needed to provide a scanner for a school. But, at a rate of one voucher for every £10 spent in a Tesco store, £44,900 would have to be spent to buy this piece of equipment, which Tesco was selling at that time for £80 retail (and obviously bought wholesale for a much lower price). According to *Which?*, a school participating in this scheme would have to encourage parents to spend £208,800 to acquire £1000 worth of computer equipment.

To date, according to the Tesco website, the company has provided over £100m worth of computers and computer equipment to the 30,000-plus schools now participating in the scheme – this is 86% of all UK schools. Based on the calculations that *Which?* made, this represents over £208bn in sales – an average of over £17bn a year. Not bad for an idea that crowns your company with the glowing halo of social responsibility as well as pleasing your shareholders. Of course, the company would argue that those sales would have taken place anyway, and that their voucher scheme really is something for nothing. Yet they actively encourage people to participate, to come to Tesco for their shopping rather than anywhere else. Tesco also lobbies head teachers by giving them copies of a letter to send out to all parents motivating them to participate and by suggesting that they should also encourage their pupils to design and distribute flyers promoting the scheme.

So, is this a demonstration of Tesco's social responsibility or just another gimmick to increase sales? Joel Bakan would say that it is the latter, as sales and profit are fundamentally important to every corporation and they will use any tactic available to help them maximise profits. If this scheme really was as munificent as Tesco would have us believe, then they could just donate the £100m worth of equipment to the schools, or better still just use it to build schools in Kenya where vegetable growers, at the mercy of the supermarket price war, are being screwed into the ground so far that they cannot afford to educate their children. Now there's a good idea! But that is never going to happen, because there is no profitable advantage in giving away money, even if it is, as this £100m is, a tiny proportion of profits. No corporation is going to do a crazy thing like that, not without generating sales. A corporate CEO might feel inclined to give away some of his or her obscenely inflated 'salary' on a private basis, but the corporation itself can contemplate this only if such philanthropy is somehow tied into creating more profit.

One of the simplest aids to maximising profits, of course, is to minimise costs, and this is where we see supermarkets at their most ruthless. Thus we come back to the relationship between supermarkets and their suppliers. Joanna Blythman, in her shocking exposé of supermarket culture, *Shopped*, has devoted a section of over 50 pages to the way supermarkets treat their suppliers. Despite this, despite the coverage this topic receives in the media and despite the fact that an increasing number of desperate farmers and growers are now having the courage to speak up against the supermarkets, bad practices go on all the time. The supermarkets call the shots, and their suppliers generally have to do what they are told. Whenever a supermarket is challenged on any issue, some glib spokesperson comes to the fore and either flatly denies what is being alleged or assures us that the company is 'looking into the matter'. The truth is they just don't care what is being said, because they are now so powerful that they feel invincible. Matters of public concern regarding our supermarkets float to the top of the day's news from time to time, but inevitably sink again as other news items take their place. Supermarket bosses know this, so each time someone has to step up to the microphone to defend a supermarket against an accusation, it is nothing more than a damage limitation exercise.

In their zeal to minimise costs as part of the formula for maximising profits, supermarkets have squeezed farmers and growers to the point of bankruptcy and beyond. Protesters outside a Tesco shareholders meeting in June 2003 expressed their anger and disgust at the way farmers are treated. One placard read, "Cheap food? 11 farmers go bust every day . . . one commits suicide every week." At that meeting, during which Sir Terry Leahy's salary package of £2,838,000 was revealed, one farmer in the audience pointed out that the average income of UK farmers had dropped to £11,000 a year (an amount that Sir Terry would 'earn' in *a day and a half*) and that 30% of farming families were living on family credit. In answer to this, Sir Terry sidestepped the accusations and blamed the state of British farming on anything and everything except the way that Tesco does business. It is four years since that meeting and nothing much has changed. Sir Terry's salary package has gone up to £3,979,000, the average income of British farmers has not gone up at all (Sir Terry could now hit their average annual income in about *one day*) and even more farmers and growers have gone out of business or committed suicide.

As Ms Blythman has shown in *Shopped*, there is much that can be said about the way any given supermarket treats its suppliers. In this chapter, we are concerned principally with how their dominating presence in the food retail market has had a detrimental effect on what we eat. Thus it is sufficient for the purposes of this book to highlight the salient points of the situation. The underlying nature of the problem is that supermarkets wield enormous power and can therefore dictate whatever terms they like. Twenty-five years ago, I knew fruit growers in the Vale of Evesham who were falling over themselves trying to get a supermarket account. It seemed like easy money because the supermarkets were such big customers. A generation later, many of these growers have gone to the wall, finding it too difficult to cope with the demands, deviousness and bully-boy tactics of the supermarkets. A combination of low prices, high rejection rates for anything less than perfect fruit and vegetables, plus the fickleness of supermarket buyers, left too many growers facing financial uncertainty. Some simply went bust, others left the industry while they still had some assets to their name.

Those farmers and growers who still supply supermarkets today tend to fall into two categories. Either they are very big operators who make big profits on small margins and high volume turnover, by being as ruthlessly efficient as their supermarket clients, or they are just ordinary farmers and growers who have unwittingly got themselves locked into the supermarket supply chain and have no alternative customers for their produce. In the area around our village, we see examples of both. On the one hand there is our neighbour, a traditional sheep farmer, and on the other hand, a couple of miles away in the next village, there is a grower of strawberries.

The sheep farmer has been a sheep farmer all his life, learning the skill from his father. He knows his job and he is very good at it. But the world has changed around him. No longer does he supply the local butchers. There are too few of them left, most of them having been put out of business by being undercut by the supermarkets. Our sheep farmer supplies Tesco now – but not directly. He has to deal with a wholesale buyer who is himself subject to the whims of the Tesco buyer. All the Tesco buyer is interested in is price, and he will place his orders with those who are prepared to sell at the price he is expecting to pay. The delicate balance between supply and demand is no longer that pure equilibrium that I studied in my economics textbooks at university. As a result of the supermarkets wielding such immense power on a global basis, it is now more a question of suppliers being told what they will be paid, like it or lump it. The Tesco buyer has no loyalty to his suppliers because he is able to source lamb from anywhere. Thus our neighbour the sheep farmer never knows where he stands. Back in the days when he supplied the local shops, he had a pretty good idea from one year to the next how many lambs he would be selling. Now he doesn't have a clue. He is dependent on the fickleness of the Tesco buyer, who is quite capable of turning round and saying, "Well, actually, I don't want any lamb from you this spring."

So our sheep farmer lives on a knife edge all the time, not knowing whether his lambs will sell once they are ready for market and not knowing whether the selling price will cover the costs of rearing the lambs in the first place, especially considering that the wholesaler is also looking for his share of profit. In the next village, the strawberry grower is the same but different. Like the sheep farmer, he has done this job all his life, as did his father before him. His business has moved from a pick-your-own operation to a mammoth polytunnel development supplying the supermarkets directly. This has had a hugely damaging effect on the local landscape, as field after field is covered in unsightly plastic. In a designated Area of Outstanding Natural Beauty, this type of development is now effectively illegal, following a High Court ruling in 2006 on a similar operation in Surrey. Our strawberry grower, however, is doing everything he can through clever brinksmanship to keep this operation going as long as possible, despite incurring the wrath of the local community. He has to keep going because, like the sheep farmer, this is all he knows. Having changed, almost seamlessly, from pick-your-own to polytunnel growing on an industrial scale, he is now locked into the system in the same way that the sheep farmer is, with all the angst that goes with it. To get out now may be too costly to contemplate, so he grits his teeth in the face of local opposition and carries on regardless, hoping that his supermarket clients will not call him one day and say, "No strawberries this summer, thanks."

Many of those who oppose him condemn his activity as being motivated by greed and selfishness. No doubt there is an element of that in how he conducts his business, but I suspect that in reality all he originally wanted to do was to make a living from growing strawberries. Like a bareback rider at a rodeo, he has hung on while the market kicked and bucked, goaded by the supermarkets to dance to their tune. Sally and I are certainly distressed by what this operation has done to our local views. We are, however, equally dismayed by the fact that there are those who rail against the polytunnels but seem unable to associate them with the activities of supermarkets. They cannot see the connection, and continue to shop at the local supermarkets, even to the extent of buying English strawberries out of season.

On the other side of the fence, the supporters of polytunnel fruit growing on this kind of industrial scale argue that this is something that Britain needs. Without it, they say, we would be importing strawberries from outside the UK, so it is good for the UK economy. They say that there is a demand for strawberries all year round and that, by using polytunnels, we in the UK are now able to extend our growing season and thereby cut down on the level of imports. No one who maintains this view is willing to accept that all-year demand is a relatively new phenomenon that has been created by the supermarkets themselves. Moreover, these same people seem unaware of the basic human hunter-gatherer instinct that compels shoppers to buy something special when they see it. Thus, if English strawberries are on the shelves in April (and cunningly marked up at a price that looks like a bargain) the average shopper will soon be reaching out, picking up a box or two and popping them in the trolley.

Thirty years ago, most people would have expected to see strawberries in June. Seasonality ruled the grocery market, and I for one (and I know I'm not alone) looked forward in anticipation of, not just strawberries, but each variety of fruit and vegetable as it came into season. The concept of all-year availability, referred to by Joanna Blythman as 'permanent global summertime', or PGST, is quite simply another weapon in the armoury of corporate supermarkets trying to outdo each other. If you can't undercut your competitor on price, undercut him by stocking something he can't get hold of. That should bring the customers flocking to your stores.

Like KVI loss-leader price cutting, PGST is now standard practice in all supermarkets. Thus anyone shopping at a supermarket is faced with the depressing scenario that the varieties of fruit and vegetables on display will be exactly the same as they were last week, or last month, or last year . . .

Supermarkets, because of their corporate nature, have a good sense of the bottom line, but no apparent concept of what fruit and vegetables look like in real life or indeed how they taste. To them, fruit and vegetables are just commodities, and damnably irritating ones at that. It must be such a headache for the profit-conscious CEO and his cohorts. No sooner has he got these things into his stores than they begin to deteriorate. Or he finds that the leeks have too much green on them to look good in their packaging. Or the apples are different sizes, or the strawberries have taken on a sad dowdy look after being locked into a chiller for a while and then trundled up and down the country's motorways. Worse than that, he gets a good seller, like asparagus for instance, that commands a high price and then suffers from a depletion in stock levels just when his sales are beginning to take off. It's all so difficult. But the supermarkets always rise to the challenge.

As a result of their best efforts over the last quarter of a century, we now have 'supermarket fruit and vegetables', which are radically different from the vegetables I remember as a child, and in fact different from the vegetables I actually buy today. Visually, they are easily distinguishable from real fruit and vegetables in that they look unnaturally uniform and unnervingly bright. The taste is poor, ranging from simply tasteless to appalling. This is because fruit is mostly unripe. And sold to us at a premium price if it is actually in a fit state to eat! The vegetables have been chilled for too long, so any natural sweetness that they might have had has vanished completely. It must also be said that, in the case of intensively grown vegetables, levels of natural sweetness are already depleted, even before the vegetables go into the cold store. Supermarket buyers are not interested in any of this. To them, a discussion on 'natural sweetness' and other such niceties is, at best, an irrelevance. They know that once a shopper is in the store the produce will sell, because the shopper has no time to leave the store and seek a better alternative elsewhere. All the buyer is interested in is a commodity that behaves itself and looks the part on the shelf until the customer drops it in the trolley and takes it to the checkout. And most importantly, all fruit and vegetable products should ideally be available at any time of year, so that the shopper can find anything anytime without having to go to a rival store.

Supermarkets achieve PGST by air-freighting supplies from all around the world, so that we in the UK can have strawberries and asparagus at Christmas, plums in spring and cucumbers in winter. Certain varieties of fruit are favoured for their good keeping qualities. No matter that Elsanta polytunnel-grown strawberries taste of nothing other than a sour reminder of what strawberries used to be. The fact is they look good for weeks, all red and shiny in their plastic cartons. The supermarket can pick them up in 40-tonne trucks in Herefordshire, transport them to a distribution depot, maybe as far away as East

Anglia, to be packaged and then transport them back to Herefordshire to be sold. All the while they keep their sheen and that just-picked look.

This perfect look, however, belies the fact that what eventually arrives on the supermarket shelves is only a proportion of what is grown. Drive up to any soft fruit polytunnel development, or in fact to any monoculture operation (e.g. potatoes) where crops are intensively produced for the supermarkets, and you will see small mountains of discarded produce. These are all the fruits or vegetables that didn't make the grade. No matter that this is our food we are talking about, or that it is all good, sound produce. To a supermarket buyer what counts is uniformity. Every carrot must be the same length; each apple must have the same proportion of colours on its skin; every capsicum must be the same size. Have you ever seen a box of capsicums grown in natural conditions, in the right environment and in season? They bear so little resemblance to the traffic light tubes you see in supermarkets as to be easily mistaken for something completely different.

Such matters are inconsequential to supermarkets. Despite the fact that supermarkets would prefer not to have to deal with such troublesome products at all, they are still seen as a 'destination category'. This means that the impression formed in the customer's mind by the enticing fruit and veg department will influence the choice of store, which is why they are sited at the entrance. Because horticultural produce looks clean, fresh and green, it acts as a magnet to draw people in. The obvious next step is to stock as many different fruits and vegetables as possible in order to get ahead of the rival competitors, and to keep those stocks up throughout the year. Of course, all supermarket chains have adopted this PGST approach, so the competitive edge with any particular chain these days comes down to small details, such as a deal on a particular line, or a particularly exotic fruit not seen elsewhere. In the end, however, one supermarket looks much like all the others. The desire to scramble to the top of the heap and stay there gives rise to some pretty aggressive corporate behaviour, with damage being inflicted not just on each other, but on everyone else, from those who supply them to the customers who buy from them.

A typical supermarket shopper might say, "I shop here because I can't afford to shop anywhere else. Everything is so expensive outside the supermarket." Such an attitude takes into account nothing except the price that the shopper expects to pay. Even the fact that the supermarket has virtually fixed this price in the first place is not taken into account – most people are unaware of the influence that the giant retailers have in 're-educating' us on our understanding of the worth of everyday food items. Many of us now feel outraged if we have to pay more than 60p for a litre of milk or £2.99 for a chicken. Very few of us stop to wonder how it is that supermarket prices are so cheap. Even fewer make the connection between the price on the shelf, the profit that is being made by the supermarket chain and the price that is being paid to the supplier. Only a tiny minority will see all the corners that have been cut, and the way our food has been nutritionally compromised, in order to sell to us at bargain-basement prices.

One of the favourite bleats of supermarkets is, "But it's customer demand – the customers don't want to pay more than this." Beware this kind of talk. To me, this is about as convincing as the Big Bad Wolf pretending to be Little Red Riding Hood's granny. Can you imagine the board of directors of a slick, profit-motivated global corporation sitting around the boardroom saying, "Hmmm, I wonder what the customers are going to demand next?" Everything a supermarket does is ruthlessly executed. That once fickle element that regulated the marketplace, 'customer demand', has been eliminated from the whole idea of global marketing. Supermarkets don't want to have to deal with the vagaries of the marketplace – they have their hands full trying to get one over their main competitors. Thus 'customer demand' is something that is created in the marketing department. Top money buys the top marketing whiz-kids, who are so good at what they do that they foist a new product (or the idea of tumbling prices) onto us and then wrap an advertising message around it that makes us believe that we thought of it first.

The price of food is about as popular a topic of conversation in the UK as the weather. Everybody appears to be fixated on the idea that food is too expensive. Where did this idea spring from? In a nutshell, from the traditional thriftiness inherent in that icon of the past, the British housewife, and from the ruthless exploitation of this mindset by nascent supermarket chains intent on stealing customers from each other. In other words, going back to post-war Britain, we find the tradition of a working husband supplying 'housekeeping money' to a wife expected to run the home on a tight budget. Superimpose on this scene the picture of the burgeoning 'convenience store', and what do we see? We see each brand of convenience store trying to persuade housewives strapped for cash that their brand offers the best prices in town.

Fast forward forty years, to a world of global brands, and nothing has changed, except for the concept of 'housewife', now consigned to the dustbin of unacceptable terminology. The price war between brands has raged all this time, fuelled by the ammunition of increasingly sophisticated advertising. The underlying message, however, remains the same: whatever the supermarket down the road is charging for their food, it is too much, so come to us for a better deal. Thus the concept of rock-bottom prices for food has become ingrained in the national psyche, thanks to supermarket rivalry.

All a supermarket wants is more market share than its rivals, and it will do whatever it has to in order to achieve this goal, whether it is dropping prices or extending its range of commodities. Thus, if supermarkets generally don't sell a particular commodity, and then one chain breaks the mould and starts stocking it, they all get on the bandwagon for fear of being left at the roadside. A good example is the fresh fish counter. At one time, no supermarket would handle such a difficult and unpredictable product. Then one of them took a chance, opening wet fish counters in its bigger stores. Before long, all the others join in. The first thing that happens is that independent fishmongers are put out of business. Next, all stores that have wet fish counters follow the normal supermarket principle of appearing to be fully stocked. Intense inter-brand rivalry means that each chain wants its stores to look better than its rivals. So each store then has to have a full complement of different fish on its stall. Elaborate displays begin to appear, with all the usual suspects, like cod, haddock, plaice, whiting and mackerel, plus a good clutch of exotics, like fresh tuna, red snappers, Mediterranean grey mullet – even parrot fish from the Indian Ocean. One-time expensive and strictly seasonal delicacies, such as salmon, scallops and lobster, add an enticing touch of luxury. This is not customer demand – this is inter-company rivalry.

This kind of corporate mindset does irreparable harm to our planet. Just taking the example of fish, the impact of suddenly having hundreds of new fish stalls opening in the last couple of decades, plus the insistence on having these stalls fully stocked at all times in stores that are open seven days a week, has accelerated the plunder of our oceans. There are many varieties of fish in which the supermarkets are not interested, and this has increased the wastage on the by-catch, to say nothing of the wastage in every store when unsold fish gets dumped. And don't believe what you are told by supermarkets singing from the green hymn sheet. If the message is, "We stock fish only from sustainable sources," this means, "We stock fish supplied by factory trawlers that are working within Government quotas." Unless you see the description 'line-caught', the fish you are buying will have been brought in by a trawler. Supermarkets are too big to work in sustainable ways.

The demand for fish is there all right – but it comes from the supermarkets, not the customers. The customers, in their sheep-like state, will always buy something if it is there, but it is the supermarket that has persuaded them they want it in the first place, make no mistake about it. When supermarkets demand exotics such as scallops, there is huge pressure on the fishing industry to deliver, in the same way that all supermarket suppliers are pressured by the quantities involved. This results in even more unscrupulous, and sometimes illegal, fishing practices, as beam trawlers rip the life out of the seabed in their increasingly earnest search for scallops and other bottom feeders. And the sudden rise of farmed fish? Well obviously, the rape of the sea has depleted our stocks and brought many species to the brink of extinction, but what a bonus fish farming has been for the supermarkets. Now they can order salmon, prawns, bass, bream and the rest all year round, specifying numbers, weight and delivery days, without having to be subject to the whims of traditional fishing practices.

I make no apologies for saying that I think supermarkets are the scourge of the earth. They are corporations, and therefore programmed to act like a pathological killer, but worse than that, they are in control of our food supply. This one fact has the ring of doom about it. Because of their huge size, supermarkets have created a new world of food supply, where bland, substandard, chemically polluted intensively produced food is supplied to them by just a handful of companies. As an aside, they have also created a waste mountain of packaging that no one wants. It is a disturbing fact that, according to the Women's Institute, 40% of all domestic waste comes from retail packaging, and much of it ends up in landfill sites. Many businesses have been lured into supplying the giant retailers on the promise of good prices and big orders, but have found themselves sucked into the vortex. Prices that start at a level that is profitable are soon whittled away once the supplier is in the loop, and those who can't cut costs to meet the supermarkets' demands for an ever-lower selling price simply go bust. The only ones left are those who are prepared to be as ruthless as the supermarkets, thus we end up with a small number of big suppliers, all with the same corporate attitude. Aggression rules, and is passed from supermarket buyer to the boss of the supply firm to the workers in that firm and anyone else unfortunate enough to get in the way.

Food quality suffers badly at the hands of the supermarkets. Suppliers trying to accept the price the supermarket forces on them and still stay in business will do anything to cut costs. There is no compunction in compromising the nutritional quality of our food if, by the use of chemicals and intensive methods of animal feeding and rearing, yields can be increased and costs of production brought down. Centralised buying and distribution means that it is virtually impossible for a supermarket chain to deal on a local basis with good fresh food from small suppliers. Where this is done at all, it is little more than a public relations exercise paying lip service to increasing public awareness about food and its provenance.

All corporations are very good at selling us a positive friendly image – that's what they pay their PR departments to do. Why? Because they want to stay in business. They are all very well aware of public feeling. They use good PR and spin to pick up on this feeling and sway opinion to their advantage. No supermarket wants any of its customers to desert it in favour of shopping at the Farmers' Market in town, so they all pick up on the issues of the day and persuade us that they have 'gone green' or are 'socially responsible' or they are 'buying locally'. But like that famous emperor and his new clothes, we are expected to take all this on board and accept what we are being told. But read between the lines and you will see something else.

An article about Sainsbury's appeared in the Telegraph on 2nd June 2007. Or at least it is a piece of writing made to look like an article, with the headline, 'Sainsbury's leads the way in supporting British produce.' It is worth having a closer look at it. Firstly, there is no journalist credited with writing it, so it has probably come direct from Sainsbury's PR department. Occupying half a page, we see that over 50% of this space is filled with a lovely picture of a wooden box full of freshly picked vegetables. Closer inspection reveals that this picture is credited to one of the mainstream image libraries, Getty Images, itself another multi-million pound corporation. The picture says nothing at all about what you might see in a Sainsbury's store, but it certainly appeals to our emotions, because it says everything about what we expect fresh vegetables to look like.

Reading the text, it becomes apparent that Sainsbury's are stocking products from a number of small producers. Fair enough. Supermarkets usually stock a few lines from smaller producers, knowing that those lines will appeal to a small selection of customers, who would go elsewhere if they cannot find what they are looking for. This message is the opening piece in the text and is designed to draw in the reader, in much the same way as the fruit and veg section draws in the customers to the stores. I know how this works – I was once employed as a freelance copywriter working for various ad agencies.

Once the reader is hooked, the text can bring in the main thrust of the piece. In this case, it is encapsulated in the sentence, "Now Sainsbury's is embarking on a three-year plan to become 'Best at British.'" This is what this 'advertorial' is all about – selling a new USP (unique selling point) for Sainsbury's. Lagging behind the likes of Tesco and Asda, the company must come up with something that gives it a perceivable uniqueness, and this is it – the promotion of British produce with the associated benefits of cutting down on its imports and saving food miles. The article emphasises this by telling the reader that Sainsbury's is 'committed to buying British wherever possible', allegedly buying 100% of its fresh chicken and turkey, 77% of its beef, 80% of fish and 64% of lamb from British sources. As an aside, this tells you nothing about the quality of these products, or about the farming methods employed in rearing the animals. Just that it's British.

Having given us this USP, the article then goes on to tell us that Sainsbury's has set up a scheme called Supply Something New and that it has sponsored the Daily Telegraph's Taste of Britain 2005 awards. So what? Call me an old cynic, but this is just Sainsbury's flying their local support banner to get one up on their rivals in the great grocery takeover game. I know they claim to stock some of the products that won the awards, but they could hardly maintain any credibility if they didn't do so. And stocking a particular line tells us nothing about the price they are paying the supplier or the other demands they are making on that supplier.

Right at the end of the article is the 'closer', a paragraph that reinforces the message to the punters, "At Sainsbury's all meat, fruit and vegetables produced in the UK are clearly labelled with the Union

Jack symbol making it easier for customers to enjoy seasonal produce and support British farmers." Read it again. It does not tell you much. As mentioned above, it says nothing about the quality of this British produce; it does not say that Sainsbury's is actually committed to a seasonal (or local) policy; it does not commit itself to buying exclusively from British producers. It is simply designed to slip easily through the net of our subconscious, so that we come away from reading the article as born-again Sainsbury's shoppers. But that's PR spin for you. Don't let it fool you. If it looks like a duck and it quacks like a duck it probably is a duck. Sainsbury's looks like a corporation and it certainly acts like one, so why should I not believe that it is one? Given that belief, I cannot accept any advertorial writing at face value. I have to ask, "What's in it for them and their shareholders?"

The preoccupation of supermarkets with their shareholders and the obsession with delivering an annual increase in turnover and profits has streamlined the food supply chain. Whatever supermarkets might tell us to the contrary, our choice is now limited by this streamlining. With the concept of PGST, supermarkets argue that our choice is immense, that we have all of the world's produce available all year round, but this is a hollow claim. The reality is that the range and choice of fruit and vegetables on supermarket shelves is limited to what each is prepared to stock, as well as being geared to what the rival stores are stocking. So it may look like all the world's produce, but it is not. It is the same few varieties, month in month out, year in year out. Last autumn, we were buying apples from our local independents. Where they were stocking at least 20 varieties of English apples picked in season (and grown locally), the Morrisons on the edge of town had the usual collection of Braeburn, Royal Gala, Pink Lady, Granny Smith (all imported) plus one token English, the good old Russet. But even this was unripe, picked too soon and not blushed with the rosy tinted skin that gives the variety its name. Like the Elsanta strawberries, a supermarket russet apple is too sour, too bland, really quite uninteresting. Just another apple. By contrast, the russets from our local man give off a scent before you bite into them and then deliver a mouthful of aromatic complex flavours. However good one might think fruit from a supermarket tastes, it is a fact that it will not match up to the real thing.

When the cherry season comes round, we go to our local grower and pick our own, choosing from four different varieties within the same orchard. The cherries are perfectly ripe and succulent with deep shiny skins and a scent that fills the car on the way home, making it difficult for us to keep our hands off our haul before we get back. At the same time, right in the middle of the season, the cherries in Morrisons have been flown in from abroad and, after being chilled, air-freighted, packed into plastic boxes and transported by road, have lost their scent altogether.

It is the same with all of the fruit and vegetables on supermarket shelves. Many would argue with me that I am getting hysterical and that it all tastes fine, but I disagree. I believe that a significant proportion of the population no longer knows how fruit and vegetables should taste. It alarms me that so many children today have no real understanding of food, its provenance, its texture, look or taste. Even the media have picked up on the fact that there are children today who are unaware of the fact that milk comes from cows and that chips come from potatoes. Supermarkets, by presenting food to us in a sanitised, pre-packed, individually wrapped way, have been a contributory factor in this demise of understanding and loss of connection between us and our food. As the quality of our food has diminished in proportion to the increase in intensified production systems, so our expectations have been dumbed down to fit in with the supermarkets' game plan of what they are prepared to sell and how they want to present it. Through the use of persuasive psychological marketing based on the advertising industry's awareness of what makes us all tick, supermarkets have taken control of the way we shop, cook and eat. The loss of understanding of the nature of food and its seasonality has left us all the poorer, creating a nation of fast food grazers with a diminishing ability to cook (brought on by a disinclination to spend time in the kitchen) and a consequent loss of connection to real food and the pleasures of eating.

Lyall Watson, that inspirational zoologist and life scientist, whose book, *Supernature*, caught the imagination of so many people when it was published in 1973, suggests that this scenario is an inevitable result of abdicating our responsibility for sourcing our own food and expecting this to be done for us by a third party. In his first book, *The Omnivorous Ape*, published in 1971, he points out that in the natural world, where *homo sapiens* is just another animal species, the logical conclusion of our omnivorous adventures is what he calls the 'supermarket syndrome'. Thus nearly 40 years ago, he predicted with uncanny accuracy our current malaise. He describes how local differences, cultures and cuisines are swept aside by global food providers. He points out that we would have access to as many foods as before, but that the same foods would be available everywhere. The symptoms of the syndrome are described as 'an increasing unwillingness to prepare one's own food, an ignorance of the techniques involved, a reliance on an ever-dwindling variety of foods, an offhand attitude to the whole question of eating, and a loss of curiosity about foods that have never before been tried.' His conclusion is that our omnivority has been sacrificed for something he coins as 'univority', a 'disease which is highly contagious and could be fatal.'

As we have seen, supermarkets are corporations. Once a corporation, always a corporation. It matters not that the supermarkets paint themselves in glowing colours. They assure us repeatedly that they are friendly, with only our interests at heart, but they remain our big bad wolf. Driven by insatiable greed, at no point in their evolution will they stop trying to be bigger and more profitable, whatever we might be told to the contrary. Far from being customer orientated, customers, along with suppliers and even their own staff, are no more than pawns in their game of maximising profits, minimising costs and keeping their shareholders sweet.

To achieve these goals, everything else is expendable – the viability of their rivals, independent shops and those who supply them. They talk nicely to their customers because they need their money and they need it translated into profits. Anyone in business needs to make a profit, but corporations are ruthless. Size matters, because economies of scale kick in and costs can be saved by cutting quality, shopping globally and centralising distribution. A reliance on air freight and road transport ensures that goods bought cheaply in other countries can be delivered to our stores whenever and wherever they are needed.

At those stores, the sales battle is fought in earnest. Supermarket shopping is a completely different experience from traditional shopping. Everything is designed to make us all spend more and to get through the system quickly, without time to think. Out goes your friendly counter service, in comes self-service and checkout tills. The idea is to persuade us to spend more than we really intended to. Although there may be three dozen or more checkouts in the bigger stores, the intention is to have just enough of them operating to create small queues. All those chocolate bars and other goodies stacked up at each checkout are guaranteed to generate a huge volume of spontaneous sales. Multiply that by the number of stores in a chain and you have a significant contribution to turnover and profit.

Self-service relies heavily on the customer being able to see what is available. Thus more space is required, hence the huge warehouse-style supermarkets that now dominate the outskirts of all our major towns and cities. This means more cars, more road use, dead town centres and soulless 'retail parks', to quote a phrase from the people who sold us this idea in the first place. Inside these huge temples of excess, the display space is mind-boggling – after all, the customer must see what is on offer.

It is here that the food maze is at its most complex, with many varieties of the same thing on offer. Innumerable variations on the theme of 'breakfast cereal' or 'yoghurt drink' bedazzle the shopper, who enters this emporium in a mesmerised state, flanked by row upon row and aisle after aisle of degraded foodstuffs masquerading as the real thing. On top of that, all manner of goods are now packaged individually so that they can be hung, mounted, or stacked where the customer can see them. The amount of packaging this involves is monumental. Inconsequential to these big corporations, this is seen as simply someone else's problem. They make it sound as if it is nothing to do with them.

Corporate activity is always disguised by clever marketing and good spin, but beware of everything a supermarket does. If it sounds 'green', you have to ask, "What's in it for them?" If they say they are selling local produce, ask questions – you will find that it is not what you think, and the truth is nowhere near the story we are being told. To put it simply, a supermarket cannot operate in the same way that a small shop operates, and it certainly cannot effectively replace the whole raft of independent shops that have been driven out of business. To operate in this customer-friendly way is far too inefficient, and the shareholders will never wear it. What we get instead is a bit of spin that tells us that Tesco et al are there for us, instead of the truth of the matter, which is that we are there for them.

When it comes to food, supermarkets simply cannot give us what we want or what we really need, despite their protestations to the contrary. What they have given us is what they want to give us, and it has all been made possible through the availability of cheap energy. This is what initially gave the burgeoning food industry its competitive edge, which was further honed by government subsidies and other perks that favoured bigger companies. Cheap fuel made it possible for these corporations to process our food in many different ways and to come up with a whole range of value-added products that swell their profits. Consumers also benefited from cheap fuel, enabling them to drive to out-of-town supermarkets to do the weekly shop. But the whole concept has a precariously bubble-like quality to it. The bubble could burst at any point in the future where the price of fuel becomes prohibitively expensive due to dwindling stocks. Our strange supermarket-dominated world is something of a fool's paradise. It cannot last, because ultimately it does not give us what we need.

The concept of cheap food has been touched on elsewhere in the text, but I say again, beware this concept. There is no such thing as cheap food. Food is a precious resource that is squandered with astounding profligacy by a profiteering culture that has foisted on us this notion of cheap food. Supermarkets, in line with the cheapskate fast food chains that sell us 'family meals' for £4.99, will have us believe that a chicken should cost no more than £2.99 and a pint of milk no more than 60-odd pence. But the real cost of these items is in the misery inflicted on the birds, the dairy cows, the farmers and ultimately on us, as we are the ones whose health suffers as a result of consuming these debased products. Cheap it might be, but we pay extra for it in other ways. We make ourselves ill. Worse than that, however, we cooperate in animal cruelty, unethical practices and the bankruptcy of farmers. Above all, the supermarkets can afford to sell you these items cheap because you are paying well over the odds for all of their value-added products, such as processed breakfast cereals, tinned foods, ready meals and silly little packets of diced carrots.

The future does not lie with the supermarkets, because globalised industry cannot deliver sustainability, which is the one thing we need to give ourselves any chance of survival. Sustainability depends on really thinking local, i.e., small independent farmers, producers and growers supplying their own local area. Supermarkets cannot do this however hard they try – their centralised operation is diametrically opposed to a 'local' system. Yet, in the short term at least, the supermarket is here to stay, because they are now too big and too powerful for anyone to stop their progress.

In that short term, the big supermarkets will also try to move in on the burgeoning 'real food' market, so beware of anything that the supermarkets do to persuade us that they are going green, organic, fair trade or sustainable. The new 'ethical marketplace' is worth £37bn worldwide – how's that for a slice of the action that the supermarkets can gobble up? It is obvious that this is going to provide rich hunting for any global retailers looking to improve their bottom line. But stay focused on the fact that 'supermarket' and 'real food' are terms that sit uncomfortably together, and you should be able to see through the hype. That's not to say that it is easy to stand up against corporate spin, for the type of economy that has operated in the developed world for the last two hundred years or so makes it heresy to criticise the corporate attitude, because 'successful companies' are seen as 'good for the economy', despite the fact that this type of economy and the consumer society it has created is nothing short of madness. Selfishness and greed are rewarded by knighthoods for the 'captains of industry' despite the fact that all the ships they steer are heading for the rocks.

There is one thing, however, that could change it all, and that one thing is us. If we, the people, were to reclaim our right to source our own food, if we were to turn our backs on the supermarket culture and begin to look for alternative suppliers for all our culinary needs, we would find that there are still enough small-scale farmers, growers, producers and independent shops to form the basis of a counter-revolution. Demand creates supply in a truly free market, and new operators would come into the marketplace. All we have to do to start it off is to say, "Okay, I'm not going to buy bread from the supermarket today – I'm going to make my own," or, "I want fresh vegetables that are truly organic, let's get on the internet and find a box scheme that will deliver them to my door." It really is that simple, and we, the people, really are that powerful.

One step at a time is all it takes. It would be a long road, no doubt. However, to quote from the wisdom of the Orient, "Even a journey of 1000 miles starts with but a single step." If we all take that single step, and then another and another, we might create for ourselves a new world order in which food is once again nutritious, chemical-free, fresh, seasonal and local and is not provided for our consumption by faceless organisations whose only motivation is money.

It is not difficult, because each time one of us makes a decision to change something, it is another step forward. One step forward is a footprint, in the same way that one voice is a sound in the wilderness. But several voices are a protest, and many footprints make a pathway. Soon you have a revolution. We are not talking war and mayhem, just a quiet revolution. A revolution that will make changes that may be hard to understand at the moment, but will have far-reaching effects beyond our own health. Our health is part of the cycle and, in order to fix it, we have to fix everything else. To change the way we shop and eat is to change the way we view the planet. The good news is that the revolution has already started.

REVERSING FORWARD

Every time it is my misfortune to have to visit one of our motorway service areas, I get a brief but intense vision of what Armageddon could be like. I don't know whether it is my bad timing, or whether these places attract a certain type of person but, whenever I call in, they seem to be swarming with the sort of Brits that have given certain areas of Spain a bad name. Swaggering about with cans of fizzy drinks and their distended stomachs and muffin tops hanging out over their badly styled calf-length trousers, they leave a trail of litter behind them as they meander aimlessly from the huge snack shop to the electronic games machines to the burger counter and back again. And that's just the females.

There are certain service areas on the M6, which I should perhaps refrain from naming, but for the sake of argument I will call Sandbach and Charnock Richard, that I studiously avoid, as they seem to act like a magnet for the leading exponents of our yob culture. Add to that, especially at the height of the holiday season, too many fractious parents, warring siblings and hyperactive kids who have just been released from the confines of overheated cars, and you have an atmosphere that is pregnant with negativity and bristling with bad vibes. When it comes to food and refreshment, there is generally very little in these places that will do anything other than make the situation worse.

The most dismal outlets of our intrinsically cheerless High Street fast food chains all seem to be located in motorway service areas. A typical junkfood burger is bad enough, but in these dreary outposts, according to those few who feel sufficiently moved to contribute to websites such as www.motorwayservices.info, eating one in certain service areas is akin to having a death wish. Personally, I feel sorry for visitors to this country who arrive at our ferry ports and follow the road signs automatically directing them to the arterial motorway system that takes them to their destination. The first time they have to stop for a break or refreshments, they must wonder what prompted them to leave the comforts of home for this outlandish place. Everything that is bad about our culture, especially our food culture, seems to gravitate towards the motorway service areas. Symbolic of Fast Food Britain and the fast lifestyle that goes with it, motorway services show us in concentrated detail the malaise that grips our nation.

From this culinary wasteland, this gastronomical desert, this black hole, there would appear to be no escape – the format has long since been set in stone by the corporations that run these places. It seems that, far from being the sort of oasis where one might relax from the pressure of driving along tediously boring anonymous, featureless roads, their sole purpose is to crank the tension up another gear. Corporate policy dictates that drivers should be enticed off the motorway to come into what is in effect a small shopping centre. They should be induced to part with as much money as possible in a variety of different ways during their visit and then get back in their cars and make way for the next wave of punters.

It seems, however, that in the midst of such aridity the occasional flower can grow, and there is one exception to the standard motorway service area that shines like a beacon. It stands as a monument to the belief that the corporate way is not the only way of running a successful business, and it is a working example of what can be achieved with a bit of creative thinking. The place I am talking about is Tebay Services, between Kendal and Penrith on the M6. This is where we are going to break our journey to Scotland.

Tebay Services has a lot going for it. It is set in rugged, beautiful countryside, in the uplands to the south-east of Shap Fells, a perfect place to stop for a break. Where another service area would undoubtedly have looked like an ugly scar on such a landscape, Tebay Northbound at least makes an attempt to blend in. With its stone walls and pitched roof, the main building has a touch of the vernacular about it, and the adjacent duck pond, with views over open countryside, adds a certain serenity. Once inside, it is immediately apparent that this is no ordinary motorway services. Rather than shiny plastic everywhere, wood and stone are much in evidence, with weighty beams seemingly supported on a huge boulder in the centre of the eating area and radiating out to the walls of the building. Picture windows add to the spacious feel of the place and look out onto the pond, the edge of which comes right up to the building.

Though the aromas drifting from the cooked dishes are very appetising (another major difference from other service areas), we decide to settle for a coffee and a scone. For us this represents a bit of market research. It seems that in this gastronomically barren land of ours, it is surprisingly difficult to find anywhere that sells decent coffee and a tasty home made scone. As for coffee and walnut cake, just don't get me started . . .

We pick a couple of scones from the self-service counter. They appear to be fresh and they are not wrapped in plastic. They have an attractive home made look, although it is hard to imagine that they are, considering the volume of such comestibles that must be sold in a busy place like this. Up by the coffee counter, we are served by an enthusiastic young man who talks us through the options. There are different coffees on order and they are all Fair Trade. We can't get a cafetière, so we settle for a double espresso each. Chatting to the woman at the till, we are assured that the scones are indeed made by them. We don't push her on this one, because there is an orderly queue forming behind us and we don't want to hold it up, so we take our tray to one of the tables overlooking the pond.

Knowing something of the philosophy of the place, I accept that the scones are made by the company that runs the services, rather than being bought in from some huge corporate supplier. Although, because of the volume they must have to deal with in a place like this, they cannot compete with genuine home made, nevertheless the scones are quite acceptable. The company that runs Tebay services, as well as a hotel and a caravan park on adjacent sites, was set up in 1971 by two locals with a vision, a farmer and a baker. The company is still family-owned and very small by corporate standards. Originally employing 28 local people, the diverse range of the company's activities now requires a staff of some 500, but the philosophy is still 'keep it local'.

In the service area itself, as well as on the company website, emphasis is put on the local aspect of the business. There is a real sense that local culture and food is important to them, and a celebration of this fact is the presence of a farm shop within the main building in both the northbound and southbound services. Fresh local meat, poultry, cheese and other dairy products are on sale alongside the jars and packets of local produce that fill the shelves. Not all of it is from the immediate area, but they fly the flag for the concept of artisan production, with fine examples of food and drink from other parts of Britain. The company claims to stock the products of 82 local producers, with 33 cheeses from the British Isles, 12 British Taste Award winners and ten different types of sausage. The dedication to thinking and buying locally extends to the company's hotel, the Westmorland, where the restaurant also relies heavily on producers and growers within the area. I am so taken with the whole place, especially the farm shop, that I wish we were staying at the Westmorland Hotel. I am quite sure that eating in the restaurant would be a rewarding experience. However, Stirling is our destination tonight, giving us only a short run in the morning to our meeting in Aberfeldy.

It does not take long to finish our scones and coffee, and we meander into the farm shop to see if we can pick up a few tasty morsels for our first meal in our rented cottage tomorrow night. The farm shop is very well stocked, and it is good to see that, amongst other things, there is a selection of our very own Herefordshire crisps from Tyrrells – a serious rival to all those hand-fried crisps out there. We buy some intriguing little meat pies to have tonight for supper (a picnic really) along with some other delicacies and some local cheese we have not seen in our own little deli back home. No doubt all this will be eaten discreetly in the bedroom of our B&B, and washed down with a bottle of wine we brought from home.

By way of a brief digression, let me tell you about Tyrrells crisps or, as their boss, Will Chase, prefers to call them, chips. Will Chase grew up on the farm at Tyrrells Court in north Herefordshire and has been growing potatoes there for the last twenty years. Until recently, he was locked into the supermarket supply chain. Like most suppliers to supermarkets, his was a thankless task and his life was full of anxiety and uncertainty, fuelled by the unpredictability of fickle supermarket buyers and a price that was hardly making him a living. He chose to do something about it before the supermarkets drove him out of business.

He came up with the idea of making hand-fried chips and converted an old potato shed into a chip making facility in 2002. The response was phenomenal, but that is because (and here I enter a personal note) they taste so good.

Soon Will was increasing his capacity and today he runs a very successful company. His anti-supermarket stance means that he will not supply the Big Four, preferring to supply independent shops instead. Currently the company supplies over 4000 quality independent shops throughout the UK, including Tebay Services. Recently, he has made an exception to his anti-supermarket rule by supplying Waitrose, because they are, to quote from the Tyrrells website, 'the only UK supermarket actively purchasing and promoting locally produced fine foods.' His dislike of the ruthlessly cut-throat Big Four made headline news in September 2006, when Tesco began illicitly stocking Tyrrells Chips. Will Chase got to hear about it and forced them to remove the stocks from their shelves.

Tyrrells' major USP is that the company itself grows the potatoes that are made into chips, so it is possible for the potatoes to be harvested in the morning and made into chips in the afternoon without even having to leave the farm. In these days of raised concerns over food miles, this is certainly something to be proud of, even though one might wish to hang a question mark over the validity of distributing the product all over the UK. The company also grows traditional varieties of potato that have good flavour. Other large manufacturers of potato crisps merely source their potatoes from brokers who shop globally for any potatoes at the right price. Like many of the places it supplies, Tyrrells' main concern is keeping it local. The company is local, its produce is local, its employees are local and its customers, though spread out all over the country, are indeed local shops supplying customers within a small radius.

What impresses us most about companies like Tyrrells and the company behind the Tebay phenomenon is their foresight and commitment to a sustainable future. There are many voices out there on the fringes railing against the prevailing systems of chemical farming and global capitalism. These same voices shout about 'sustainable farming', 'buying local' and 'growing organic'. Big business just ignores them, dismissing them as nothing more than a bunch of cranks who want to turn the clock back, put the economy into reverse. But this is not the case. Those 'cranks' can see the folly of what we are doing. They can see that we cannot go on doing it, that to do so is to risk everything, the very survival of human society. Admittedly, this can sound cranky, but I know that those who voice these opinions (and I count myself amongst them) are sane. Far from wanting to turn the clock back and put the economy into reverse, we simply understand that we need to return to more traditional ways of farming and the sustainability that this return implies. A bit like backing out of deep mud on the forest track to find a firmer route, this is a reverse move that will take us forward.

When a company such as Westmorland Ltd is prepared to commit itself to an enterprise like Tebay Services, we 'cranks' know that we are not alone. This is a company that certainly puts its money where its mouth is. Not for them the tokenism of the supermarket 'organic selection', bland-tasting and plastic-wrapped along with the rest of the sanitised products in the vegetable section, but a full commitment to the idea of sustaining a local community by buying products grown and farmed within that community and employing people who reside there. This is such a big step to take in the face of modern global capitalism, but it works. Westmorland Ltd has shown us that, even with something as hopelessly lost as a motorway service area, it can still be run as if people matter. Emphasis can be placed on good nutritious food, grown and farmed locally and supplied to those who visit the services. The profit that this generates goes back into the community, not into the inflated salary package of some CEO analysing the annual accounts in some glass palace a world away from the customers whose money generates his profits.

Interestingly, Westmorland Ltd does not claim to be organic, although many of its local suppliers do. No doubt the company recognises that the term 'organic' can be misleading in the same way that 'Fair Trade' does not always denote the kind of trading environment in which we would like to believe. In the philosophy of Westmorland Ltd, the first thing to concentrate on is to reinstate the local community. Once the community thrives, with farmers, growers and producers within the community able to sell their produce at a price that will keep them in business, then the rest will follow. Already some of the farmers and growers supplying Westmorland are organic in their methods, but the word becomes irrelevant in a situation where agricultural and horticultural activities take place in a non-chemical way.

In sourcing supplies for our B&B, we deal with a number of farmers and growers directly. Very few of them get hung up on the word 'organic'. We have no worries about them, however. We have visited all of them, seen their farms, talked to them about how they go about their business. Without exception, they care. They care for their animals and their husbandry methods are excellent, so much so that they remind me of my grandfather and his neighbours. It would be so easy to see my old Grandpa through the rose-tinted glasses of childhood memory, so it is very comforting to meet people today with the same approach to farming as he had. All of them have opted out of the madness of getting locked into supermarket supply chains, preferring to find their own customers by selling through Farmers' Markets or simply by word of mouth.

Though the word 'organic', as applied to the growing of crops or the rearing of animals, was unknown to my Grandpa in that context, it had already become an issue while he was still farming. As the Second

World War came to an end, so the British government became preoccupied with finding ways of ensuring that self-sufficiency became a reality. New ideas based on chemically-enhanced crop yields were gaining credence at the expense of traditional thinking. What has since become known as conventional farming really began only as a result of the Agriculture Act of 1947. In the previous year, the Soil Association was born. The Beveridge Report of 1942 was the result of an investigation into the state of the nation's health, and the founders of the Soil Association were genuinely interested in seeking solutions to our health crisis. Advocating that agriculture should be the basis of a preventive health service, the founders were attempting to help the nascent Health Service to hit the ground running. However, life is never that simple.

With the devils of chemical manufacturing companies whispering in the ears of gullible government ministers, the good sense talked by the Soil Association was largely ignored. The chemical companies won the day, and Britain was on the road to ruin. The Soil Association didn't go away, however. Although the last surviving founder member, Lady Eve Balfour, lived long enough after its inception to see Britain's agriculture, food production and Health Service all highly dependent on chemicals, the Association's message about the connection between sustainable farming practices, healthy animals, nutritious crops and the health of the nation was a hugely powerful one. As a result, the Soil Association is now widely recognised as the definitive authority on organic practices and sustainable farming. Anyone out shopping can be reassured by the Soil Association logo that what they are buying has at least been approved by a trustworthy authority.

Within the EU, all organic food must meet certain minimum standards, and each EU country has its own regulatory body. In the UK, it is the United Kingdom Register of Organic Food Standards, which regulates the activities of six certification bodies in the UK. The Soil Association is the oldest and largest of the six, taking care of around 80% of UK certifications. Its pedigree ensures that there is much public trust in the Soil Association, but pressure from the supermarkets to subjugate the idea of organic produce to their global buying policy has begun to erode this trust.

Going back to the principles set out by Lady Balfour and her co-founders, the production of organic food should ideally be locally based, but the supermarkets want everything now and they want it in all their stores at the same time and at the right price. So they import. Currently around 56% of organic food sold in the UK is imported. Worse than that, organic food is treated no differently by the supermarkets than any other type of food. Thus it is grown in monoculture fields in many other countries, then air-freighted in, transported to distribution centres and then on to the outlets around the country, where it arrives cleaned up, chilled and lifeless. A dead carrot is a dead carrot, even stamped with the word 'organic'. In addition, due to their tremendous buying power, the supermarkets may not have paid much more for such organic fruit and vegetables than they do for conventional crops, yet the price on the shelf is jacked up to reflect its perceived higher value.

Customers buying organic produce from the supermarkets often say that it is not worth the extra money. I would agree with them. I would say that it is not worth buying any fresh produce from any supermarket, organic or otherwise, because supermarkets have no idea how to deal with this type of product. Their modus operandi simply does not allow them to treat fresh produce with the sensitivity it deserves. Recognising this as a problem, and understanding that it mostly applies to imported produce, the Soil Association recently announced its intention to withdraw organic certification from imported foods. This may help, but it will not solve the problem of how the supermarkets operate and how this affects the quality of our food. At the risk of becoming repetitive, it is impossible to trust a corporation whose driving force is the need to maximise profits. As we have seen in the previous chapter, corporations cut costs wherever possible to achieve their prime objective.

When it comes to organic foods, the supermarkets recognise the huge financial opportunity this represents and they want to cash in on it. In order to call the shots, the supermarkets are buying up small organic producers and then selling own-brand organic food. What the customer does not see, however, is the fact that, as owners of these small organic producers, the supermarkets will exploit loopholes in the system (as they do with any other system) to cut corners. Standards drop and the result is, for example, that dairy cows and chickens, though technically described as organic, are still raised in confinement. In the UK organic industry, it seems that the whole issue of animal welfare is treated seriously only by the Soil Association. The other five certification bodies are more relaxed in their approach to imposing standards. In countries from which we import, standards may be even lower. In the USA, animals reared under 'organic' conditions are allowed to be kept in confinement so long as they have 'access' to the outside – but they don't actually have to be let out, so of course they are not. In addition, animals may be fed less than natural diets, and crops may be grown in huge monoculture prairies.

All of this is precisely why we would go that extra mile (literally, but still within a very small radius) and buy 'non-organic' meat from a farmer who is willing to show us around his farm, rather than buy any organic meat from a supermarket. The supermarket system extends the food supply chain too far. Those who buy their fresh produce from a supermarket actually have no idea about what they are buying. The traceability records that nowadays appear on packaging are literally not worth the paper they are printed on. They are as irrelevant as the nutritional information that appears on packets and tins. What does all this coded information actually tell you about the provenance of the product? Very little, if anything, that is of any use. Supposedly there for our own peace of mind, and as a reassurance that the supermarket is doing everything it can to source the best products for its customers, in reality these traceability codes are no more than another smokescreen, misleading us in the same way as the RSPCA Freedom Food logo. This badge supposedly informs the buying public that animals on farms awarded Freedom Food status have been afforded the following five freedoms:

- freedom from fear and distress
- freedom from pain, injury and disease
- freedom from hunger and thirst
- freedom from discomfort
- freedom to *express normal behaviour* (my italics)

Frankly, this is laughable, and brings into disrepute the supposedly good name of the RSPCA, which it is worth remembering stands for the Royal Society for the *Prevention of Cruelty to Animals* (my italics again) At the time of its inception in 1824, animals were considered to be no more than commodities to be used for food, work and pleasure. One of its objectives was to persuade the general public that animals should be treated with respect. How disappointing it is to see that, over 180 years later, the Freedom Food logo is actually covering up cruelty that in many ways is worse than that which was prevalent in the 1820s. Sadly, the standard of animal welfare that this logo is supposed to guarantee is aspirational rather than mandatory. The checks applied to farms that are awarded the badge are inadequate. In any case, there appears to be no strict requirement to stick to the letter of the five freedoms, and stories are leaked to the media of farmers who abuse them and get away with it. In their own defence, the RSPCA, according to the Ecologist magazine (April 2007) says that its welfare standards are 'deliberately practical and achievable' and can thus be put into practice 'on both large- and small-scale farms, and cover indoor and outdoor systems.' In reality, this means that the Freedom Food logo can appear on food from intensive production units. Personally, I find it impossible to equate the picture of intensive production with the list of five freedoms. Standing outside the barbed wire perimeter of a typical intensive poultry unit, it is quite obvious that four of those five freedoms are simply not available to the birds within. They may have 'freedom from hunger and thirst', but that's it. Like the 'organic' label on supermarket food, the Freedom Food badge is just another empty symbol used by big business to get away with unacceptable practices whilst throwing the consumers off their guard.

There is really only one positive thing that can be said about such labels on supermarket food and it is this: if one were to follow the provenance trail to its source, through the line of middlemen between producer and final consumer, one would be so shocked at the corner-cutting involved in producing a profit for all of those involved in the chain, one might be tempted to stop shopping at supermarkets altogether. That would be a result, because every pound not spent in a supermarket and spent instead within the local community is a little bit towards a brighter future, a future in which people are in charge of their own lives. Maybe then the importance of community can be regained, superseding the naked avarice and selfishness that is the essence of globalised corporate capitalism.

All those on both sides of this debate postulate and pontificate about who is right and who is wrong. Big business calls up its cohorts in the shape of spin doctors, advertising agencies, marketing departments and 'experts' and attempts to persuade us that their way is the only way. Meanwhile, the pro-organic lobby, composed mainly of individuals and small organisations, claims that its alternative is the only workable one. At times it seems as if the pro-organic lobby is all talk and no action. This is only to be expected in a situation where idealism is pitched against profiteering. This is precisely why it is so inspiring to call in at Tebay Services and see the idealism in action.

Westmorland Ltd is a working example of the viable alternative to our current domination by giant corporations. There are those who maintain that the corporation has a finite life and that it will die a natural death, whilst there are others that say that globalised thinking, as a concept, will be killed off by the onset of diminishing oil reserves. Both of these may be true. Many hope that this will be the case and that we can look forward to an improved future. At Tebay Services, however, we can see that future already. Without waiting for the world to change, Westmorland Ltd has shown us that change can be a reality and that the future will look like this.

Local food from local suppliers sold in shops that employ local people, a buying experience so much more satisfying than the present form of shopping anonymously with strangers. The least we can do is to support the thinking shown at Tebay. Each one of us can do something today to change our shopping habits. Even if it is just a gesture, like buying a chicken from the Farmers' Market, it all counts. Maybe next time, something else in addition to the chicken will be bought from the Farmers' Market. The 'alternative' shopping basket will grow. The important thing is to do *something*. We can see what a sustainable future looks like. We can see how real, seasonal, locally sourced food is good for our health and the health of the planet. And all we have to do is to make a move towards that new future. How hard can it be?

It is not hard, but it requires effort. We must make this effort to seek out those who subscribe to the 'local' ethos. And checking out the supermarket for local produce is not the answer. They simply pay lip service to the idea. Supermarkets cannot do 'local'. It is a logistical impossibility for them, because of their huge size. Just think about it. Even if one store in a chain decided to give 'local' a try as an experiment, it would fail. Can you imagine the chaos around by the delivery bay? Instead of one 40-tonne truck turning up and disgorging pallets of neatly packaged produce, there would be a queue of local suppliers snaking around the corner, each transporting a few odd boxes of whatever they are producing. The store's warehouse manager would be tearing his hair out trying to sort it all. Chaos would ensue in attempting to keep the shelves stacked. Even if the logistics of supply could be controlled, the sheer number of people passing through even one store in a chain would mean that stocks would run out too quickly. To quote from a Welsh hill farmer who tried to sell his lamb direct to his local Tesco, "They said there was no point in taking me on, because what I had to offer would sell out in four hours, so it was a non-starter." And there you have it. Supermarkets are not the answer when it comes to food that is truly local, seasonal, organic and from sustainable sources.

At Tebay, we have been shown the door to a sustainable future. All we have to do, each one of us, is to walk through it. To many, this might look like a door to the past, but, if you are out walking and you take the wrong fork on the footpath through the forest, it makes perfect sense to go back to the place where you know you took the wrong turn and then continue your journey in the right direction. Globalised chemical food production does not work. We need to reverse our 'progress', return to the traditional farming practices we left behind fifty years ago and then we can go forward to a future of sustainable farming, healthy crops, healthy animals and nutritious food for all.

BRINGING HOME THE BACON

Refreshed and uplifted by the experience of buying food not just in a farm shop but in the unique location of a motorway service area, we are looking forward to the next leg of the journey through the craggy north of England and the southern uplands of Scotland. As much as I hate motorway driving, the spectacular scenery north of Penrith is some compensation. It is my turn to drive now, giving Sally a break and a chance to drink in the dramatic views on this glorious afternoon. From time to time, we see the old A6 alongside us, and it reminds me of travelling up to Scotland as a young boy on a family holiday, my Dad clutching the wheel of our old Ford Anglia, determined to coax the 1200cc engine to pull this car full of people and luggage over Shap Fells and Beattock Summit. Life was altogether slower in those days and undoubtedly better in many ways. But this is no nostalgia fix. I have merely come to understand that living life at a faster pace does not necessarily represent an improvement, especially when there are so many negative ramifications that are written into the contract that we have made with the Devil of Progress.

Take for instance the sheep transporter that is coming towards us on the southbound carriageway. Nothing unusual in that, you might think, and indeed it is a common sight. But it is also a relatively recent sight that symbolises another change in our farming practices that impinges detrimentally on the quality of our food. In the name of efficiency, the slaughter of animals has been centralised into huge 'factories of death'. The thousands of small abattoirs that used to exist, one in every local community, behind every butcher's shop almost, have all but disappeared in response to EU laws that appear to favour the big companies at the expense of the small local operators. By shutting down the small abattoirs, the independent butchers' shops that depended on them were denied a source of supply. The small farmers that worked with these independent butchers thus lost an outlet for their animals. The result is that shops close, farmers go out of business, animal welfare is seriously compromised, animal husbandry is sacrificed in favour of intensive rearing systems and the nutritional quality of our food is impaired.

The sheep transporter, full of terrified animals crammed together with no room to move, is ripping along the motorway, bound for some giant factory slaughterhouse. There these poor frightened creatures will be dispatched without ceremony by people who have no feelings for them. They are just doing a job, and a job that makes such demands on the slaughtermen in terms of time efficiency that it removes practically all traces of humanity from them as they 'process' the carcasses as quickly as possible. They really have no time to think about what they are doing. Like soldiers in battle, their minds are numbed. Callousness and indifference rule in such places.

And then there are the consumers, those who buy the finished product. All they see is a joint of lamb wrapped in plastic and sitting in the supermarket chill cabinet. It could easily be pork, beef or poultry – the process is the same. Most people don't think beyond the price on the wrapper, let alone the contents. Leading busy lives, with too many other things to worry about, most people do not want to know how the meat got there. Trimmed joints and cuts of neatly packaged meat do not have the same visual effect as seeing a quarter of beef hanging in a butcher's shop. With supermarkets, we are one more step away from the whole idea of sourcing our own food, and that makes it so much easier not to think about what is in the packaging. But turning a blind eye to the malfeasance that underscores our meat production industry does not condone it or make it acceptable.

We as a species are omnivores, eating everything from leaves, fruit and nuts to insects to fish and animals, so I am not saying that we shouldn't be eating meat. What I am saying is that, since we like to call ourselves civilised, we have a duty of care towards all those domesticated animals that we rear for food. Since abdicating our responsibility for finding our own food, however, we have unwittingly sanctioned the rise of cruel and sadistic intensive farming practices. Justification for all this brutality, we are told, is the demand for cheap food. Yet this is not so. This implies that we, the consumers, have made these demands and that the poor old supermarkets, always struggling to keep up with their difficult and demanding customers, have merely complied with our wishes. The truth is that, since the end of the Second World War, our government has made it a priority to provide cheap food and the supermarkets have merely leapt on this as a competitive weapon. As we have seen in Chapter 6, each tries to outdo the others in terms of 'good value', 'affordable food', 'money-saving offers' and all the rest of it. Phrases like 'Every little helps' and 'That's Asda price' reinforce the idea in our minds, whilst the supermarkets play havoc behind the scenes with producers, growers and other suppliers in order to drag down the prices and still remain profitable.

I must stress again, there is no such thing as cheap food. Cheap food comes at a huge price. Part of the price we have paid for all this 'cheap' food is the loss of morality, sensitivity and the simple regard and respect for our fellow creatures that should be inherent in a species with such a large brain. We have allowed ourselves to become de-humanised, simply avoiding the issue of animal exploitation whilst we pick our way through the supermarket chillers looking for a nice joint for the weekend. Then there are the farmers and growers. We get cheap food and they get to subsidise us through the prices imposed on them by the supermarkets. To me it seems unjust that, because so many of us have lost sight of the real price of food, so many providers of that food are facing stress, loss of earnings and even bankruptcy, with the suicide rate amongst farmers higher than the national average.

Perhaps the most significant element of the true price we pay for our cheap food is our failing health. In the brightly lit sanitised atmosphere of our giant supermarkets we don't have to think about the meat we are buying. We might imagine fields of happy bullocks or a pig snuffling around a sty in some farmyard somewhere, but the reality is a long way from this sepia-tinted image. The sheep transporter on the motorway is a very small part of the industrialised factory system that has taken over from where farming left off about fifty years ago. Where the farmers of my Grandpa's era gave us good healthy meat to eat, modern factory farming gives us poor quality meat, tainted by chemicals and other toxins, nutritionally impaired, bland in flavour and tough in texture.

The presence of the transporter on the motorway today is a visual reminder that even sheep are not safe from the perils of intensive practices. It is believed by many that lamb is the safest meat to buy because sheep cannot be reared intensively. It is true that it is sheep one tends to see out in the country grazing the fields, a fact that became quite obvious when so many flocks disappeared in the wake of the foot-and-mouth outbreak in 2001. However, all is not necessarily as it seems. Many sheep farmers are indeed grazing their flocks on what looks like traditional pasture land but is in fact perennial rye grass, that disastrous, chemically supported, nutritionally depleted monoculture that has replaced the wild flower meadows of my Grandpa's day. In addition to this, the most common hybrid breed (a cross between a Texel ram and a Mule ewe, itself a cross between a Bluefaced Leicester and a Blackface or Swaledale) has been adapted to suit modern feeding practices. Like dairy cows, they are being raised on high protein cereal feeds. They are bred to be unnaturally early lambers, the ewes giving birth in the winter months in order to provide new season spring lamb around February and March.

Sold at premium price, spring lamb is a goldmine for the supermarkets (though not for the farmers) but it is a meat that you should beware of. Even if it is organic, buying it from a supermarket means that you are running the risk of it having been raised on a combination of cereal and rye grass. Because of this it will lack flavour as well as texture, and may well be contaminated with chemical residues and growth hormones. Left to nature, lambs would be born in the spring, when new grass is at its richest. It is only the money-driven marketplace that has made demands on our ewes to provide us with lambs at a time when natural food is scarce. So lamb is available at Easter when there is a peak in demand, but it is killed too young and has not had the benefit of a nutritious feed.

No doubt there are many people who simply accept that this is how lamb should taste, and who never think about the fact that the meat may be contaminated in some way, but it is well worth seeking out a local supplier, maybe at your nearest Farmers' Market, from whom you can buy slightly older pasture fed, single breed meat. For a real taste sensation without compromising tenderness, try hogget, meat from a yearling sheep. Mutton, which has undeservedly suffered bad propaganda and crafty spin to become nationally reviled, is nothing more than mature lamb, in the same way that beef is mature veal. It is also extremely tasty, and can be as succulent and tender as any beef. As with any other type of meat, there may be some issues with age. It is well known that in the past tough old sheep were palmed off on an unsuspecting public, literally mutton dressed as lamb, an expression that has unfortunately given mutton a bad name forever. But new season lamb, killed at four months old, can never get close to the real taste of hogget or mutton, and can be bland and uninteresting by comparison, especially if it has been fed on a substandard diet.

Buying direct from the farmer via a Farmer's Market not only gives you the opportunity to buy more mature, tastier meat, but also means that you can talk directly to the person who rears the animals. Thus you can ask questions. You can find out what the sheep are being fed on, which breed is being reared, how old they are at slaughter. We are very lucky in Herefordshire to have quite a few sheep farmers who specialise in rare breeds and, within a 10-mile radius, we can buy meat from Ryeland (our local breed) Balwen, Kerry Hill, Herdwick and Jacob, all of which are grazed on rich traditional pasture. The texture, tenderness and taste of the meat from these animals are exceptional.

A look at the website of the Rare Breeds Survival Trust will reveal 56 breeds in the UK, with such wonderfully evocative names as Castlemilk Moorit, Badgerface Welsh, Manx Loaghtan, Clun Forest and Soay. Each of these breeds was originally confined to a particular part of Britain, having characteristics that made it ideal for that area. The theory of 'local breeds for local conditions' applies not just to sheep, but to other farm animals too, as well as to crops and vegetables. In an ideal world, we would all be enjoying the fruits of our own locality. It is an ideal worth working towards. Rearing animals or growing crops suited to a particular 'terroir', as a wine producer might call it, ensures food that is of premium quality, rather than the bland homogeneity of breeds and varieties that are hybridised to survive anywhere. Supporting farmers who rear rare breed animals is a step in the right direction. The next logical step would be to go back to rearing only those breeds that are particularly suited to local conditions, but that situation is likely to remain an aspirational and impractical ideal.

It is mainly the supermarket trade that, over the last twenty-five years, has driven the demand for intensively reared sheep and young spring lamb, but there are some pockets of resistance to intensive rearing. A few independent butcher's shops still remain and continue to be supplied from small local farms. There has also been an increase in interest in Farmers' Markets since the foot-and-mouth outbreak in 2001. So it is still possible to find meat from sheep that have been traditionally reared, even if they are Texel crosses rather than single breeds.

Traditionally reared pork and beef is often more difficult to find, possibly because these animals are considered to be harder to farm or because both have received bad press from misguided health pundits, who have condemned pork for being too fatty and beef for simply being 'red meat'. On the plus side, TV programmes such as *Jimmy's Farm* have had some success in creating a new wave of interest in traditional pig farming and an awareness of the existence of once-common local breeds. Presumably, for any 21st century disillusioned urbanite seeking new fulfilment in re-inventing himself as a country boy, pigs are more appealing than bullocks, with an endearing quality that makes them more popular. Pigs are big favourites with adults and children alike, and they are looked upon with some affection. This is good news, for no animal bred for food, apart from poultry, is more roundly abused than the intelligent, sensitive and happy-go-lucky pig.

My Grandpa kept pigs on his mixed farm, but I was very young at the time and my memories are confined to playing in the old pig sty and being told stories of how the ancient 'pig bench' came in handy when it came to slaughtering. By the time I was old enough to be more aware of real life on the farm, Grandpa was on the verge of retirement. What I do remember, however, was the canteen at Worcester Royal Grammar School, which opened in my second year at that venerable seat of learning. We felt quite privileged to have our school meals cooked on the premises in our own kitchens, and I recall that the taste was far superior to the bought-in meals that I had experienced in my first year there. Having our own kitchen meant that kitchen waste accumulated. It was thrown into a couple of enormous aluminium bins behind the kitchen, but it wasn't simply potato peelings and cabbage cores. All the waste from the tables used to go in there too.

Inquisitive as to what happened to these huge bins, I asked one of the dinner ladies.

"Oh, the pigs'll have that," I was informed.

I was amazed. I asked her why.

"Oh, pigs'll eat anything," she assured me.

This little snippet of information stayed with me, filed away somewhere in the back of my mind, but it came rushing out again many years later when my brother got himself a job on a local farm. There he looked after sheep and pigs, and he confirmed that the pigs were fed on 'pigswill', basically kitchen waste from schools and factory canteens. I was horrified.

"But surely," I protested, "Everything is mixed up together, and the pigs will be eating all sorts of things, vegetables, bread, cakes and rice pudding – *and even bits of pork!*"

"Well, they seem to like it," said my brother.

Pigs are omnivores, it is true, and it could be argued that there is no reason why omnivority should prevent them from eating their own kind. Indeed, that other great omnivore on this planet, Man, has also been known to eat the flesh of his own species, and in some parts of the world no doubt still does. However, there is evidence that it is not a good idea. Look up '*kuru*' on the internet and you will see that it refers to a disease contracted by certain New Guinea tribesmen with a penchant for eating other people. Almost always fatal, *kuru* is seen as a similar disease to BSE and its human equivalent, CJD. Thus, at a biological level, there appears to be a case against eating your own kind.

My personal feeling is that it is so obviously wrong for us to eat each other, and I would say the same thing applies to pigs. As a naïve schoolboy, however, I came to accept the fact that pigs were eating pork, but I was appalled that they were being made to eat food that we considered fit only for the bin. I thought about the words to the song '*On Ilkley Moor Baht'At*', in which a young man out courting Mary Jane on the moors is warned that he might catch his death of cold, and would thus have to be buried. His body would subsequently be consumed by worms, which would in turn be eaten by the local ducks, and the ducks would then turn up as Sunday dinner, the implication being that the young man would ultimately be eaten by his friends and neighbours. I could vividly see this scenario played out in front of me with the pigs and their pigswill. The pigs eat the pigswill, which includes bits of pig, and then we eat the pigs. It all seemed somewhat unsavoury to me. What I didn't know then, of course, was how bad it was really going to get.

The farm where my brother worked had a barn full of pigs, or so it seemed. This was the early 1970s, and pig farming was about to go into a hyperdrive of intensive production, but on this farm it hadn't quite happened. Pig production was in full swing but could hardly be described as 'intensive' by today's standards. The pigs here roamed freely in one part of the farm, and it was really only the sows and their weaning piglets that were kept in the barn. The farmer was raising a lot of pigs, but this was still essentially a mixed farm, with sheep, a few dairy cows and some arable and root crops. Although I have never been back to that farm since those days, it would not surprise me to find out that it is now another monoculture centre, assuming that it even exists as a farm anymore.

Monoculture is prevalent in modern farming because of the corporate stance that 'farming is a business like any other' and therefore requires the same attitude towards costs, efficiency of production and bottom line profit. Applying this to the farming of animals automatically translates into cruelty and exploitation. When pigs, or bullocks, sheep or poultry for that matter, become mere units of production, their lives count for nothing, and those who farm this way seem able somehow to divorce themselves from their innate humanity and pile misery upon misery on these unfortunate creatures. Perhaps I should not be surprised. When I think that at one time civilised European countries were quite capable of treating other human beings from Africa simply as a cargo and a saleable commodity to be transported in abominable conditions in the holds of ships on their way to the slave plantations of the Caribbean, I should find it easy to accept the cruelty and callousness of modern animal farming. But I don't. Instead I rail against the arrogance of *Homo sapiens* and the installation of a belief system that states that Man possesses some kind of divine right to 'have dominion over the fish of the sea, and over the fowl of the air, and over the cattle, and over all the earth, and over every creeping thing that creepeth upon the earth.' This sounds to me like a bullet point in a corporate manifesto, and I can see how it has led on to the creation of factory farming.

Pigs reared on factory farms do not have to endure the extreme hardships and absolute inhumanity that existed on our despicable slave ships, but life for them is still full of stress, pain and fear. The object of the exercise on a factory farm is to produce the highest output for the lowest cost. High volume concentration of animals (units of production) plus modern machinery and growth-promoting drugs generate economies of scale. Animals kept in these confined conditions are prone to sickness and general malaise, so are regularly dosed up on antibiotics to keep them going.

Intensive pig production takes place in large warehouses where the floor space is divided up into pens, each of which houses so many pigs that behavioural problems are rife. The pigs are stressed and fearful. In a vain attempt to protect their own space, they resort to tail biting. For the 'farmer', the answer to this is to dock tails and clip teeth, mostly without the use of anaesthetic. It doesn't stop the problem, but there is less physical damage to the flesh of the pigs. In their pens, the pigs are fed a controlled diet which will include the growth-promoting drugs designed to bring them up to optimum weight in the minimum amount of time. Because animal fat has been demonised by certain diet gurus and members of the medical profession, the pigs' feeding regime is also controlled to produce meat with minimum fat cover. As an aside, it is virtually impossible to get real crackling on a joint of pork from an intensively reared animal.

In the worst of the intensive piggeries, the sow stall and farrowing crate are the norm. The sow stall is used for pregnant sows as a means of confinement away from possible attacks. Although it reduces the number of miscarriages, thus helping with profitability, there are obvious serious issues regarding the welfare of the sow. Movement is restricted so that the sow can do no more than stand, sit or lie down. She cannot even turn around. In many instances, the sow is put into this severely restricted situation for the whole of the gestation period of nearly four months. With the farrowing crate, the sow is kept caged in a separate section from her piglets, so that they have to feed through the bars of the cage. Again this helps profitability as it eliminates the chances of a sow sitting or lying on her piglets and killing them, but it is another animal welfare disaster.

Ceaseless campaigning by organisations such as Vegetarians International Voice for Animals (Viva!) have resulted in sow stalls being outlawed in the UK, but they are still fashionable in other big pig farming countries such as the USA, Canada and Denmark. The farrowing crate is still used universally, and for 70 days of the year, sows have to endure this confinement whilst weaning two to three litters every twelve months. It is a bleak, desolate, mentally devastating existence that casts a long shadow of shame on us all. Articles such as one by Antony Barnett that appeared in the Observer on Sunday 19th October 2003 have helped to bring to our attention the barbaric practices that go on in the name of pig farming, but it does not stop the industry from growing ever bigger. Corporations such as the US giant Smithfield Foods have a duty to their shareholders, and expansion is an activity which continues ceaselessly. In the US today, it is not unknown for some pig production units to be housing upwards of a million pigs. Smithfield have recently expanded into Poland, one of the newest members of the EU, and see an opportunity to industrialise a rural industry that works on traditional lines producing around 18 million pigs a year. Thus the juggernaut of industrialised factory farming rumbles on, crushing all before it.

The controlled feed given to pigs in these intensive units is mostly soya bean protein, other feed grains and meat and bone meal (MBM). MBM is a by-product of the industry that renders down the waste products from industrial slaughterhouses. All of these feed products have fuzzy lines of traceability and provenance, partly because of the global nature of industrialised farming. Soya bean protein at the very least will be from chemically dependent monoculture, but may even be from GM stock, and MBM may also be contaminated as a result of purchasing raw materials from a wide range of suppliers. It is actually difficult to know what these pigs are being fed on, but it can be said with some certainty that their diet, controlled for optimum finished weight, is well short of what might be described as natural.

Thus we have a situation in which animals are kept in deeply stressful and mentally debilitating conditions, given feed of dubious provenance and industrial content, given drugs to promote growth and inhibit disease, and then packed off to huge processing slaughterhouses in overcrowded transporters. They endure a journey that jumps their stress levels into the realms of the terrified and then, whilst in this state of almost violent distress, they are summarily killed. Their carcasses are processed with as much speed as the system will allow and before long another batch of plastic-wrapped joints of pallid pork with no fat cover is on its way to your local supermarket. The taste of this insipid and watery meat is bland and uninteresting, which to me comes as no surprise, given the way in which it has been produced. I am quite familiar with the taste of genuine pork, and this stuff is no more than a pale memory of the real thing. Should I feel privileged that I have eaten real pork and I can tell the difference? I don't know. What

I do know is that I feel depressed by the thought that a large number of consumers have absolutely no idea what pork should taste like and so are unable to make the comparison.

Traditionally, any pork meat that could not be sold at a premium price in the butcher's shop, for example the shoulder, belly and hocks, was sold for stewing or was made into sausages. Any offal not sold directly was used for haslet or faggots. In the making of brawn, even meat from the head would have been used. The rest of the animal too, including skin, hair and bones would be used in other industries. Nothing was wasted. That is no longer the case. Prime cuts of meat, such as legs, loin joints and chops, are what end up in supermarket display cabinets. Shoulder meat mostly goes to the ready meals industry, and some of the rest (belly, hocks, etc) goes into the manufacture of factory sausages and other 'pork products', such as tinned chopped pork. Much of what would have once been used in the subsidiary industries of travel goods (bags, etc) or the manufacture of brushes is surplus to requirements today. It can end up as pet food, reconstituted animal feeds (which can be fed to cattle, sheep or pigs) or simply consigned to the incinerator.

That great British stand-by, the humble pork sausage (and indeed beef and lamb sausages too) has long been a wonderful by-product of the butcher's shop. A busy butcher's shop, in its daily trade of preparing for sale presentable cuts of meat, accumulates a good quantity of meat offcuts as well as cheaper, less popular cuts. It is an excellent use of resources to gather these up, mince them and combine them with seasonings and a binding agent such as breadcrumbs, and make them into sausages. A cooked sausage is an excellent and tasty way to eat these odds and ends and cheap cuts that might otherwise be too difficult to prepare and consume. Sausages, deservedly popular, have been on our menus for centuries, remaining a perennial favourite in British culinary culture.

The popularity of the sausage, however, has left it open to exploitation by food industrialists hungry for more profit. Taking the principle of mincing up the offcuts and other hard-to-handle bits of meat, unscrupulous manufacturers don't think twice about mincing up anything that they cannot sell in any other way. They work on the principle that if it is minced finely enough, i.e. emulsified, no one will know the difference as long as the finished product looks vaguely pink. By law, a sausage must contain at least 30% meat, or 42% for a pork sausage. This is such a low percentage that it easily leaves the system open to abuse. On top of this of course we have the question of what actually constitutes 'meat' in the legal definition. Prior to 2003, it could mean MRM, or mechanically recovered meat, which is basically a paste flushed from meat bones. This fact made it into the media, and the EU was prompted to change its labelling laws.

Since 2003, MRM can still legally be used in sausages but it cannot count towards the minimum percentage. Fat and connective tissue (tendons, sinews, gristle and skin) are permitted. Having had hands-on experience of making sausages, I can tell you that a certain amount of fat is essential, otherwise the sausage will not remain moist during cooking. Industrial manufacturers, however, count the fat as part of the minimum meat requirement, and up to 30% of this can be fat. Up to 24% can be gristle, as is the case with some supermarket own-brand packs of sausages. Out of the minimum 42% pork meat required by law to be in a sausage, only 20% of the whole sausage is therefore likely to be lean meat. The rest, apart from the fat and gristle, will be mostly a proprietary crumb mix composed of cheap wheat, flour and salt, along with water, artificial colours such as E100 and E180, preservatives E210 and E239, other artificial colourants, stabilisers, flavour enhancers and bulking agents.

According to an article in the Independent on 30th October 2006, Britons eat around 175,000 tonnes of sausages every year, with two-thirds of this £530m market passing through the tills of the top five supermarket chains. Much of this turnover is generated from the cheaper end of the market, home of the dodgy sausage, such as Asda's 'smartprice' sausages at 49p for a 454g pack of eight. Does anyone buying such a pack ever stop to ask how it is possible for Asda to sell at a price that should set off all the alarm bells? The listed ingredients give us a clue. They include wheat flour, protein isolate, soya, wheat starch, salt, pork rind and all the usual chemical additives. By contrast, premium organic sausages cost £3.90 for a 500g pack. To my mind at least, even these should be viewed with suspicion, coming as they do from the same factory systems as the smartprice version, the only major difference being that the pigs are fed on organic feed. Think about it. To supply a retail chain like Asda, a producer has to deal in huge quantities. Asda's premium organic sausages might well be far superior to their smartprice alternative, but they are still the product of what has been called the 'industrial organic' system. The sausages we buy for Aspen House cost *less* that Asda's £3.90 per pack (£7.80 per kg) but we can *guarantee* their provenance, the quality of the meat and what is inside the sausage casing.

There are indications that the British public are getting wise to the dumbing down of our traditional bangers but, in the same article, a spokesman for Kerry Foods (who own Wall's, Bowyers, Richmond and Porkinson) is adamant in defending the industrial sausage, saying that sausage sales at that end of the market continue to grow. It is a sad fact that once-trusted household names such as Bowyers and Richmond are now such big organisations (and part of an even bigger one). Thus it is inevitable that, whatever they might tell us through their marketing and PR, their product is factory made. This means that it is virtually certain that the meat used is coming from intensive pig farms, some of which will be in other countries where regulations are more lax than in the UK, and that any products made from it will be propped up with a variety of industrial additives. There is no connection between the pig farmer at one end of the supply chain and the consumer at the other, therefore it is impossible to obtain satisfactory answers to any questions that might arise regarding provenance, traceability or husbandry. The only way in which we can be guaranteed the right answers is to deal directly with the person who rears the animals or, as a very good second best, the butcher, farm shop or box scheme that buys the product for resale.

Pork also provides us with bacon, gammon, ham and a huge selection of continental charcuterie. Traditional methods of curing and smoking have given us gastronomic icons such as salami and Parma ham, as well as our very British dry-cured and smoked bacon. Curing bacon in the traditional manner can be done either by dry curing or by wet curing. With the former, the curing is done by rubbing a mixture of salt, saltpetre and possibly some sugar onto the pork and leaving it for several days, during which time the salt works its way into the meat and 'cures' it in such a way that the meat can then be kept for a longer period of time than would be possible in its fresh state. With the wet curing method, the pork is immersed in a brine solution, but wet or dry, the curing process results in water being leached from the meat as the salt penetrates. The expulsion of water represents an overall weight loss of between 15% and 30% on the dry weight of meat.

To an industry committed to maximising profits and minimising costs, this is simply not good business sense. So new methods of curing have been invented that get over the problem of weight loss. Modern industrial curing injects the meat with a curing 'pickle' of brine and chemicals, and the curing takes a matter of hours rather than days. With this method, the meat is cured from the inside out, rather then the other way around. Any loss of water is simply made up via the injection process, to such an extent that the water content is actually *increased* by 15% of the dry weight. The injection of water into the fibres of the meat has become such a successful process that it is now used in other areas of the fresh meat industry. Fresh pork, chickens and other poultry are now injected with water, a weight gain for which the customer unwittingly pays.

Whilst on the subject of curing, it is interesting to note that, from time to time, the finger of blame is pointed at cured meat products as being carcinogenic. The cry goes up, "Eating bacon gives you cancer! Sodium nitrite is a killer!" But the truth of the matter is a long way from what we are told in the media reports that follow these research announcements. The trouble is, once again, that none of this research makes any distinction between poor quality food and the real thing. Thus all cured pork is deemed carcinogenic. Stop and think about it, though. Fresh and cured pork products that have come to us via the intensive pig farms and factory processors are quite likely to be carcinogenic. Personally, as I value my health, I keep well away from this kind of industrial meat. On the other hand, pork or bacon from a carefully reared animal that has been fed and cared for in the proper manner, far from doing you harm, will be full of nutrition.

Sodium nitrite has always been used in the curing industry. It gives ham and bacon its distinctive pink hue. I have cured pork to make ham and bacon, and I know that you need only a minute amount of this substance to do the job. I also know that it is treated with respect. Apart from any other consideration, it imparts a peculiar flavour to meat if used in too large a quantity. Traditionally, we didn't eat much bacon or ham, both being precious resources that gave us meat to take us through the winter months. Today, bacon finds its way into snacks such as the ever-popular BLT sandwich, and ham has become another ubiquitous commodity item. Pink and shiny, unappetising slices of the stuff can be found lurking on every supermarket deli counter.

Consumption of these meats, to say nothing of factory sausages and tins of processed 'chopped' ham and the like, is quite likely to do your body some harm. In addition, the level of sodium nitrite is unacceptably high, being used indiscriminately in the food industry to liven up the colour of grey lifeless meat. So, what is this chemical all about? Sodium *nitrite* is produced in the body through the action of saliva on sodium *nitrate* (a salt of nitric acid, an essential plant nutrient taken up by plants from soil as their principal nitrogen source). It is important in controlling bacteria in the stomach to prevent gastroenteritis. The body produces more sodium nitrite than is consumed in food. Green leafy vegetables, and root vegetables, provide 85% of dietary sodium nitrate, which may be converted to nitrite during digestion.

Far from being harmful, therefore, it is a natural salt. When added to meat cures, it does the job of giving the meat an appetising colour, as well as contributing to the preservative properties of the curing salt. As the old adage goes – everything in moderation, which includes the curing salts as well as the cured meat itself. Cured meat was never the everyday item it is today and, in addition, it used to be far better quality than the substandard low-grade commodity product consumed today. Traditionally cured meat, eaten in sensible quantities, is fine, provided it is real meat. But, move into the realms of factory food and, as ever, you are in trouble.

Bacon can also be smoked. Originally this was done simply by hanging a piece of bacon in the chimney of an open fireplace, where the bacon would be gently smoked over a few days. These days, purpose-built smokers are available in which this ancient but somewhat haphazard process can be replicated, but with more control over the finished product. The smoked bacon we use at Aspen House is made on the farm where the pigs are reared and where all the meat is prepared for sale at Farmers' Markets. It is smoked gently over oak sawdust chippings and the taste is exquisite. The food industry, however, has no time for this kind of smoking, as I found out when, around eight years ago, I spent a short period of my life working for a local butcher, a man I saw as a hero standing his ground in the face of the terrifying onslaught of the giant retailers. I admired his defiance and determination to succeed and to give his customers first class meat and service. As much as I was impressed by his skill with the butcher's knife, his dedication to presentation and his understanding of the way in which meat should be handled to get the best from it, I became alarmed by the way in which he 'smoked' his bacon.

The pork for his bacon was supplied by a small producer of organic rare breed pigs. It was gorgeous meat, and the dry cure that was rubbed onto it was a finely balanced mixture of salt, saltpetre, sugar, mustard and herbs. The finished bacon had a flavour that was as good as I have tasted, and it was a perfect demonstration of the best meat being treated in the best possible way to produce a taste that was second to none. But then it came to smoking the bacon, and I noticed that there was no smoker at his production unit.

Although the production unit was new and purpose-built, it did not include a facility for smoking food. I was intrigued as to how 'home smoked' bacon was available in the butcher's shop without this facility. All was revealed in the shape of a 5-litre can that was pulled from under a shelf in the storeroom. According to the label, it came from Kerry Foods and, according to the orange and black warning symbol on the can, it was harmful to health. I was advised to treat it 'with respect' whilst I was given a demonstration of how it works. All that was required was to hang the side of bacon on a meat hook with a tray beneath to catch any drips, and then the smoke flavour was simply painted on with a 2" paintbrush. If you wanted a deeper colour or a smokier flavour, you just gave it another coat. Then it was allowed to dry for about an hour and it was ready to slice. Thus a process that would traditionally have taken at least a couple of days was completed in just over an hour. Another triumph for the inventive artificial food industry. And another toxic food additive being unwittingly consumed by those who bought this bacon, including me.

At that time, eight years ago, in common with many other people, I knew that all was not right with our food. In the closing years of the 20th Century, who could not be aware that the selling of food had been taken over by supermarket chains and that the taste of fresh food had somehow diminished? My concerns drove me to buy my meat from the butcher for whom I worked and my vegetables from the little shop next door to him. I was still shopping in supermarkets, but my food shopping was mostly done elsewhere. Although I watched smoke flavour being painted onto a side of bacon, I still trusted my boss, the heroic independent butcher. It was a few years later and much further down my road of discovery that I understood exactly what it was that I had witnessed. It registered as a shock that someone like this stalwart independent could be taken in by the glib sales pitch from the Kerry rep.

I have travelled a long way since then and made many discoveries. I have come to understand so much more about the huge 'flavour' industry that has grown up alongside the industrialised food processing industry. For those of you who would like to read a detailed account of how the flavour industry works, Eric Schlosser's great exposé, *Fast Food Nation*, is powerfully descriptive. Such detail is not essential here but a few facts will not go amiss.

The flavour industry, according to Schlosser, is huge and secretive, reluctant to divulge information about the unique chemical formulae used in the manufacture of flavours not only for the food and drink industry but also for the perfume, cosmetics and household goods industry. Essentially, the process of creating a flavour is the same no matter what the final application is. The basic science behind the smell of your washing up liquid is no different from the smoke flavour that I saw painted onto sides of bacon. Development of the 'science of taste' grew up in the USA where, just off the New Jersey Turnpike, lies the heart of the global flavour industry. Here dozens of firms, including huge companies like International Flavors & Fragrances, are busy producing, within the same laboratory complex, everything from flavours for breakfast cereals, fast food fries and fizzy drinks to the world's leading brands of perfumes, including Estée Lauder's Beautiful, Lancôme's Trésor and Calvin Klein's Eternity. Both 'natural flavours' and 'artificial flavours' are produced in these laboratories and find their way into everything from soap bars to chocolate bars. Working on the theory that the aroma of a foodstuff is responsible for 90% of its flavour, scientists in these vast labs have produced a huge range of flavours whose main job is to put some taste into bland processed food.

Check the ingredients listed on practically any commercial food product, whether it is a breakfast cereal, a fruit drink, a tin of beans, a jar of mayonnaise or a frozen ready meal, and you will find either 'artificial' or 'natural' flavour listed. Both are man-made chemical additives produced in the laboratories of the flavour corporations. The only difference is that, in order to describe something as a 'natural flavour', it has to comply with a slightly different set of regulations from those that describe artificial flavours.

My experience eight years ago has made me realise that the industrialisation of our food is now so advanced, and so insidious in its infiltration of the vast range of commercial food products, that it has become an almost insurmountable task to understand exactly what we are buying. If it is possible to go into a traditional butcher's shop and buy smoked bacon that isn't smoked, then it must be said that the long fingers of the industrial mycelium have indeed crept unseen into even those extremities of the food industry where tradition still thrives. It is a sobering thought, especially when one considers that this butcher was not knowingly dousing his bacon with a potentially toxic substance – he merely thought he was saving time and money.

Time and money are of course valuable to the success of a business. Indeed, a surplus of money represents a profit, and a business without profits does not last long. There is an argument for diverting the funds currently available under the umbrella of the EU Common Agricultural Policy into organic and sustainable farming, to help those farmers who wish to convert to organic to do so without failing financially, but I believe that this is not the whole story. I believe that we must find a way to re-establish the true value of real food. The concept of cheap mass-produced food has led us all down a blind alley. If it remains the policy of those who dominate the retail food market to demand homogenous food production and to continue to drive down prices, we are all losers. The animal transporters that we see on our motorways are just one indicator that we have already gone too far down the wrong route, but to get back on track we have to question seriously our relationship with the animals that provide us with food.

WHAT'S MY BEEF?

Saddened by seeing the animal transporter, we drive (
for a while. A sheep transporter on the motorway is easy t
just another vehicle amongst the thousands that crowd t ⌐ᴗ main
arteries of our road system. Most of us are in too much of a hurry in this
modern world. It has been speeded up to the extent that many people
have lost their grip on the principle of 'it is better to travel than to arrive'.
By concentrating on the destination, however, it is all too easy to miss
all that happens on the way.

In common with so many others, both of us had a tendency to be
like this at one time, caught up in the maelstrom, the surging flow of
modern life, propelled forward by the sheer force of it. Moving to Aspen
House has helped us to change. We no longer set our sights solely on
the destination. Thus we have discovered that it is indeed true that it is
better to travel than to arrive. It is so much more rewarding to see all
that is around you and to marvel at what the journey has to offer.

Essentially, it means that whenever we go anywhere, whether it is
for an afternoon of walking, or a few days off, or a trip to Scotland to
see an inspirational author, the pleasure of the experience begins as
soon as we leave home. Frustration at road delays become a thing of
the past, because it becomes quite possible to weave the experience
of the delay into the fabric of the journey. To many, this will sound trite,
to some it will sound bizarre and to others, arrogant. However, no one
gets there any quicker by getting in a bad mood about the traffic. It
works, and it makes the journey more enjoyable because so much gets
noticed that might otherwise get missed.

The downside is that sheep transporters get noticed too. We
would rather not see them, or indeed any other manifestations of the
way animals are abused in the name of farming. To us, farming implies
good husbandry, in the same way that gardening implies tending the
soil and caring for the plants that grow in it. Thus good husbandry is
caring for animals that are farmed, which implies that they should never
be transported for miles up and down motorways, from farm to market,
from market to another farm, from farm to slaughterhouse. To us, this
is thinking globally instead of locally, all for the sake of money.

We have already observed that money is necessary – our modern
world would be difficult to operate without it. Money is a functional
common denominator that puts a definable value on all goods and
services. It allows one to see how much everything costs, and it
enables a business to assess how much profit has been made. Money
should never become the goal, however, because once it does all
human compassion and reasonableness seem to be pushed to one
side as avarice takes over, fuelled by the mistaken belief that more
money equals more happiness. Apply money-orientated thinking to the
farming of animals, and human benevolence takes a back seat. Non-
involvement with the process of farming is justified by the belief that we

somehow superior to the 'dumb animals' that we exploit. It is therefore quite acceptable to do with them as we will, so long as we can increase the bottom line.

Is it not true, though, that in another context, that of domesticated pets, we have a completely different relationship with animals? It is another example of our fabled double standards that we can simply choose to ignore the unremitting degradation bestowed upon farm animals yet jail a man for being cruel to his dog. Anyone who has ever had a pet, or anyone who has a garden, must know that animals and birds can be so like us in so many ways that it is not difficult to give them human qualities. Were it not for this understanding, we would never have had cartoon characters like Bugs Bunny or Tom & Jerry, never enjoyed The Muppets or films like Lassie, Dumbo, The Lion King or Babe. Some would argue that this is nothing more than anthropomorphism, but I feel that our affinity with other living things is innate.

Even the tiny songbirds that populate our gardens are in essence just like us. When I am digging or preparing the ground for planting, one of our resident robins will always come close to see what I am up to and maybe grab a worm or two from under my spade. In the light of humanity's heightened awareness of climate change, there is an added poignancy to each encounter with this bright-eyed, bold yet timid little garden companion. I am always pleased to see these cheerful red-breasted sentinels. The way they watch over us as we work is very comforting. Though they remain on their guard, their inquisitiveness and apparent lack of fear encourages the kind of relationship with the other creatures on this planet that we seem to have lost.

As I watch the robin and the robin watches me, I feel that sometimes we are not too far from the kind of telepathic bond that we must have once enjoyed with our natural surroundings, before greed took over and we began systematically to foul our nest and destroy this unique and precious Garden of Eden. What we are about to lose becomes poignantly apparent as I watch this little ball of fluffy feathers. *Homo sapiens* (Latin for 'wise man' . . .) through the misguided precepts of religious authority, has claimed dominion 'over all the earth' and, in his arrogance, has put himself above all other creatures and the whole of this living planet. I feel sure that such folly will topple our species. The planet itself will eventually recover of course. After all, it is millions of years old, and our dominant species (or should that be 'the virus of humanity'?) has been hell-bent on destroying it for a mere 200 years or so. The planet will eventually shake us off and get back to normal.

Meanwhile, the robin and I continue to watch each other intently, he, for all his inquisitiveness, with a sense of wariness. After all, to him I am one of the enemy. But I'll try to work on the telepathy, and maybe I'll be able to persuade him that I understand the bond between us. Are we not alike? Do we not have the same basic structure? He has muscles, bones, sinews and organs just like I do. Though he could hide in the palm of my hand and his tiny legs are thinner than toothpicks, his heart beats just like mine and his brain processes information about the outside world just like mine. If only we all understood just how close we are to the rest of nature . . . there might be hope for us yet.

We have all seen the whales and dolphins on the TV. We know that animals have feelings. We know when our pets are sulking, just as well as the farmer knows why his cows won't go near the shed where the pigs have recently been dispatched. Yet when we prostrate ourselves at the altar of the God of Money, we easily forget all this and will happily condone the barbaric mistreatment of animals in the name of profit, saving money on the feeding and welfare of animals in a supermarket-driven price squeeze, and saving money at the tills when we proudly go home with our £2.99 chicken.

Of all the farm animals that have suffered abuse at the hands of Man, we must make special mention of those gentle bovines that provide us with beef. Modern day cattle are descended from the mighty Aurochs of ancient times, which finally became extinct in 1627, a fact commemorated on a monument in the Jaktorów Forest in Poland. The fine old breeds of the British Isles, mottled Longhorns, red and white Shorthorns, Black Finchbacks and the Doddies of Scotland, the ancestor of the Aberdeen Angus, have all sprung from the gene pool of the Aurochs. Prior to the 1700s, cattle were still mainly looked upon as work animals but, as the population of England began to increase dramatically through the 18th Century, the focus of attention switched to their value as a source of food. Wealthy landowners with time and money to spare became interested in selective breeding of cattle to increase the meat yield. This was the first tinkering of exploitation, and was taken up as a cause by one Robert Bakewell, a tenant farmer from Leicestershire.

In the 1740s, Bakewell began crossing his Longhorns with other breeds that displayed desirable characteristics, finally producing a hybrid that was stockier than its Longhorn forebears, with a tendency to gain weight quickly on a lighter diet than average. Bakewell, spurred on by the potential profit in these experiments, was soon breaking moral and ethical taboos in his quest for the perfect beast. Animal incest was no barrier to him as he mated his bulls with several generations of their own progeny in order to fix the traits he desired via inbreeding. Hybridisation and a preoccupation with creating the best meat-producing cattle became the new fixation with many people inspired by Bakewell's work.

By the turn of the century, there were at least 32 agricultural breeding societies competing with each other to produce the biggest, meatiest animals, culminating in a monster Great Hereford Ox, six foot four high, ten feet in girth and armed with horns about four feet long. This giant of an ox weighed in at over 5000 pounds. Prize bulls became the star attraction of the increasingly popular agricultural shows, which were instigated by nascent organisations such as the Royal Agricultural

Society of England, given its royal charter by Queen Victoria in 1840 and showcasing its activities in what quickly became the Royal Show. Other agricultural societies followed this lead. By the early 20th Century there were shows throughout the land, the biggest of which survive to this day. And still the prize bull, with the looks of a bodybuilder on steroids, is the star of the show.

This muscled look does not appeal to all, but the methods used to achieve it are essentially no different from those methods used in creating new varieties of flowers. The hugely ostentatious chrysanthemums, dahlias and roses that attract millions of people to venues such as the Chelsea Flower Show are the results of selective breeding and precise manipulation of individual characteristics to produce the desired result. If we find this acceptable, then we should have no problem with the breeding of beef cattle. What we should worry about, however, is what happens to the cattle once they become part of our industrial food chain, but we should understand that modern factory farm exploitation began with Bakewell's attempts to produce a more profitable animal – more meat for less cost.

Britain, famed for roast beef and home to the new beefed-up bovines, began a profitable export trade to other parts of the world, notably the USA, where British breeds soon ousted the far skinnier, slow-maturing Texas Longhorn from its number one slot. The herding of cattle and the eating of beef became something of a national pastime as the 19th Century gave way to the 20th. By the 1960s, the USA was home to innumerable steak houses and hamburger chains. The quantity of beef consumed was phenomenal. Burgers alone were being consumed at the rate of 200,000 a minute.

In order to satisfy this level of demand, changes occurred in the way beef production was managed. In passing, it is useful to note that such a high level of demand was not simply a growing insatiability for all things meaty. In part, the demand was created artificially. By marketing the idea that meat is eaten in greater quantities by the wealthy and socially superior, both cattle farmers and cereal crop farmers in America found that they could benefit from economies of scale. Although their margins were relatively small, their turnover was high and the bottom line benefited positively. There is much that can be said about the disastrous impact of this symbiotic marketing relationship between cattleman and cereal grower, an impact that is now being felt on a global scale, but for the moment let us look at just one aspect of it – the way it cruelly exploits beef cattle.

Cattle are ruminant herbivores, which means that they eat grass and ruminate. With stomachs divided into four compartments, cattle are able to break down the tough fibres and cellulose in grass and convert them into something digestible. The first of the four compartments, the rumen, is where primary fermentation takes place, after which this partially digested material, or 'cud', is regurgitated for a second mastication, when the animal is said to be ruminating or 'chewing the cud'. Copious quantities of saliva are added by the ruminating animal, helping to break down the material into manageable particles before it is re-swallowed. It can then pass through the remainder of the animal's digestive system.

In America, a taste was developed for beef that had been finished on corn, adding a proportion of corn to the diet for a short period before slaughter. The taste was considered superior to beef from purely grass-fed animals because there is more marbling (intramuscular fat) in corn-fed beef than in the traditional pure grass-fed version, and the meat is considered to be more tender in the cooking as a result of this. More importantly for profit-motivated ranchers, however, was the fact that beef cattle gained weight on corn. Thus, by the middle of the 20th Century, it had become normal practice to add corn to cattle feed, which inevitably led to the inclusion of a greater proportion of other cereals too. Good news for cereal growers and cattle ranchers, but not particularly good news for cattle, as these herbivores are not equipped to deal with grains. Too much grain in the diet gives cattle acid stomach, which makes them ill and increases the chances of passing on *E.coli* to humans. It is also far less nutritious for cattle to be fed on grain, and consequently less nutritious for those who subsequently eat the beef.

Whilst cattle feed was being supplemented with grains and cereals, changes were also occurring in what should have been natural pasture land. The drive for post-war self-sufficiency on both sides of the Atlantic gave us chemically dependent agriculture, one spin-off of which affected grazing lands. Farmers were persuaded that traditional old mixed pasture was out of date and woefully unproductive. 'Out with the old, in with the new' was the new battle cry as ancient pastureland was ploughed up and replaced with a monoculture of perennial ryegrass supported by ammonium nitrate fertiliser. Ryegrass looks lush, as do any crops high on chemical nitrogen fertilisers, but it is nutritionally impaired. Whereas traditional mixed pasture supports many different species of grass, herbs and wild flowers, each of which puts out a different root system, a monoculture root system penetrates the ground to the same depth all over. The varied root systems present in ancient species-rich grazing, each growing to a different depth, are very efficient at extracting the maximum value of mineral and nutrients from the ground. Perennial ryegrass, by contrast, is able to extract minerals from one depth only. For the cattle that eat it, this represents a poor, nutritionally depleted diet.

Watch any cattle on traditional pasture and you will notice how they graze selectively. They might almost be described as choosy, but this is perfectly natural, as the animals know instinctively what they need for optimum nutrition. In a ryegrass monoculture there is no choice. Each part of the field is exactly the same as any other. It might sound a little whimsical to say that cattle on ryegrass are bored with their food, but wouldn't you be? Effectively starved of nutrition by this lack of choice in their diet, beef cattle have only commercial feeds to turn to for variety, but their alimentary systems are not built to deal with anything other than low-grade fodder such as grass and hay. Despite this basic biological fact, profiteering has led to beef cattle, like their milk-producing sisters, being routinely fed not just corn and other cereal grains, but soya bean meal for extra protein, as well as a bizarre variety of unwholesome 'supplements' that find their way into proprietary feedstuffs, such as chicken litter (including feathers and manure) rendered down chicken or pork meat, processed restaurant leftovers, out-of-date pet food and meat and bone meal derived from sheep. As we saw in Chapter 5, the ultimate perversion is that some cattle feeds even contain bovine remains. I am but a humble layman, an inquisitive observer of life as we know it, and my opinion is therefore unqualified by anything other than common sense, but it seems to me that to authorise animal cannibalism in the name of profit is a step too close to insanity.

From my observational point of view, there seems to be no mystery in the fact that cattle succumbed to mad cow disease. The mystery to me is why so many hours of intellectual discussion have ensued in trying to explain the reasons for the sudden appearance of this disease in the mid 1980s, and to defend the new feeding regimes. Surely it is obvious that changing the diet of a true herbivore into that of an omnivore without the due process of normal evolution is madness. Of course it is useful from an academic point of view to know that cows may well have developed BSE as a result of eating the remains of sheep contaminated with scrapie, and that its cause was a new kind of pathogen called a prion, but somehow it all looks to me like a smokescreen to justify the manipulative and exploitative nature of man. And after all the talking is done, the factory farming of animals still continues as if nothing has happened.

Even when it was suspected that BSE might be transferred to human beings, the government and the appropriate industry authorities formed a huddle to work out a united stance against public fears. Officially being told about BSE in 1987, the UK government waited another two years before convening a committee under Oxford zoologist Sir Richard Southwood to investigate the possibilities of BSE being transferred to humans. Predictably, the findings of the committee were that it was 'most unlikely that BSE will have any implication for human health.'

It was only three years later that the first human cases were brought to the public attention. These were not BSE in its original form, but a variant of a similar disease already recognised in humans, Creutzfeldt-Jakob disease (CJD) causing rapid neural degeneration and even death – vCJD is nearly always fatal. Between January 1999 and December 2006, 165 people were diagnosed with vCJD, of which 158 have died. It is far too early to tell how many more deaths might occur from this disease worldwide, but cases of indigenous BSE, with all the implications this carries for vCJD, had been reported in up to 18 European countries by 2001. Since then it has been estimated that the disease may be present in many other countries outside Europe, including Canada, the USA, South Africa, Japan and the Balkan countries. According to the latest information from the Office International des Epizooties (or the World Organisation for Animal Health) 24 countries, including the UK, have reported at least one incidence of indigenous BSE up to May 2007.

The gravity of a situation like this is quite clear. Common sense cries out to be heard that creating unnatural diets for domesticated animals is intrinsically wrong and has serious consequences for humans as well as the animals. Yet those who profit from such grotesque practices continue to do so. Some token modifications to their modus operandi might be brought into practice as the result of new legislation designed to appease public concerns, but generally speaking, it's a case of 'plus ça change, plus c'est la même chose.' Unencumbered by conscience, agri-business will continue to do whatever it feels is necessary to generate ever-increasing profits or, to put it another way, to indulge in what Colin Tudge, in his book, *So Shall We Reap*, calls 'cut-price husbandry'. In this morally depleted modern world, the corporate credo of minimising costs and maximising profits overrides everything, including common sense, the principles of sound husbandry and a respect for other living creatures.

We have already seen how dairy cattle are abused and exploited for the sake of increased milk yields. We have seen how this manifests itself in the fattening up of beef cattle, and in the feed they are given. The abuse is then compounded in the way beef cattle are reared. Increasingly in the UK, this is along the lines of 'feedlots', an intensive system that now accounts for most of the beef production in the USA. The idea of a feedlot is that the cattle are confined in large sheds that look like industrial warehouses rather than allowed to roam and graze freely. The more confined the animals are, the less they are able to move around, and the less they move around, the less energy they use, so a greater proportion of the calorific value of their feedstuffs can go into fattening them or, as the image-conscious beef industry prefers to call it now, 'finishing'. Whilst confined in this way, it is possible to feed them on a computer-generated high protein feeding programmes to bring them up to finished weight as quickly as possible. Great for profits, bad for animal and human nutrition.

In the USA, the home of the hamburger, the predominance of so many fast-food burger chains like McDonald's, Burger King and Wendy's, means that the demand for beef is enormous. The effect of this on the way beef is reared, fattened, slaughtered and sold can make for stomach-churning reading. Books such as *Fast Food Nation* by Eric Schlosser set out in microscopic detail the corruption and bad practice that has come to epitomise the industry that supports the West's fast-food lifestyle, and films such as Morgan Spurlock's *Supersize Me* have brought all the issues to the public attention. Anyone wishing to know more about the US beef industry and the burger chains that it supports has a wealth of material to peruse. What is of more concern here is how these practices have been adopted by our own beef industry in the ever-increasing intensification of farming. For the last 50 years, the UK has looked to the US farming industry for guidance and has eagerly taken on board all of those innovative but ultimately inhumane and unsustainable ideas. Confinement of beef cattle on controlled diets is just one of them.

Confinement stresses the animals and makes them more prone to disease, so they are regularly given antibiotics to keep the incidence of disease to a minimum. Other antibiotics are used as growth promoters. The use of antibiotics in farming has increased twenty-fold in the last 50 years, and that brings with it other problems. Overuse of antibiotics results in drug resistance, which of course requires ever stronger drugs to combat possible illness. The drug resistance is passed on to humans who eat the beef from these animals, resulting in a crisis in the health industry.

Steroids, or growth hormones, are regularly fed to cattle to accelerate weight gain. Some natural hormones such as testosterone, progesterone and estradiol are administered along with the synthetic hormones, zeranol and trenbolone acetate. The presence of environmental estrogens (rather than those made in the body) act as endocrine disruptors in humans, thereby altering the body's natural hormone balance and creating an excess of estrogen. Such an excess has been linked to reproductive cancers (breast, testicular, prostate) and the incidence of these cancers has risen sharply in the last fifty years. According to various medical bodies (for example, the Cancer Prevention Coalition) there is an undeniable connection between these cancers and 'the uncontrolled use of hormones in meat.'

The intensive farming of beef cattle, or any other type of intensive animal farming for that matter, is fatally flawed in terms of the health of the animals, the health of those who eat the meat, the cost of supporting the industry and the environmental impact created by the inordinate amounts of chemically contaminated waste products that cattle feedlots and other such operations generate. In terms of public health scares, the industry staggers from one crisis to another and shows no signs of ever improving. The UK BSE crisis and the subsequent issues with vCJD haunted us though the 1980s and 1990s and, just when it appeared that some kind of control might have been regained, Britain was struck by the foot-and-mouth epidemic in 2001. By the time it had run its course, 6 million animals had been slaughtered. Our green fields were devoid of sheep and cows as 2001 rolled into 2002. Ten thousand farms were affected by the orders to cull and incinerate all animals within any known areas of infection, leading to the heartbreaking loss of many pedigree herds which were probably unaffected but which were slaughtered anyway on the orders of a governmental 'just in case' policy.

If anything positive came out of this epidemic it was the way in which it highlighted the ramifications of an intensive farming culture that necessitates buying, selling and transporting animals all over the country. The first case of foot-and-mouth in 2001 was confirmed in a pig in Essex, but the pig had come from a farm in Northumberland. Within days, new cases, also traced back to this same farm, were reported in Herefordshire and Devon, nearly 400 miles away. Animals are bought at large centralised auction markets and transported all over the country to be reared on intensive farms, and then they are transported again to centralised slaughterhouses. Many smaller abattoirs were closed in the 1990s, cutting the numbers nationwide from 1300 to about 300, bringing new problems into the farming industry, as discussed in the last chapter.

Industrialised farming carries horrendous risks, as does the application of the corporate credo of maximising profits and minimising costs, compounded by the ongoing price war between supermarket giants determined to outdo each other in the provision of cheap food for their customers. The cost of the BSE crisis was at least £5 billion, to which we can add the cost of the foot-and-mouth epidemic of £2.7 billion. We must again ask the question, what is the real cost of cheap food? Like the flour in our bread, the milk products, including cheese and those oh-so-healthy yoghurt drinks, our bacon, pork and lamb, the roast beef of old England, if it comes through industrialised supply channels, is more likely to attack our over-burdened immune systems than to give us the nutrition our bodies need. We may well think we have spotted a bargain when we see the beef mince on special offer at the supermarket, but we are paying a heavy charge for it that will never appear on the price ticket.

GO TO WORK ON AN EGG

On every occasion that I have travelled to Scotland, and there have been many times over the years, I have been surprised by how little time it takes to drive through the Southern Uplands from the border at Gretna to Glasgow. Even in pre-motorway days, when it was still the A74, it seemed to take no time at all.

I suppose the reality is that it is less than 90 miles from Gretna to the centre of Glasgow. That great metropolis seems to be upon you once you see the signpost for Lanark, so it is only about an hour's drive from Gretna to Glasgow. The traffic also seems far less heavy after Carlisle, though there is no logical reason why that should be. Perhaps I am just being fanciful, relaxing into the bleak upland scenery and knowing that I have left behind the huge urban sprawls of Birmingham and Manchester. Just knowing I am in Scotland makes me feel better.

On this trip, it is raining as we approach the outskirts of Glasgow, but we don't care. Britain has a maritime climate, so there is no point in worrying about the rain. As the wipers arc rhythmically across the windscreen, the built-up environs of Scotland's commercial and industrial heartland appear through the glass to be etched against the grey early evening sky. There was a time when one had to cope with the congestion that such a built-up area precipitated, but today the motorway system takes us around the east of Glasgow without our having to slow down. The exit for Stirling comes up before we know it.

The rain is heavy as we pull up outside the B&B and splash up to the front door.

"Dreadful weather," says the man who answers the door.

We agree, but only to be sociable. He shows us up to our room, unlocking the door and ushering us into what looks like a tartan showroom. It's everywhere. The carpet, bedspread, cushions and curtains.

"Very nice," I squeak weakly. I am lost for further words, but I do wonder why there are some inhabitants of Scotland who still have such a distorted understanding of their own heritage that they have to perpetuate the picture postcard whimsy of Queen Victoria and her eccentric reinvention of a country subjugated so harshly by the English in 1746.

Luckily, we are in holiday mood and we have a bag full of comestibles, including a bottle of wine and the goodies that we bought at Tebay Farm Shop. Drawing the tartan curtains, plumping up the tartan cushions and making ourselves comfortable on the tartan bedspread, we tuck in. Later, the rain having stopped, we explore Stirling, deciding that a brief perambulation on a damp evening is probably not going to do it justice, which of course gives us a good excuse to organise a return visit some time in the future.

The next morning, we enter the breakfast room, not without a little trepidation. It was on the strength of what we saw on the internet that we made this booking, but we have found from past experience that even a good website is no guarantee of a good breakfast. We sit down at a table just behind the door. Soon the lady of the house enters and immediately adopts a kind of arms-akimbo stance.

"Happens every time," she informs us.

We give her non-comprehending blank looks.

"I lay up the best table over there by the fireplace and people always sit somewhere else," she elucidates.

We smile politely and commiserate with her whilst trying not to get involved. We both know that this would not be Sally's opening gambit in our own dining room. Neither would we ask our guests to help themselves from a selection of the usual cereal suspects – mostly bearing the Kellogg's logo. We certainly wouldn't have any of these industrialised cereals in our breakfast room. Although we do offer organic cornflakes, the truth is that we would rather not even have these because, organic or not, they are still a processed breakfast food and we think there is so much more to choose from. However, old habits are hard to break and we have so many guests who prefer cornflakes to any other cereal that we feel we must have some in stock.

Passing on the cereal, we sip our orange juice whilst waiting for the cooked breakfast to arrive. Call us pernickety, but we are not enamoured by the taste of the juice. No disrespect to our hostess, who after all is merely following convention, but this orange juice has little flavour. It just tastes like watered down concentrate. To us, orange juice is something that you squeeze from an orange. Everything else is a poor imitation, including the brands that are described as 'fresh-squeezed'. It all serves to illustrate how we have all been cheated by those who purvey industrialised foods. Over the years, we have forgotten how things should really taste. We end up believing the persuasive sales pitch on the carton that we are drinking something pure, nutritious, fresh and uncontaminated that is going to give us essential vitamins and keep us in good health. If only that were true.

The cooked breakfast arrives. It looks passable, but in reality is fairly standard stuff. The sausages look as if they are hand made, so they probably come from the local butcher. The bacon also looks and tastes as if it might have come from the same source. Remembering what we had seen on this B&B's website, we are satisfied that some of what we are eating has been sourced locally, so that's a plus point. And then it all goes badly wrong when Sally's scrambled egg appears.

It is pale, watery, solid and possessed of a slightly repellent odour. Rather than the glossy creamy softness one would expect from something described as 'scrambled eggs', it has that overcooked look that you might expect in a self-service breakfast bar in a tired hotel. We assume that it has been precooked and has been sitting in the oven keeping warm until ready to serve, but the colour does not compare favourably with the colour of the yolk on my fried egg, so presumably it is not from the same batch, and it smells unpleasant. The unhappy conclusion we come to is that it has probably been bought from the cash-and-carry as a convenience food (easy to use – just pop it in the microwave, heat and serve!) and could well be made of pasteurised dried egg. Whatever its provenance, it is inedible, and remains on the plate. We find the whole experience dispiriting, not because Sally has been given a cheapskate alternative to real eggs, but because the person serving it either does not know the difference or does not care. Either way, it is a sad indictment of the state of our culinary awareness.

After breakfast, we get on the road, relieved to know that we have some fresh farm eggs with us in our box of provisions. Although we are sure that we will be able to find some real eggs when we reach Aberfeldy, it is always handy to have some in stock. We are already talking about having scrambled eggs for breakfast tomorrow in order to expunge the memory of this morning's experience from our minds.

When I was at school, food was important, but it had its place in an ordered life. Breakfast was prepared and served by my father, and he, my brother and I would sit down at the dining room table and eat the meal together, with Toto the Cairn terrier sitting bolt upright (in his best meerkat pose) at a polite distance in anticipation of any bacon rinds that might be surplus to requirements. My mother, not being an early riser, didn't join us.

The three of us sat and ate either porridge or cereal, followed by eggs of one description or another. I could never decide which was my favourite. Soft boiled eggs with toast soldiers were delicious, but I remained ambivalent about the pleasure of eating the white on its own once the final scrape of yolk had been consumed. Fried eggs were perfect with bacon from the local butcher, but we did not have bacon every day. Omelettes made a rare appearance at the table, but scrambled or poached on toast rivalled the boiled eggs and soldiers for the number one spot.

I loved eggs and, with my brother and I doing our best to get through the day's supply from the chickens at the bottom of the garden, I got through large numbers of them. It was about this time that an advert for the Egg Marketing Board was released, extolling us to 'go to work on an egg'. The advert intrigued me. I was impressed with the play on words. Language in general, and English in particular, fascinated me, especially its power to communicate ideas. One poster for the ad showed a man in a bowler hat sitting astride a huge egg. In one hand he carried a briefcase, whilst the other held on firmly to his bowler, lest it fall off in the wind caused by the speed at which he was travelling. Three meanings were apparent to me: a man using an egg as a means of transport to get him to work; a man sitting at the table and 'going to work' on the egg by cutting off the top to get at the yolk inside; and a man setting himself up for the working day by having eggs for breakfast before he leaves.

Impressed by the ability of these six words to convey at least three meanings, I also became aware of the power of persuasion inherent in them, the power of someone to change the thinking of someone else by the clever use of words. When I was 17, I chanced upon a book by an American author, Vance Packard, entitled *The Hidden Persuaders*. It was truly revealing. The book, published in the late '50s, talked about the advertising industry in America and how powerful it was becoming, even then. As I progressed through the book, I began to understand quite clearly that practically everything we buy is 'sold' to us.

In America, as advertising turned into the new science of marketing, the 'hidden persuaders' were using psychology and subliminal suggestion techniques to sell the American people not just a few everyday items but what amounted to a complete 'lifestyle'. The newly coined phrase, 'consumer goods', came to describe everything from kitchen utensils to complete kitchens and from garden accessories to garden furniture to cars and holidays. To fit in with the image being created by the adman, new foods and new ways of eating were being given the designer treatment. The powerful nascent youth market was the main target for this relentless bombardment of advertising propaganda, but the wily businessmen milking this profitable market hedged their bets by demanding that their advertising and sales teams found new markets to aim at too. Soon no one would be safe from this insatiable desire to sell products to us. From the cradle to the grave, the adman was out to get everyone and, as techniques improved in the US, so their methods were copied in Britain.

And the humble egg? That fundamental foodstuff, that essential wholefood, was itself undergoing a transformation as the age of consumerism rolled out. At the time of the advert that had so inspired me to take a closer look at the techniques of advertising, the egg, in Britain at least, was seen as a staple. By being exhorted to go to work on an egg, we were indeed being encouraged to eat eggs, especially at breakfast, still seen then as the most important meal of the day. But behind that advert, something was happening.

The ad was being run on behalf of the Egg Marketing Board. This had been set up towards the end of 1956 to rejuvenate an egg industry in terminal decline, the reason for which is quite likely to have been that people in Britain had got used to living without real eggs during the war and the nine years of rationing that followed it. The idea was that the Egg Marketing Board would buy up all the eggs produced in the UK, grade them, endorse them with a mark of guarantee (the famous 'little lion' stamp) and market them through registered packhouses. By 1968, the Board was handling the processing of 8,280 million eggs a year, but the system by which it was run was deemed to be hopelessly bureaucratic and inefficient, and there were calls for the Board to be scrapped. It did eventually close down in 1971.

A total of £12 million pounds had been spent on advertising by The Egg Marketing Board. This included the 'Go to Work' series and the little lion, but still people remained unconvinced about the quality of the eggs. Many stated quite clearly that they did not trust the Board's guarantee and would prefer to buy farm-fresh eggs. So, as long ago as 1968, this central authority was trying to persuade us that the judgement of a third party, i.e. a government body, was more reliable than our own, but the people did not agree. Though eggs had practically vanished from the menu for the 14 years up to the end of rationing in 1954, most people could remember what a real egg tasted like, and they knew that the ones with the little lion stamp were poor imitations of the real thing.

This did not deter a government determined to increase Britain's food production to new ambitious levels. During the life of the Egg Marketing Board, agriculture, which included egg and chicken production as well as other meats and cereal crops, was swiftly being transformed into an intensive system of production supported by the introduction of chemical nitrogen fertilisers to boost yields in the field. Crops were also dusted or sprayed with pesticides to keep insect predators at bay. Herbicides were used to control weeds. These chemicals were dangerous to the environment and toxic to humans, but such issues were not addressed in the relentless pursuit of production and cheap food for all.

As much as we were being persuaded during the life of the Egg Marketing Board that we should eat more eggs, suspicion about methods of production was aroused by the fact that these new eggs bearing the little lion stamp were of inferior quality. However, unless you happened to know a commercial egg producer, it was very difficult to find out why they were inferior. Today we have a much clearer idea, but forty years ago, information was more difficult to obtain and the media generally were not interested in running stories about eggs.

At the same time as this was happening in Britain, the egg in America was about to receive some bad press. Although the egg has been a highly prized natural food for centuries, certain American food scientists, whilst studying the relationship between cholesterol and heart disease, concluded that eggs were bad for the heart. Ultimately, as we shall see, this turned out not to be true, but the pronouncements of scientists were, back in the dark days of the '60s and '70s, difficult to shake off. Thus public confidence was badly dented and the egg suffered. Instantly shunned by a population concerned by the rising incidence of heart disease, sales nosedived. Such negativity is unjustified.

In many ways, the egg is a perfect food, packed with nutrition and high quality protein. An egg contains eleven essential nutrients, including the nine amino acids that the body cannot make itself. In addition, it has fifteen important minerals and vitamins, including B vitamin foliate (helpful in reducing birth defects) and the highest concentration in any food of B vitamin biotin – vital for healthy skin, hair and nails, as well as being important in the digestion of fat and protein. A major ingredient in eggs is lecithin. Also an essential component part of every human cell, lecithin helps the body to digest excess cholesterol and fat. It is an important source of choline, vital to the development of the foetal brain and the protection of memory cells. Egg yolk is rich in antioxidants, especially the carotenes, lutein and zeaxanthin, which help to keep the eyes healthy and even demonstrate a potential use in fighting colon cancer. Each egg contains only 5 grams of fat (of which 1.5 grams are saturated).

There is, as we can see, much that can be said in praise of the humble yet spectacularly nutritious egg, but not all eggs are the same. If the eggs have come from hens foraging for food in a natural way rather than from hens laying to order inside a gulag chicken shed, their nutritional value is at its highest. Rich in Omega-3 fats, which help to prevent the 'diseases of civilisation' – diabetes, heart disease, obesity and depression – the eggs from these natural foragers also have the right balance of Omega-3 to Omega-6 (approximately 1:1). An egg from a typical indoor production unit has twenty times more Omega-6 than Omega-3 – a dangerously disproportionate balance, as a predominance of Omega-6 creates a greater propensity towards the above-mentioned diseases.

Leaving aside for the moment the problems of industrialised egg production, let it be said that an egg in its natural state is a vital foodstuff. Yet in the early '70s the American Heart Association declared that the egg was a danger to the heart, thus negating at a stroke (no pun intended) everything we as a species have understood about eggs for centuries. This declaration was based on evidence put forward by a group of food scientists who had been working on the causes of heart disease. In doing this, they assumed that there must be a 'safe' level of cholesterol in the human body. The belief was that any cholesterol in food had a direct impact on the cholesterol level in the body. Thus the inescapable conclusion was that eating cholesterol-rich foods should be strictly limited.

It would be quite understandable to believe that any figures produced by a body of scientists for a 'safe' level of cholesterol would come about as a result of painstaking research and double-blind analysis. But if you thought that, you would be wrong. Gina Mallet, in her book *Last Chance to Eat*, unearthed the truth behind the findings of the food scientists. In 2002, she had interviewed Dr John J McNamara, the executive director of the Egg Nutrition Centre, the egg lobby based in Washington DC. He described how a group of food scientists got together in 1968 to discuss their belief that consuming cholesterol-rich foods should be contained within a safe level, but found it impossible to decide what that level should be. Finally, it was agreed quite arbitrarily that the limit of cholesterol intake should be 300 milligrams per day. Average human consumption of cholesterol is approximately 580 milligrams per litre of blood per day, and the consensus was that a safe level should be about half that figure. This is not science, it is simply guesswork. And very damaging guesswork too, considering the repercussions it was to have on health.

As an innocent bystander without a degree in science, I am baffled by this kind of arbitrary thinking. My own simple calculations tell me that, if we have approximately 5 litres of blood in our bodies, and the corresponding cholesterol level is 580 milligrams per litre, then the daily 'use' of cholesterol by the body is 2900 milligrams. So how did this particular group of food scientists arrive at 300mgs/day as a safe level of consumption? Surely the figure should be 1450 mgs/day. It is of course all history now, and all the myths surrounding cholesterol are as strong as ever. So, going back to said scientists . . .

An egg contains about 278 milligrams of cholesterol so, in effect, what the scientists' recommendation was saying was that eating one egg a day virtually took up the whole of one's cholesterol allowance. Thus the egg shot to Number 1 on the Banned Foods list – all that cholesterol in one hit! The negativity surrounding the eating of eggs has remained to this day, despite the fact that the recommendations of this particular committee of food scientists was rendered meaningless by subsequent findings that the whole cholesterol issue is far more complex than originally thought. Cholesterol is created through the way the human body processes food, not by foods that contain cholesterol. Or, in other words, the level of cholesterol in the blood is largely determined by the action of metabolism in making, using and disposing of cholesterol.

It took nearly twenty-five years before cholesterol was understood to the degree it is today. By 1999, the egg finally received a clean bill of health, following publication of the Hu-Willett study from the Harvard School of Public Health. By then of course a whole generation had grown up with the received wisdom that eggs could cause heart attacks. It takes a long time to shake off this kind of entrenched belief.

So, eating eggs is okay then? In principle – yes. In practice, however, and in our modern food industry, nothing is quite that simple. During the 25 years or so up to 1999, those dark days when misguided food scientists were being challenged by understandably irate egg producers, the egg industry was progressively being cranked up to ever-greater industrial levels. Thus, by the time the wholesome egg had been pronounced fit for human consumption after all, the industrial system under which most eggs were produced had severely compromised the nutritional value of the egg.

In this country, the Egg Marketing Board had set the ball rolling or, more accurately, set the egg rolling, for that was one of the innovative highlights of industrialised egg production, building wire cages for hens through which they drop their eggs onto a conveyor belt that takes the eggs away to be packed. In the pursuit of greater efficiency, hens became confined in ever-larger sheds containing thousands of cages, each crammed with three or more hens.

These egg factories are abominable places. The stench alone is overpowering, but the conditions in which these birds are kept are simply inhumane. I believe that there is no way we, as sentient beings, can justify such heartless cruelty towards other living creatures merely for the sake of efficiency and profitability at rock-bottom prices. These birds are no more than tools of an unbelievably cruel trade. Crammed in their cages in a prison without natural light, the hens lose the natural rhythm of egg laying. Completely trapped, the hens cannot roam free, nest or forage. They are fed and watered in controlled amounts and on feed made up of the cheapest of ingredients. After all, profit is the watchword here, and profit is hard to come by when your selling price is being driven through the floor by aggressively competitive giant retail chains trying to impress their customers with the low prices of basic foods.

In the natural world, hens require a good mixed diet with a high proportion of protein, which they acquire by foraging for insects, grubs and worms. Cheap factory chicken feed has protein in it, but it can come from beef fat, beef bone meal, rendered dead cats and dogs and even poultry, adding, as with beef and pork production, a sadistically cannibalistic element to the whole feeding process. So, what happens when you pack hens into overcrowded conditions and feed them an unnatural diet? You've guessed it – they get sick.

Pathogens thrive in these conditions, and the main culprits are *E. coli*, campylobacter and *Salmonella enterides*, the latter producing a mild form of typhoid fever in humans. In susceptible people, this can be dangerous or even fatal. Inevitably, when salmonella was first discovered in eggs in the 1980s, a new food scare was on the loose, scattering around yet more confusion about the egg as a basic food. The egg industry, concerned as ever with the bottom line, were not too interested in finding out what was causing salmonella to appear in eggs. Effort was instead focused on stopping the spread. Vaccination was introduced in Europe, and it is now common practice to feed battery hens with antibiotics like fluoroquinolone (to which, of course, the bacteria inevitably become resistant).

People were already scared about the amount of cholesterol in eggs. Now they were spooked about the presence of pathogens, not helped by media coverage that created a new rampant food monster out of the salmonella bacterium. In an effort to calm things down, and to point out that salmonella was not necessarily the killer it was made out to be, Edwina Currie, our Health Minister in the late '80s, famously declared that in fact most of the eggs on sale in our supermarkets at that time contained salmonella. This statement caused uproar. The egg industry was baying for her blood. The media, noses twitching with the scent of a new scandal, were building pillories, and the government was squirming with embarrassment. Mrs Currie lost her job as Health Minister, but the twist in the story is that she was actually telling the truth. In such diabolical conditions, salmonella can easily make its way into eggs, usually via cracked shells. If the hens themselves are infected, eggs can be invaded by salmonella before being laid.

Cholesterol is one thing, toxicity is quite another. Public alarm at the fact that eggs might be infected with life-threatening pathogens has forced governments and big business to think again about production methods in factory farming. Under pressure, the European Union has conceded that battery egg production should be phased out by 2012. In July 2001, Marks & Spencer announced that it would become the first UK food retailer completely to eliminate from its shelves eggs produced from battery hens. M&S now sells only free range and organic eggs, a policy also adopted by Waitrose. This initiative represents a landmark in retailing, and sounds like really good news for the consumer.

However, an industry that currently produces 8,940 million eggs a year is still a big industry. M&S and Waitrose are relatively small players in food retailing, so they can afford to be choosy when it comes to eggs, but the bigger supermarkets still demand huge quantities of eggs at a low price. 74% of the UK's total egg production still comes from caged hens, with only 20% coming from free-range systems and a mere 6% from barn systems. Factory egg production persists because it is big business, and the mantra is, as we know, 'minimise costs, maximise profits'.

Big business pulls strings that control governments, so it is interesting to look at exactly what is meant by the EU's claims that battery production will be phased out by 2012. What it actually means is that 'barren' cages will be banned and will have to be replaced by 'enriched' cages, a directive that became operative in 2003. So what exactly is an 'enriched' cage? Basically it is bigger than a conventional cage, allowing each bird 750 sq cm of space, together with a 'nest', perching space and scratching area. From 2003, existing battery cages must also be enlarged, to a new minimum of 550 sq cm per bird (up from 450 sq cm).

Such cold facts tell us little, so it is interesting to read what has been written by investigators from Race to the Top, a project set up in 2002 to track supermarket progress towards a greener and fairer food system. The project was set up as an alliance of major organisations, seeking the cooperation and participation of our leading supermarkets. After a successful pilot year in 2002, plus one report published in 2003, Race to the Top mysteriously fell off the radar. However, the information that was collected is still available on their website, and it is there that a visit to a 'state-of-the-art' egg production unit is described.

The unit in question was operated in Nottinghamshire by Deans Foods, suppliers of battery eggs to several of the multiples. They also supply free-range eggs to M&S. The visit was made prior to the 2003 recommendations regarding size of cages, so the hens were still contained in an allocated space of 450 sq cm. There were three vast sheds at the site, each around 110 metres long and housing around 100,000 hens, confined five to a cage in a five-tier system. In total, 309,000 birds were involved in producing a weekly output of 1.7 million eggs. The cages had sloping mesh floors so the eggs rolled forward into a section out of reach of the birds to await collection. Droppings passed through the mesh bars of the cage onto boards from which they were periodically removed. Artificial light, ventilation and temperature control within the sheds was almost entirely automated. The whole operation was controlled by just four staff.

So what about barn and free-range systems? In barn systems, the hen houses can be vast and hens have no outdoor access – they are just not caged. Barn systems can be either 'perchery' or 'deep litter', the former giving the hens access to perches and feeders, whilst the latter merely gives the hens a floor area that is covered with a litter of straw, wood shavings or other similar material. In both systems, nest boxes and communal nests must be provided. But we are still talking about huge sheds, typically housing in excess of 50,000 birds with up to 6,000 birds per colony. In free-range systems, European Egg Marketing Regulations stipulate that hens must have continuous daytime access to runs which are mainly covered with vegetation (extremely difficult to achieve) and with a maximum stocking density of 1000 birds per hectare (395 birds per acre). However, some sheds can house up to 32,000 birds in two 16,000 bird colonies. The majority of laying hens in the UK are in colonies of 16,000.

With flocks of this size, and despite the stipulation for outdoor runs covered with vegetation, the reality is that industrial free-range egg production is not so very different from standard cage production. The hens are still cramped, and the reality is that the nervousness brought on by the overcrowded conditions, and the pecking order imposed by dominant hens, means that they are in fact reluctant to venture out of the shed. However we look at it, they are living an unnatural life and being fed on a controlled feed of dubious provenance. Nutritionally, this type of free-range egg, though the name suggests something altogether superior, is alas disappointing in terms of eating quality, taste, colour of yolk and nutritional value. Sadly, this often applies to the organic version too. It may be organic, but if it is produced under factory farm conditions, there is still no guarantee of nutritional quality, let alone taste. Organic hens themselves may be housed under exactly the same conditions as free-range, but fed on a different grade of food, its principal difference being that it will be of organic origin. So the conclusion is inescapable: beware the industrialised egg. The simple message is that if the eggs you are eating come from any large producer, the quality and nutritional content of the egg will be compromised to some extent.

It would not be fair to make sweeping generalisations and say that all organic and free-range eggs produced in large quantities are of inferior quality. Much depends on the size of the operation, the conditions in which the birds live and the husbandry methods employed. Part of the problem is that, despite the coding system used on egg boxes, we really have no way of addressing these concerns.

We are too far removed from the original producer. You may be lucky enough to know a producer personally, in which case it is easier to find answers to these important questions. However, most people are not in this position. If in any doubt, just don't buy mass-produced eggs. These days there are so many farm shops, farmers' markets, veg box schemes and private individuals who sell eggs from their homes, that it should not be too much trouble to track down your own personal supplier, even if you live in the heart of a city.

For me, nothing beats buying eggs directly from a farm, where you can see the hens living the natural life and you can taste the difference in the eggs they lay. I realise, of course, that there are no farms in the middle of cities (well, actually, that's not quite true – there are, for instance, 17 city farms in London . . . check out websites such as www.farmgarden.org.uk) but there are often Farmers' Markets, wholefood shops or organic shops, so it is always worth just checking these out.

There is at present a wind of change in our food industry and, although it will take a huge effort to break the stranglehold that the giant corporations have on the production and sale of our food, demand for better food should, under the normal laws of economics, be met with an increase in supply. We can but hope that in the unreal world of the corporation, the real laws of economics can apply, but there is certainly evidence that this can be the case, and one example of this working in practice is the egg production at Clarence Court.

Owner, Philip Lee-Woolf, has gone back to basics at Clarence Court. He recognised that, not only has intensive egg production compromised the nutritious quality of eggs, but also the battery hens themselves were compromised to such an extent that, even in the best conditions, the eggs they laid were very low grade. In Lee-Woolf's opinion, it all went wrong back in the days when the Egg Marketing Board was running its 'Go to Work on an Egg' campaign. The desire to intensify production and, at the same time, to bring down the price of eggs, meant that new hybrid hens began to appear. The emphasis shifted from quality to quantity and most breeders, farmers and producers became obsessed with the idea of producing more for less and bringing the price of eggs down.

At Clarence Court, Lee-Woolf has developed two pure breeds of hen to lay his eggs, the Old Cotswold Legbar and the Mabel Pearman Burford Brown. Legbar eggs come in a beautiful array of pastel colours – blue, pink, peach, ivory and green. They look like a Farrow & Ball paint chart. The Burford Browns on the other hand are deep brown thick-shelled eggs. At their best, both have gorgeous deep yellow yolks and are packed with flavour. According to Lee-Woolf, the breed is reflected in the taste, but the old rare breeds are far more unpredictable than their new hybridised cousins, called upon to lay at least one egg a day without a break until they drop from exhaustion.

In terms of quantity, the Clarence Court hens don't lay so many eggs as the new hybrids (Burford Browns lay about 180 a year, Cotswold Legbars around 240, and the hybrids about 350) but the quality is undeniably superior. Add to this the fact that the hens at Clarence Court are looked after in the best possible way and you are talking about eggs as they used to be. Old breeds, pasture foraging, small flocks, plenty of space – these combine to produce excellent eggs. The business at Clarence Court has grown phenomenally, an emphatic indication of the growing demand for real food, and the distinctive egg boxes are available in all Waitrose outlets and selected Sainsbury's branches. Personally speaking, we will not buy these eggs, but that is because we do not shop in supermarkets. We realise that we are very fortunate in having some excellent alternatives in our area, and we gratefully take advantage of this. Also, it must be said that we are still dubious about the flock sizes that are necessary at Clarence Court to keep the supply going at the required level to supply two supermarket chains. Yes, these eggs are better than the average free range, but they are still not as good as the real thing, and they cost much more than the £1.50 a dozen that we pay for eggs that are guaranteed to be laid that morning. It is, however, very good to know that progressive thinking companies like Waitrose are prepared to listen to their customers and stock products that come from producers who understand the true meaning of real food, nutritional value and humane animal husbandry. Even though I cannot see how the supermarket approach to retailing can ever truly give us the kind of real food we need, let us hope that the example set by Clarence Court and others is an indication of positive change that might just lead onto a better future.

part two

BAD FOOD AND FAILING HEALTH

How giving up real food
has compromised our health

THE GOOD DOCTOR

When it comes to any consideration on how our food has been compromised over the last 50 years, a large part of the problem is the lack of understanding and awareness of what the problem is. For many people, it is a failure to recognise that there is a problem at all. In the same way that someone driving through England on a typical summer day finds it difficult to accept what is being publicised about climate change, so it is difficult for some to understand that there is a problem with our food when, to them, all appears to be well.

Leaving Stirling and the experience of the inedible scrambled eggs, Sally and I can see clearly that we, the British, have far too little innate appreciation for what is good and what is not. To the landlady of our B&B in Stirling, there was nothing wrong with the eggs she served Sally. In fact, it could be argued that she was proud of the standard in her dining room. But it was not the standard we had expected after we had read her website, and those scrambled eggs blew a huge hole in her whole philosophy. Would the owner of a French auberge, or an Italian trattoria, ever make scrambled eggs like that? We think not. British cuisine, or the perceived lack of it, has become the laughing stock of our more food–conscious European neighbours. Speaking personally, we believe that there is much to be admired in British cuisine, and we praise those high-profile chefs who are prepared to make a stand for our home-grown produce and for a culinary tradition that once knew how to handle it. It is not enough, but it's a good start.

It appears to me that our grasp of basic cookery skills has been undermined by the industrial revolution, the alacrity of post-war governments to make a Faustian pact with the chemical companies on the promise of abundant food for all, our increasing enthusiasm for a fast-food lifestyle and the phasing out of cookery lessons in our schools. Whatever cooking skills were utilised by ordinary mortals prior to the industrial revolution were quickly whittled away by the new urbanisation taking place around nascent heavy industries. The great migration of displaced rural labourers in search of work in the new cities and towns created huge sprawling slums and a growing ill-fed, poorly educated, badly paid underclass. Food was about survival not culinary skills, and a large proportion of the working class of the 19th Century have been described as living on a subsistence diet, the main features of which were white bread, margarine and refined sugar, all products of the new industrialisation.

Today the slums are gone but the lack of interest in, and consequent limited understanding of, food is endemic in our culture, together with an inability to distinguish between good and bad food. That limited understanding leaves us open to abuse by unscrupulous industrial food producers, and our increasing intake of the products with which they ply us puts our health at serious risk. Of all the people who have presented erudite and persuasive arguments against the industrialisation of our food and about the health risks involved, one man's work stands out as being amongst the best, because of its contemporary setting and the clarity of its message. That man is Dr Walter Yellowlees.

As a resident GP for 33 years in the Aberfeldy practice right in the heart of Perthshire, Dr Yellowlees was able to observe at close quarters the effect that industrialised food was having on his patients over this period of time. So inspiring and evocative is his book, *A Doctor in the Wilderness*, that we feel compelled to meet him. That is the reason for our trip to Scotland this spring.

Leaving the A9 at Ballinluig and heading west to Aberfeldy brings welcome relief. Modern arterial roads are quick but soulless, symbols of an exploitative world, their only purpose being to join urban centres together with all possible speed. Such roads are no more than a means to an end. The A827 to Aberfeldy, by contrast, is the sort of road it is a pleasure to travel. The sort of road that grows organically over a period of time, following old drovers' routes and well-worn pathways between hamlets and villages.

From Ballinluig to Aberfeldy, the road follows a natural course along the valley of the River Tay as it winds its way through the peaks of the southern Grampians. Hidden around every bend is something unexpected, a view across the valley, a stretch of road through ancient birch and oak trees dappling light onto the gently tumbling river, a timeworn milestone, relic of an older era and a reminder of how little this road has changed over the years. After all that motorway driving, it is so relaxing to be following the meandering valley of the Tay, travelling with the natural contours of the land rather than cutting straight through them. That, and the romanticism of being on the old 'Road to the Isles', makes the last ten miles of this journey an absolute pleasure.

Whilst in Aberfeldy, we will be staying in a holiday cottage on a farm owned by friends of the good doctor, John and Pam McDairmid. In a world of agri-business, where small farmers go bust at a horrifying rate, the McDairmids are survivors, keen to uphold their rural lifestyle without selling their souls. The farm, the intriguingly named Mains of Murthly, is high on a hill above the local distillery, commanding views over the valley. It is now effectively run by Calum and his wife Nicky, the next generation of McDairmids.

This enterprising farming family have done what a lot of farmers have had to do to keep their farms viable but out of reach of the stranglehold of agri-business. They have diversified. Whilst still producing organic beef and lamb, the McDairmids grow soft fruit and let out holiday cottages. Housed in one of the original 300-year-old farm buildings, Calum has set up a magnificent two-storey showroom of hand-crafted solid wood furniture, as well as a huge range of classy household accessories. Called *Spirit of Wood* to reflect the use of solid hardwoods in the construction of the furniture, this is a showroom well worth visiting. More than anything though, it demonstrates the kind of creative thinking that can be applied when a farmer is not prepared to give in to the madness of modern farming methods. The whole enterprise at Mains of Murthly scores highly on organic and eco-friendly credentials. It is an inspiration to all.

Having introduced ourselves to John and Pam, we unload the car and head into Aberfeldy to meet Dr Yellowlees for lunch at his home. Responding to the knock at his door, the good doctor makes us most welcome. At 90 years old, he is a living monument to his philosophy of healthy eating and could easily pass for a man 20 years his junior. Over a light lunch of home made bread and soup, served in home made soup bowls (on retirement, he learned the art of pottery) the talk is of real food. Dr Yellowlees tells us something of his experiences during his time as a GP, but mainly we talk about gardening and the delights of growing your own vegetables despite the efforts of wind, weather and the local wildlife to discourage such noble efforts. We talk of food and the deep satisfaction of eating clean, fresh food that is in season and, by definition, locally produced, preferably straight from your own garden.

Our meeting has to take place on our day of arrival, because Dr Yellowlees is going to Edinburgh the next day on a short break to see one of his sons. Totally independent, he will drive himself to the station, catch the train to Edinburgh, spend the time on the train either reading or researching material for his next book, and meet his son at the other end. We find his outlook on life quite inspirational. I hope that when we reach his age, we are equally as full of life. After lunch, we arrange to meet again on his return, after which we stroll around the town to see what Aberfeldy has to offer.

For Dr Yellowlees, life as a GP in the Aberfeldy practice began in 1948. By the time he retired in 1981, our nation's food had changed dramatically and with it our health. Long before this time, history tells us that the Highlanders of Scotland were a hardy, healthy long-lived race, some say the tallest and most muscular of all European peoples. When the Duke of Atholl instigated the Highland Clearances in 1784 by forcing from their homes the inhabitants of Glen Tilt, it was recorded that, of the 600 crofters thus evicted, none was shorter than six feet, and 17 inches around the calf. Seven-foot giants were not unheard of. These crofters also lived long useful lives, mostly still active in their eighties and beyond and many living to over 100 years old.

The staple diet at the time consisted of oatmeal porridge, barley or oat cakes, vegetables (potatoes, turnips, kale) wild fruits and honey, milk, cheese, butter and eggs, with river fish and some meat from wild deer or beef cattle. Dr Yellowlees records that this dietary tradition was still the norm when he arrived in 1948. At that time, rural agriculture was still being conducted along time-honoured lines, with small family-run mixed farms in the area covered by the Aberfeldy practice. This stretched from fifteen miles west of the town halfway along Loch Tay, taking in Glen Lyon, Fortingall and Kenmore, through to Strathtay and Ballinluig ten miles east of Aberfeldy. Certainly a formidable territory to cover back in 1948, but one which represented a good cross-section of the local population.

Much of what constituted the basic diet of the area was grown on the many small farms within it. The principle of local food for local people was the abiding philosophy, although no one at that time necessarily saw it like this. In the same way that my Grandpa had no need to use the word 'organic' in its modern sense, so the people who lived in the upper Tay valley in 1948 had no conception of 'keeping it local' in terms of the political issue it has become today. They were merely doing what had always been done. The principle of mixed farming, using stock rearing in combination with traditional crop rotation, kept the land fertile and productive. Produce from the land, consumed locally, was fresh and nutritious. Enough was grown to satisfy local needs, and the farmers worked in a close bond with nature.

It would be too easy to look upon this scene with a misty nostalgic eye, to sigh and yearn for the good old days. Just writing about past times in glowing positive terms lays one open to criticism and prompts mutterings about 'rose-tinted glasses'. Not in the case of *A Doctor in the Wilderness*, however. Here we have a book written by someone whose job it was to look after the health of the local inhabitants under his jurisdiction. He entered the Tay valley area when the picture described above typified the way of life that existed then. Nearly 60 years later, he still lives there. His work as a GP gave him the kind of observational opportunity not available to a white-coated lab technician in a sterile research environment full of albino mice. Dr Yellowlees was in the position of what you might call an observer in a unique experiment with real people, over a period of more than 30 years, on the effects of a changing diet.

By the time he retired, that traditional way of life was all but gone. Chemical farming has found its way into the upper Tay valley and there are now too few small-scale mixed farms to supply local needs. How sad it is today to see a delivery lorry that has travelled from some far-off distribution warehouse parking outside the local supermarket, discharging its metal cages of processed food, just a few doors down from the local butcher. Even the butcher himself cannot get all of his meat from local suppliers anymore. Although his beef is first class, mature, well-hung and pasture-fed, it comes all the way from a farm near Aberdeen. It tastes delicious, but it is no longer local, such is the impact of monoculture cash-crop farming on this quiet area of Perthshire. The butcher is still there, one of the last independent butchers in the area, but he knows that the future of his shop is limited by how much time he is prepared to devote to it.

In order to give his turnover a boost he, like the McDairmids, diversifies, offering his customers a range of products not normally associated with a butcher's shop. Cheery enough with his patrons, he drops this jovial facade to confide in us that he is saddened by the lack of knowledge demonstrated by the parents of young families who come to buy from him. They are only one generation removed from those whom Dr Yellowlees would have been treating in the early days of his career, yet they have already lost so much and are out of touch with the food they eat. The smell of a butcher's shop is now alien to them, and the sight of blood is disturbing to their modern sensitivities. They are not vegetarians, however. They come to his shop to buy meat, but they have become used to seeing it synthetically cleansed of all the 'bits' and wrapped in clingfilm on a shelf in a supermarket chiller. No smell to worry about and no need to handle the meat itself.

Losing the sense of involvement with our food in this way is dangerous. The traditional diet prevalent in the Tay valley, or anywhere else for that matter, came from the land, produced and grown by local people for local consumption. Most people would no doubt have grown a few potatoes and vegetables in the back garden, and everyone would have been in touch with where their food came from. As the rot of chemical farming set in, it would have poisoned not just the land and the crops grown on it but also a way of life that had sustained these Highlanders for centuries. Mixed farms gradually gave way to monocultures, the harvests from which would be sold on to the factory food industry, and the local population gradually came to rely on 'imported' food, coming back into the Tay valley from those same food factories.

As this transformation took place, so Dr Yellowlees observed a change in the health of his patients. Halfway through the 20th Century, the infectious killer diseases of the 19th Century were effectively under control. Typhoid, cholera, diphtheria and TB had been virtually wiped out with the help of better sanitation, better housing and better methods of treatment. It has been said by those who survived the Second World War that, as the end of hostilities was declared, the nation had never been healthier, despite having had to endure years of rationing. We can presume that this was indeed the case in the upper Tay valley. Gradually, however, Dr Yellowlees noticed that his patients were succumbing to new diseases, those ailments now often referred to as the 'diseases of civilisation'. Not infections transmitted by pathogenic organisms, but debilitating conditions precipitated by the breakdown of bodily defence systems, illnesses that are now all too familiar to us – cancers of many kinds, coronary heart disease, diabetes, arthritis, osteoporosis, even Alzheimer's disease, asthma and depression.

I have already suggested that it creates the wrong impression to call these the 'diseases of civilisation'. This gives civilisation a bad name. The human species has created many civilisations over the centuries which have come and gone, but there is no record that these older civilisations suffered from the raft of maladies now threatening to undermine us, although reference has been made to diseases exclusive to urban areas. No, our modern illnesses are the 'diseases of industrialisation', brought on by a new approach to food production, unprecedented in human history, the origins of which can be traced back to the onset of what is known as the Industrial Revolution. As we saw in Chapter 4, as early as 1820, the adulteration of staple foods had already reached sufficiently high levels to prompt Frederick Accum to publish his *Treatise on Adulterations of Food and Culinary Poisons*. The kind of corruption described by Accum formed the foundation of what was to come. Though we have said goodbye to the days when green tea was coloured with verdigris (copper oxide) and black tea was coloured with lead, the chicanery of the modern food processing industry has simply become more sophisticated. Most processed food today contains an additive or two. E-numbers, artificial colourings, artificial flavourings and a whole range of specific chemicals fill the ingredients lists on all factory food products.

In order to obtain official sanction, manufacturers go to great expense to get some of these additives approved for food use, but that does not make them safe. Aspartame, once listed by the Pentagon as a biochemical warfare agent, has been approved for food use by the US Food and Drug Administration (FDA), and thereafter by other similar agencies around the world. Yet it is seen by many as one of the most toxic and controversial food additives ever produced, allegedly linked to leukaemia and lymphoma. Sold commercially under names such as Canderel and Nutrasweet, this neurotoxin is ubiquitous in its application, finding its way into more than 5000 commercial products, especially fizzy drinks, jams, breakfast cereals, diabetic products, diet preparations, even prescriptions and everyday drugs. When an additive is widely recognised as being unsafe (even the FDA admits that aspartame has a number of unpleasant side effects) yet is given official approval, any sane person has to question the presence of every other additive normally found in commercial food products. But this is so difficult to do, because we are misinformed and lied to. Disinformation, commercial sleight-of-hand, advertising propaganda and spin prey like leeches on our gullibility and innermost fears, and we struggle daily to extricate the truth from conflicting reports. For every scare story, there is another that countermands its claims, and in the end it is as easy to do nothing as to attempt to discover the truth.

Thus, despite the efforts of Accum and others like him who have voiced their misgivings over the last two centuries, industrialisation of our food has continued from Accum's day to the present, driven by a new type of economy in which the only goal is ever-increasing production and wealth. In the last 50 years, the graph has risen sharply. Industrialisation is now global, and all the problems associated with it have increased to staggering proportions. One result is that our species, a species that has been on this planet for millennia, has finally lost touch with its food supply. Abdicating our responsibility to seek and gather our own food from source, we prefer to give that responsibility to profiteering middlemen whose inclination to cut corners and compromise the nutritional value of our food is as strong as ever it was in Accum's day.

Worse than that is the equally sharp rise in marketing techniques. It seems that the more adulterated our food becomes, the more slick is the advertising that tells us how wholesome it is. Hence the popular belief that there is nothing wrong with our food and that there is no problem in sending children to school with a lunchbox containing a bag of crisps, a white bread sandwich, a Mars bar and some sweets. Many parents believe that a chocolate bar will give the child a much-needed energy boost during the day. The truth is that this kind of snack, offering nothing much more than sugar, inferior fat and some over-processed milk products will give the child a short sharp sugar rush of energy that wears off quickly and leaves the child hungry for the next fix.

Walter Yellowlees saw the people under his jurisdiction dismiss the food of their fathers and grandfathers in favour of the new glamorous products beginning to appear in the shops. Who wants to be bothered with stirring the porridge for half an hour when all that is needed is to break open another packet of cornflakes and watch the golden flakes tumble into the breakfast bowl with a satisfying rustle? Bathed in factory milk and topped with a good sprinkle of white sugar, just as would have been shown in the new television ads, and there you have it – a breakfast that the proprietary manufacturer insists is going to set you up for the day. Never mind that there is no fibre in this over-processed flake of maize. Never mind that the nutritional content is so depleted by the processing that the law insists upon the manufacturer replacing the lost nutrients with synthetic equivalents. And never mind that the sugar – white, over-refined, pure sucrose – will deplete your B vitamins and lead you down the dark vale of raised blood sugar levels, probable diabetes and possible disruption of your whole hormonal system. Why worry about such things when the advertising on the packet clearly states that this is a healthy breakfast? And no health warnings about the sugar even though, as we will see in chapter 13, sugar is the most dangerous of industrial 'foods'.

As processed foods continued to fill the shelves in our shops, and the associated advertising campaigns continued to persuade us that it was all doing us so much good, so traditional foods fell out of favour. This was as true in the Tay valley as in any other part of the UK. At the same time, the loss of local mixed farming took away many of the choices we once had, and gradually people began to lose touch with where their food came from. Growing your own vegetables began to be seen as a hobby for retired old fogies, not the sort of thing to be distracting the new forward-looking generation. Why grow your own when the local supermarket has everything you need? To the new post-war generation, with their sights firmly set on earning their slice of the new affluent society, growing vegetables was decidedly uncool.

In the excitement of a new age, what no one could see was that the new foods that were so eagerly bought were as insubstantial as the prefab houses that were being built and as valueless as the new consumer goods that were proliferating in the new throwaway society. We were being sold a dream that dispensed with old values in favour of a new utopia where everything worked with the push of a button and food came ready wrapped and ready to use. Like Faust and his lust for power and knowledge, our lust for this new world came with a price. Faust was prepared to take a chance on giving up his soul to the devil at the point where he reaches the zenith of human happiness and understanding, because he believed that this point would never be reached. He thought he would get away with it. Our price was to give unto the devil of consumerism what it is that defines us as human, our 'soul' if you like. We, like Faust, also thought we would get away with it. But we have not. We are paying the price now, as we lose contact with the sources of our food, with each other and with nature, whilst increasing numbers of us succumb to new degenerative diseases that we have no real hope of curing.

RACING DOWN THE ROAD TO RUIN

Whilst Britain was still in the grip of post-war rationing, Dr Yellowlees, just a few years into his career as a GP, was already having serious misgivings about the underlying cause of ill health amongst his patients. He concluded that 'unwise use of the land was one of the factors leading to the declining health and vitality of the Scottish people'. He had studied the work of Sir Albert Howard who, in his book *Farming and Gardening for Health or Disease*, had made the connection between healthy soil, healthy plants and ultimately the health of humanity, confirming the observations made by Lady Eve Balfour in *The Living Soil*. What the doctor could see all around him was land, previously farmed successfully on a mixed farm rotational basis, going under the plough to re-emerge as fields of cash crops drenched in chemical fertilizers and pesticides.

This demolition of traditional farming took from the people the opportunity to live off the land. Even as early as the 1950s, cheap industrial foodstuffs were being imported into Aberfeldy (in common with the rest of the UK) eroding the diet that had sustained the area for centuries before. As the doctor observes, many of his patients 'seemed to live by opening cans'. Not a good thing. As George Orwell once remarked, "We may find in the long run that tinned food is a deadlier weapon then the machine gun."

Two major changes were occurring simultaneously. Firstly, the health of the soil was being compromised by the escalating use of chemicals to boost yields. Secondly, the products of this increasingly unhealthy soil were being sold to industry merely to be processed into commercial foodstuffs, thus knocking out any remaining nutrients. By the time these 'foods' were available for sale in the shops, many of them were so badly depleted of vitamins and minerals that they had become virtually useless as a life-giving source of nutrition.

Dr Yellowlees could see this and he could see what it was doing to his patients. Practising what he was preaching, he set about creating a small market garden venture in Aberfeldy, run on simple organic principles, in order to give the local inhabitants a chance to buy some nutritious food and also perhaps to encourage some of them to follow his example and create vegetable gardens of their own. But he was swimming against the tide. As his GP workload increased, so his spare time dwindled, and his venture became restricted to simply growing vegetables to meet the needs of his family.

In 1960, the British Medical Association published two booklets, one on bread and the other on sugar. In support of what was happening in agriculture and food manufacturing, these two booklets stated categorically that 'plenty of white sugar' was good for children and that white bread was 'every bit as nourishing as wholemeal'. Though Dr Yellowlees contested these claims in a letter to the *British Medical Journal*, his protests fell on deaf ears and the caterpillar tracks of the industrial food juggernaut clattered on. How difficult it must have been to make a stand for sanity against the mighty, though evidently misguided, BMA. And should we not, in our own contemporary setting, remember these misguided views when faced with some of the outrageous claims made today about nutrition and health? As Dr Yellowlees demonstrates in *A Doctor in the Wilderness*, observation and common sense are important tools when searching for the truth. When faced with information from 'official' sources, or indeed directly from corporations and industrial manufacturers, we would do well to ask ourselves who stands to benefit from all of the assertions made.

Of course it is all too easy not to ask questions. Unless one is prepared to look behind the words of advertising slogans, it is easy to fall under the spell of seductive suggestions as to how our lifestyle might be enhanced by eating this or that proprietary product. By the 1960s, with the increasing presence of television in our homes, we were becoming a nation hooked on processed food products and the slick sales patter that went with them. Around Britain, millions of people were starting the day on a breakfast of processed cornflakes or other branded cereals, swimming in milk from an industrial dairy and sweetened with white sugar. This was followed by toasted white bread spread with margarine (or, more recently, low-fat spreads) and industrially produced sugary marmalade, all washed down with low grade tea, sweetened, often heavily, with yet more refined sugar. Coffee lovers, meanwhile, were getting hooked on the quick and easy instant coffee brands.

We Brits also loved our lardy cakes, Chelsea buns, Victoria sponges and the rest of the sticky treats found in the bakers' shops of my schooldays, but we were unaware of the degraded flour and poor quality vegetable fats that were increasingly being used in their manufacture. And at any time of day – another cup of sweet tea. Living the life of Reilly after the end of rationing, we claimed that we'd never had it so good, yet the quality of our food was deteriorating year by year. By the time Dr Yellowlees retired from the Aberfeldy practice, we were a nation in poor health. In the quarter of a century since then, we have become riddled with the diseases of industrialisation. Though the medical profession insists on telling us that we are all living longer, this conceals the fact that so many of us are losing quality of life in our later years. Dr Yellowlees, a monument to his own philosophy and a vindication of all that he espouses in terms of health and nutrition, is in his nineties, yet he is still living an independent life in his own home. Such healthy nonagenarians are rare indeed.

During the span of his career as a GP, other voices have joined those of the good doctor and his mentors. Research has been done by people who care. Many a noble organisation, such as Patrick Holford's Institute for Optimum Nutrition, has been established. Unafraid of flouting received wisdom, such spokesmen have shared with us their new knowledge of how the body works and how it responds to good nutrition or the severe lack of it. In addition, there are many books, journals, reports and websites that concur most emphatically that processed food is the foundation of so many of society's ills. Yet the corporations still tell us a different tale, and their way of doing business still maintains a stranglehold on food production.

Our problem now is to find the threads of truth that run through the fabric of claims, counterclaims, disinformation and blatant fabrications that constitutes the information industry in which the food processing giants cloak themselves. Pull on any one of these threads and the cloak will begin to unravel.

Let us start with the basic breakfast staples mentioned above. As we saw in Chapter 4, all mainstream proprietary breakfast cereals are nutritionally depleted. The basic ingredients, such as wheat, rice or maize are likely to have been grown under intensive conditions, possibly from genetically modified stock and undoubtedly processed in giant mills. Further processing, using high heat, pressure and extrusion equipment, then turns these raw materials into the flakes and shapes that tumble from the packets into our breakfast bowls. The advertisements for these products are full of soothing phrases designed to calm those of a nervous disposition who might have heard some bad news about all that processed food out there. The big names in the breakfast cereal market do their best to persuade us that at least we can have a decent healthy breakfast at home before we head out into the jungle of our fast-food world. But we are being conned. As Sally Fallon points out her book *Nourishing Traditions*, the over-processing of proprietary breakfast cereals leaves them potentially toxic and actually quite difficult to digest.

To reiterate what was said in Chapter 4, there may be a whole range of vitamins on the list of ingredients, but these are not the vitamins inherently present in the whole grain – any such natural vitamins have all been destroyed by the processing. The vitamins you see listed are merely synthetic equivalents that the manufacturers are obliged to put back into the cereal to give them some semblance of vitality, but their potential benefit is heavily outweighed by some of the other added ingredients, notably sugar and salt. According to Sally Fallon, this kind of proprietary preparation can have a more adverse effect on blood sugar than refined sugar and white flour. In addition, as we saw in Chapter 5, the milk that is splashed onto these cereals is likely to come from an industrial dairy and it will be pasteurised, homogenised and semi-skimmed. This is the milk of choice for so many people in the UK today, a choice we have been persuaded to take by the food industry based on alarmingly specious claims about milk and its fat content.

Everything else that is present on the breakfast table, sugar, bread, low fat spread (butter has also been black-listed) and marmalade will almost certainly be industrial in origin. Therefore, rather than being the healthy start to the day that we would like to believe it to be, a breakfast like this is going to put our bodies under stress instantly. The sugar alone gives our immune and endocrine systems a blow they could well do without. Each of us is equipped with an immune system that is designed to protect our bodies against any invasive entry from unwanted bacterial predators and harmful toxins. Its health depends on the intake of foods rich in nutrients, vitamins and minerals. If we eat food that contains ingredients harmful to health, our immune system is embattled and grows tired, like combat troops on inadequate rations.

Thus if we eat poor quality food that is also potentially toxic, we are trapped in a vicious circle. The antibodies go out to fight, but they are not up to full strength, so they are not guaranteed to win. Going back to our typical breakfast, the risk of harmful ingredients (e.g. pesticide residues, additives) in the wheat and grain products, the poor quality milk and the predominance of sugar, all cause a defensive reaction in our immune system. Having finished our breakfast, we might then head for the office, where we might consume several cups of poor quality tea or instant coffee during the day, plus a snack from the sweet trolley and a quick bite to eat at lunchtime from the sandwich bar (yet more nutritionally depleted bread) or one of those ubiquitous High Street fast-food outlets. On each of these occasions, the antibodies come out fighting again, but they are not getting the nutrition they need to be effective, and they grow weary.

So, what happens? Toxins and other harmful pathogens begin to penetrate our defences. One thing in our favour is that our antibodies form an elite fighting force that is second to none. It takes a lot to overcome. Thus, although the immune system might be put under enormous stress, it can take a very long time before it finally breaks down. It can take years. This is precisely why many people who are constantly putting their immune systems under stress are oblivious to the fact. If the body begins to show signs of weakness, the symptoms are often ignored, or put down to some other cause, such as a late night, too much to drink, bad day at work, a row with a partner. As a consequence, we now live in a world where an increasingly large number of small but irritating and debilitating symptoms or 'niggles' affect a very large proportion of the population, and are largely ignored.

Headaches, tiredness, irritability, depression, acne, PMT and certain allergies tend to be accepted today as a natural consequence of our increasingly fast lifestyle, but this is only partly true. All of these niggles and more can also be symptomatic of a damaged or ineffective immune system. Tell this to most people and you risk ridicule. Normal reaction to such suggestions is to say, "There's nothing wrong with me that a good holiday won't cure," or "I feel fine. Apart from feeling knackered, I'm in good nick," or "How can there be anything wrong with me? I go for a run twice a week, I'm down the gym three times a week and I hardly ever touch junk food."

One has only to look at pictures from the horrors of Hitler's concentration camps, Japanese prisoners during World War II or the victims of famine and drought, to realise that the human body will stand an immense amount of punishment and still manage to survive and recover. Life is notoriously tenacious.

The modern diet is not entirely devoid of nutrition, but it is severely depleted in vitamins, minerals and trace elements. Thus we do not look like famine victims, because we continue to eat, but what goes on beneath the skin may tell a different story. Most of us look reasonably normal, but how many of us suffer from one or more of those little niggles? Though they may be no more than irritations, such symptoms could quite easily be caused by an imbalance in the body's systems. In much the same way that it is now being recognised that our whole planet works like a carefully balanced mechanism, so our bodies are, or should be, a mirror to that idea. The human body should reach an optimum peak of fitness and vitality in a condition that is referred to as 'homeostasis'. This describes the point where all physiological systems exist harmoniously in a stable equilibrium, each in perfect balance with all the other elements.

Animals in their natural unpolluted habitat can be said to enjoy physiological equilibrium, but Man, with his impaired immune system, has long since fallen from this 'state of grace.' In common with all living things, we are surrounded by billions of bacteria and viruses, all seeking refuge in any body that will give them the nourishment they need to thrive and multiply. Once our defences have been breached and an imbalance created that is not corrected, a domino effect can be set up that can ultimately affect all our bodily systems. Such imbalances can so easily start with the food we eat. Our alimentary system, our gut, contains both friendly and potentially harmful flora, bacteria and other organisms. One of these is a parasitic yeast called *candida albicans*, which exists inside all of us quite naturally, and normally presents no problems. Yeast, as any baker will confirm, is capable of almost explosive growth, given the right kind of nourishment and the right conditions in which to multiply. In the case of *candida albicans*, its nourishment of choice is sugar and the conditions within our stomachs that favour its growth are brought on by stress, drugs or poor food. If, as a result of the latter, the body's immune system is in an impaired state, this hungry and opportunistic yeast will slip through weakened defences and invade the gut.

Industrialised food puts our immune systems under constant attack. The white blood cells of our immune system, the phagocytes and lymphocytes, fight back on many fronts, tackling antigens and pathogens in what is effectively one-to-one combat. Food of this nature, though, can carry a whole variety of pesticide residues, other toxic chemicals, harmful metals and carcinogenic compounds. Thus it is a force to be reckoned with. The lack of nutrients in the food denies the immune cells the ammunition they need to fight with, so the defence they mount can be ineffective. In this mêlée, *candida albicans*, or Candida as it is more commonly known, proliferates unimpeded and subsequently mutates into a mycelial fungus which penetrates the wall of the digestive tract, thus opening up a portal for the seepage of toxins directly into the bloodstream. The mycelia spread outwards towards the body's extremities, toxins follow and our bodies are likely to begin to show unmistakeable signs of malfunction.

Candida is the big C-word, the one that the medical profession is reluctant to utter. Although it is a known fact that this yeast lives within us, it appears to be difficult for the medical profession to accept that an overgrowth of Candida might be responsible for a large number of modern day ailments. It is even more difficult to accept that a bad diet might precipitate the internal circumstances that give Candida the opportunity to dominate. In the case of vaginal or oral thrush, your doctor will quite happily tell you that it is caused by the Candida yeast, but the symptoms are external and that makes diagnosis much simpler. To talk about Candida in the stomach or digestive tract is a grey area medically speaking, hence the reticence to discuss the possibilities of how Candida disrupts the body internally to generate external symptoms. Perhaps it is because Candida is present in everyone that it tends to get overlooked by doctors seeking the causes of particular diseases or conditions.

Nevertheless, many exponents of complementary medicine accept that, in the right circumstances, generally in the presence of a weakened immune system, Candida can indeed run riot. The doctor that will describe vaginal thrush as a Candida infection, or candidiasis, will also tell you that a body might become susceptible to it after a course of antibiotics. It is an accepted fact that antibiotics kill friendly bacteria as well as those they are designed to eliminate, thus weakening the immune system. What the doctor will not tell you is that an immune system weakened in any other way, e.g. through poor diet, might also generate the right circumstances for Candida to proliferate.

The reason for this might lie in the way the National Health Service is run today. Firstly, it is a reactive institution. It reacts to the presence of a problem rather than working to prevent the problem occurring in the first place. Secondly, it is in the grip of the giant pharmaceutical companies, whose mission seems to be to create a reactive drug for every ailment, from a runny nose to cancer. Thirdly, the poor GPs employed by the NHS are, like so many government employees, held to ransom through target-driven 'incentives' and campaigns. Success in the medical world is measured by 'results' against a given target. A GP's answer to external Candida is to prescribe a drug or chemical-based ointment designed to clear it up. However, all this remedy will do is to push the Candida from the surface to manifest itself in some other way, perhaps hidden from view.

In today's health service, prescriptive drugs rule. It seems that harassed GPs have no time to explore a patient's symptoms adequately. A drug is available to suppress every symptom, including those that manifest themselves as side effects of being given other drugs. Thus the UK, taking its lead once more from the USA, has adopted a 'pill for every ill' healthcare culture. In such an environment, it is difficult to open up a meaningful discussion with your GP about something as elusive as Candida in the gut, just one more of the diseases of civilisation, but the one that nobody talks about.

The problems that we face today from these diseases are problems caused at a fundamental level, that of the food we eat. If we could put that right, so many of the bodily ills we suffer, and of course the subsequent ills suffered by the society within which we live, could be eliminated. This sounds like a pious hope, a vision of a new utopia but, to me at least, it sounds like something worth working towards.

One of the main challenges to this ideal is the seventeenth century approach to medicine. Symptoms are traditionally treated in isolation, rather than holistically. The drug companies have taken this idea to its logical conclusion, hence the absurd situation of patients being prescribed a huge list of different drugs for different jobs rather than finding out what actually ails them. Some doctors, like Dr Yellowlees, appear to have an instinctive and vocational feel for what they do which allows them to diagnose medical problems in a truly holistic way, but such people are rare. For the most part, the medical 'industry' today is geared to reactive symptom-specific remedies. This approach misses the point that if someone is suffering from Candida overgrowth in the gut, for instance, this might manifest itself as athlete's foot or constipation.

Our nutritionally depleted food diminishes the efficiency of our internal bodily systems. In particular, our carefully tuned immune system is weakened, allowing an internal imbalance to occur in favour of unfriendly organisms such as Candida. An overgrowth of Candida shows up as any one of a number of common ailments, which the medical profession then treats with drugs. Subsequently, the drugs have a further adverse effect on our immune system. Thus we have tied ourselves into a vicious circle, simply chasing the symptoms around the body instead of repairing the real damage. This is bad enough, but it gets worse. Take the case of Candida again. The Candida yeast thrives on certain substances which are abundant in our over-processed modern diet. Having given Candida a chance to spread and dominate, we then ensure that it lives happily ever after by feeding it the things it loves, most notably pure refined sugar, a favourite of all yeasts, certainly a big hit with Candida and quite possibly the worst industrial food known to Man.

"But I hardly have any sugar," is a plea heard so often these days. The bad old days, when everyone had two spoons of sugar in the many cups of tea consumed during the course of an average day, would appear to be long gone. There is so much more awareness of the harmful effects of an over-consumption of sugar, and the popularity of sugary cakes and the like has certainly fallen. If only it were that easy, just giving up cakes and sugar in your tea. But it is not. Sugar gets into everything, from breakfast cereals, bread and marmalade to tins of beans, chopped tomatoes, ready meals and meat products to the more obvious fizzy drinks, chocolate bars and snacks. It even finds its way into savoury snacks. When it comes to the huge range of industrialised foodstuffs, the presence of sugar, in the form of sucrose and its many derivatives, is ubiquitous.

Almost by stealth, this useless commodity has crept into our daily diet to such an extent that the health of the nation is under serious threat. Everything we eat, from our breakfast to microwave meals to that last cup of drinking chocolate at night, is polluted with sugar. When we look at the statistics that show the alarming increase in the numbers of people afflicted by such malfunctions as diabetes, heart disease, obesity and the various cancers, the inescapable conclusion is that we are indeed roaring along the road to ruin like a joy rider on Ecstasy. Or should that be sugar?

JUST A SPOONFUL OF SUGAR

In the centre of Aberfeldy is a converted Grade-A listed watermill that has been sympathetically restored and converted into the largest independent bookshop in the rural Highlands, with three floors of books. It also serves brilliant coffee in its coffee shop on the ground floor. Its ethos is proudly displayed for all to see. On the menu at the counter was written: '*We do not sell high sugar content fizzy drinks manufactured by global corporations. Nor do we sell drinks made by firms that divert precious water supplies in the developing world from the local population in order to make their drinks.*' All in all, a perfect place to meet Dr Yellowlees on his return from his brief trip to Edinburgh.

We had the feeling, as we sipped our coffee, that he does not approve of this dark beverage. He is not alone. Many nutritionists believe that the benefits of coffee are outweighed by its harmful effects. Patrick Holford, of the Institute for Optimum Nutrition, goes as far as to say it is potentially carcinogenic. Our real food ethos tells us that all of these people are probably right and that it would be desirable to eliminate coffee from the diet altogether. At the same time, however, we have great respect for my grandfather's philosophy of 'a little of what you fancy does you good.' And there is no doubt about it – you can't beat a good cup of coffee. Thus we look upon it as a weekly treat. Or, in the case of The Watermill in Aberfeldy, a twice-weekly treat. After all, we are on holiday, albeit a working holiday.

A day of self-indulgence does not stop with the coffee. Our philosophy on a naughty day is 'might as well be hung for a sheep as a lamb,' so a scone and butter usually accompany the coffee. On our first visit to the Watermill, we were seduced by the home-made carrot cake, so we thought we might try that again. Tempting the doctor to a slice, however, turned out to be an unproductive exercise. We hadn't really expected him to accept this offer, knowing his stance on sugar, but we thought that there might be a chance that he would subscribe to the same philosophy as us.

He just gave us that look, as if to say, "You know how I feel about sugar."

We admired his fortitude. Weak-willed by comparison, we ordered ourselves a slice of carrot cake each, but the guilt was there, and I didn't enjoy this piece as much as the one I had devoured earlier in the week.

There is a good reason why Dr Yellowlees shuns sugar so conscientiously. He believes it to be the root cause of most of our ills. As we have seen, in his 33 years as a practising GP, he saw the health of his patients deteriorate in direct proportion to the increase in processed foods that steadily became the norm. His research into why this should be took him to the works of two eminent nutritionists, Sir Robert McCarrison and Surgeon Captain T L Cleave. The former had written a treatise called *Nutrition and Health*, which set out to explore the relationship between these two, ultimately concluding that, in order to enjoy good health, one must build a solid foundation of good nutrition. Surgeon Captain Cleave, during his life as a Royal Naval medical officer, and through the years of his retirement, also studied the relationship between good health and good nutrition. He came to a precise and astoundingly simple conclusion about the modern diet: Man has no ability to deal with the refined carbohydrates that are created by industrialising our food.

Surgeon Captain Cleave had two major interests. One was his work, through which he demonstrated a zealous desire to understand the causes of illness and thereby to learn the art of prevention. The other was his love of nature. He had what Dr Yellowlees describes as 'intuitive skills in understanding the ways of beasts, birds and fish.' He could see clearly that animals in the wild were perfectly adapted to their sources of food as they occurred in nature. Even though they preyed on each other, all animals live in a natural harmony with their sources of food. But they clearly do not suffer from the degenerative diseases that so afflict modern Man.

The reason for this, Cleave concluded, is that Man is the only species on Earth that tampers with its food and alters it in such a way as to make it unnatural. More specifically, the process of refining carbohydrates creates new 'foods' that our bodies are simply not capable of dealing with effectively. Our evolution has not kept pace with the advances in food refining, and we are in fact trying to survive on food which is literally alien to our systems.

Sugars abound in nature and are found in the green leaves and stems of plants, in vegetables and in fruits. In a natural environment, our bodies are equipped to eat these natural foodstuffs and then break them down as they pass through our alimentary systems, extracting from them along the way the starches and sugars which provide the energy source that our bodies need to survive. What our bodies are not equipped to do is to consume refined sugar by the spoonful.

Using an example illustrated by Dr Yellowlees, we can see why refined sugar is such a problem. In a natural sugar-bearing plant, a beetroot for example, the sugar content represents about 10% of the weight of the beetroot. If we eat the beetroot, our bodies would break it down as it moves through the digestive tract, and the sugar would be extracted and made available to the body as a source of energy. In order to acquire the equivalent of the few spoonfuls of sugar that might be sprinkled on the average breakfast cereal and stirred into a cup of tea, one would have to eat about 450 grams of beetroot. To reach the average levels of sugar consumed daily by a person in the UK today one would have to eat around six large beetroots. Logic tells you that one would feel satiated long before the sixth beetroot had been consumed.

Assimilating sugars via a breakdown of natural carbohydrates has other real benefits too, in that vitamins, minerals, proteins and fibre come as part of the package, and that the proportion between all these is naturally balanced. Pure refined sucrose has none of these elements. It consists, as has been said so often, of nothing but 'empty calories.' Pure sucrose, with no nutritional value, and available in unnaturally large quantities, puts our bodily systems under massive stress. Yet the consumption of sugar has for centuries been a significant and normal part of our daily diet, so we prefer to look upon it favourably and persuade ourselves that it does no real harm.

Within the medical profession, some doctors will say that, providing you are reasonably active, and can burn off the extra calories, sugar is fine. Sugar has become so much part of our daily lives that we are oblivious to the detrimental effect on our health. Let's face it, even doctors can have a sweet tooth and, when trying to justify what amounts to a craving, developing a convincing argument in support of it is not difficult. Many medical and nutritional experts today seem unable, or unwilling, to point the finger at sugar as a serious threat to good health. Though they agree that it is not beneficial for us because it provides us with too many calories, they fall shy of stating that it is actually harmful and should be banned from the diet altogether.

On the rare occasions when something is said about the damage that sugar causes, the big guns of the sugar industry come out blazing. In 2003, for example, the World Health Organisation produced a new report on the dangers of consuming too much sugar. The report's guidelines stressed that sugar should form no more that 10% of an average person's diet. There are many that would say that this figure is dangerously high and is obviously aimed at industry approval, but let us accept that this is the figure that the WHO quoted. The sugar industry would have none of it. They hit back at the WHO and, via the mouthpiece of the US Sugar Association, which includes giants such as Coca-Cola, Pepsi-Cola and General Foods, accused the WHO of being 'unfair, misguided and misleading.' Companies such as these support a sugar consumption limit of 25%.

We can see quite clearly from this what we are up against. Although there is a growing understanding of the dangers of refined sugar, giant corporations who make billions out of selling their sugary drinks, snacks and processed foods are so powerful, and so devious in the way they promote their products, that they will not let a little thing like a WHO report get in the way of their profits. Sugar has been around too long and has become too profitable, and the fat-cat corporations do not want us to give up consuming it. Their arguments for sugar are made to sound plausible, but one must remember that there was a time when tobacco companies also sounded plausible when they tried very hard to convince us that smoking was no more than a beneficial social pastime. If we can but stop for a moment to think clearly for ourselves, we will see the other side of the story.

The other side of the story in this case is that sugar really does damage our health. Here we face a biological dichotomy. It is an established fact that sugar is essential to life, because it provides the fuel that we need for energy, and energy is what drives all our cellular processes, from thinking to running. However, at a natural biological level, human beings obtain the sugar they need from starch, which we are able to break down through chewing and enzymatic digestion into glucose molecules. The bonus for us in this process is that we pick up other elements of natural food, vitamins, minerals, proteins fats and fibre, all of which have roles to play in keeping the body fit and healthy. All of these elements enter the bloodstream via the small intestine and are transported to wherever the body needs them, the glucose destined for fuel to be converted into energy. Though complex in construction, the system is beautifully simple, akin to controlled precision engineering. And that is its essence – control and precision.

Throw into this carefully balanced system a spoonful or two of refined sucrose, and the system falters. It is not built to receive sugar in this way. In order to metabolise refined sugar, devoid as it is of any other components apart from sucrose, the body must call on its own reserves of vitamins, minerals and enzymes. Thus an ingestion of refined sucrose will be dealt with, and balance will be restored, but at a cost to the body itself. As Sally Fallon points out in *Nourishing Traditions*, the consumption of refined carbohydrates in the form of sugar (and white flour) is dealt with by the body's reserve defences, but it may be likened to drawing money out of a savings account. If one keeps making withdrawals without any deposits, funds will soon be exhausted. Of course, not everyone has the same level of reserves within the body. Some people have more in their account than others, and such people may be able to survive for a long time before showing signs of depletion. With some people, it might even be passed down to the next generation before anything adverse manifests itself. But the principle applies to us all, and none of us is able to escape the ravages of this deadly substance.

Many fine works of research have been published over the years that contain detailed, well reasoned and convincing arguments that label sugar as a serious health hazard. Cleave's excellent 1974 publication, *The Saccharine Disease*, should be read alongside John Yudkin's *Pure White and Deadly* and William Dufty's *Sugar Blues*. John Yudkin was Professor Emeritus of Nutrition and Dietetics at the University of London. His book, though out of print and relatively hard to find now, has been described as 'scholarly, comprehensive and quietly devastating.' William Dufty's book, written with all the verve of someone who is passionate about his subject, pulls no punches in explaining why sugar turns us into addicts.

In the face of a mountain of evidence condemning sugar, a great many people have righteously given up sugar in tea and coffee. They don't sprinkle it on their cereals in the morning and some even shun sticky buns and Mars bars. However, as we saw in Chapter 12, sugar is everywhere. It is an essential ingredient in the food processing industry, used as a flavouring in everything from bacon to cheap honey.

It is in salad dressings, condiments, pasta sauces, ready meals, low-fat spreads and probiotic drinks. When it is not listed as sugar, it masquerades under the guise of glucose, fructose (even glucose-fructose syrup) fruit sugar, maltose, dextrose, lactose (milk sugar) corn syrup or modified corn starch. Getting slightly more obscure we have glycogen, sorbitol, maltodextrin, monosaccharides, polysaccharides and the enigmatically named invert sugar. Over in the health section, we might see brown sugar, Demerara sugar, Muscovado sugar or just raw cane sugar. They sound healthy and tasty. They are not – they might well be tasty, but they are no more healthy than those glittering white crystals. Sugar is sugar, no matter what the colour, and the amount of sugar present in some processed foods is phenomenal.

An article in The Times in April 2007 revealed that the consumer magazine *Which?* had turned its attention to sugar, and investigations had revealed the high doses of sugar present in some meals. One ready meal of crispy beef in a sweet chilli sauce was found to contain 67g of sugar, the equivalent of 16 large teaspoons of sugar hiding in one ready meal. This typifies the problem with extrinsic sugars, in other words, those sugars added to our food rather than being present intrinsically. They are being added to our foods by big manufacturers and we are consuming them quite unknowingly. If sugar is present in a manufactured food, it must be declared on the label. Thus the information is technically being made available, but in reality is not being noticed by us. Very few people have the time to scour the labels on everything they eat.

As mentioned above, the World Health Organisation has recommended that sugar forms no more than 10% of a person's average daily food intake. Let's put some figures to this. Take an average woman aiming at 2000 calories a day. 10% of this equates to roughly 50g of sugar by weight. This is around 12 teaspoons. An average man at 2500 calories a day would be getting through the equivalent of 15+ teaspoons. This is a huge quantity of sugar. If you weigh out 50g of sugar on your kitchen scales, you will be appalled by the size of the heap that this forms. But it is not difficult to get through this amount. Take one bowl of, say, maple and pecan crunch breakfast cereal and add to that one healthy flapjack for your mid-morning snack. That brings your total up to about 45g, and you haven't yet popped out at lunchtime for a cappuccino and a croissant or perhaps a can of something fizzy. If the latter has a sugar base, rather than an equally damaging chemical substitute such as aspartame, this could add another 37g to your total, or another nine teaspoons.

Those whose lives are somewhat less abstemious than shown in this little illustration can very easily find themselves bumping up their sugar intake to dangerous levels. Our inherent taste for sweet things has been exploited by a food industry intent on keeping us as customers for life. An increasing number of babies are no longer breast-fed and this gives manufacturers their first opportunity to cultivate that sweet tooth that gets us hooked on all things processed. Baby and infant formula milk are sweeter than breast milk, and follow-on formulas can contain 60% more sugars than normal milk. A bottle-fed baby, in its first eight months of life, can consume 30,000 calories more than one that is breast-fed. Baby foods, with legal authority to contain up to 30% sugars, help to imprint this appetite for sweet tastes that leads on to a predilection for sweetened snack foods, which of course includes so-called 'healthy options', such as low fat yoghurts. A typical low fat yoghurt may be virtually fat-free, but might still contain up to 7% sugar.

Savoury snacks can be just as bad. Even something as obviously salty as the reconstituted potato snack, Pringles Originals, contains dextrose. Flavoured crisps carry sugar in everything from Thai sweet chilli flavour to basil and balsamic vinegar flavour. The food industry has created a palette of some 30,000 varieties of artificial chemical flavourings to add sweetness to our processed foods and keep our sweet tooth honed up. No one mentions the potentially addictive nature of sugar, but the food industry knows only too well that if they can get kids hooked on sweetness they will always be able to sell their products as the kids grow up.

Hooked on sweetness really means hooked on the sugar drug. The problem with refined sugar is that it gives the body a big hit. Without having to be extracted slowly from within plant-based carbohydrates, it is converted to blood sugar very rapidly, giving you an energy boost and the high that goes with it. Reaction in the body stimulates the pancreas to release insulin to reduce the level of blood sugar and this brings on a low. The body then needs another hit, and the subsequent rush of energy feels good, as does the high. Like caffeine or nicotine, the body starts to depend on its next fix, and it becomes extremely difficult to wean it off this need for sugar. Figures for consumption of sugar indicate that we are certainly losing this particular battle. From a per capita consumption of around 4lbs of sugar a year at the beginning of the 18th century, the average today, in the US at least, is around 170lbs per person per year. The UK is not far behind.

Suggestions of health risks, including the likelihood of putting on weight, are dismissed by the industry. Its stance is that eating is all about calories and that all calories are equal. It puts the blame squarely on the individual, saying that it is up to each one of us to make sure that we are not consuming more calories then we require. As far as organisations such as the Food and Drink Federation are concerned, sugar is 'a natural carbohydrate' and a source of glucose, 'the vital fuel for the brain and body' and 'an essential part of an active lifestyle.' To those who take such a stance, it is of no consequence that so many of us find it difficult to actually monitor our own levels of sugar consumption, due to conflicting messages and the difficulty of interpreting information written on packaging.

Despite the industry's stance, the health risks are well researched and well documented. Books such as Sally Fallon's *Nourishing Traditions*, Nina Planck's *Real Food*, and Lynne McTaggart's *What Doctors Don't Tell You*, are all valuable and finely detailed dissertations on the impact of processed food on our health. If you are interested in investigating the subject in depth, one or all of these works would be an excellent place to start. For the purposes of this book, we can simply summarise.

As mentioned previously, the body is a beautiful example of precision engineering. All the systems that keep us functioning at optimum levels are finely tuned and inextricably linked to each other. This state of equilibrium means that, when everything is in tune, no part of our bodily function is out of balance. If we consume real foods in their natural state, our bodies are ideally equipped to digest them efficiently. The sugars and starches we need for energy are broken down and digested slowly, entering the bloodstream quietly over several hours. If we were to go without food for a while, our endocrine system will act to release glucose reserves in the liver, but just enough to restore balance once more. Blood sugar levels are regulated by insulin from the pancreas and hormonal input from the thyroid and adrenal glands.

Refined sugar disturbs this finely tuned regulation mechanism alarmingly quickly, provoking a dramatic reaction from the endocrine system, which goes into action like fire-fighters at a blaze. A flood of insulin and hormones brings the threat under control and equilibrium is restored. If another hit of refined sugar takes place, the system comes out fighting again. But like those fire-fighters, precious reserves are used up as the situation is brought under control. If it happens too many times, the reserves run out and the fine tuning is impaired, with some parts of the system going into a state of constant alert and other parts becoming run down and defective or ceasing to function altogether.

Those who are likely to subject their bodies to this kind of constant sugar barrage are, unfortunately, also quite likely to have a penchant for a diet high in refined and processed foods – you might say it goes with the territory. The resulting lack of vitamins, minerals and other nutrients will leave such a person all the more vulnerable to a potential breakdown in the endocrine system. This in turn opens the door to a number of pathological conditions, those now familiar modern day degenerative diseases, allergies and obesity. Conditions such as depression, learning difficulties and behavioural problems can also be traced back to this original root cause.

With regular sugar attacks on the body gradually overcoming the body's ability to maintain control, the balance of blood sugar can eventually be disrupted on a permanent basis. Once the scales tip, a body can be left in a state of high blood sugar (hyperglycaemia) or low blood sugar (hypoglycaemia). A case of high blood sugar can easily precipitate diabetes, leaving the sufferer exposed to the possible danger of blindness, tissue degeneration, heart disease and diabetic coma. Injections of insulin can keep the coma at bay, but it may not be able to stop the other problems. Hypoglycaemia on the other hand, may not display such severe symptoms, but it is not to be trifled with. Low blood sugar can leave a sufferer listless and lethargic, inclined to depression and ultimately Myalgic Encephalomyelitis, more commonly known as ME, or chronic fatigue. Seizures, allergies and migraine are also common symptoms. Treatment of low blood sugar is often reduced to no more than advising the patient to eat something sweet when they feel a low sugar emptiness coming on. Such a remedy does little good, however, when the sufferer is as likely as not to tuck into a snack bar. The sugar rush from this might alleviate the symptoms temporarily but will also impinge on the body's delicate balancing mechanism, as will any sugar hit. The problem is therefore not likely to go away, and quite possibly will develop into something more serious. That our medical profession is capable of making this kind of recommendation is indicative of the fact that sugar is still widely accepted as being no more that a source of calories.

Contentious though it might be, there is no escaping the fact that studies have shown that sugar consumption, possibly through the stress caused to bodily systems, can lead to heart disease. The buzz phrase when it comes to heart disease is 'saturated fats'. This is generally taken to mean animal fats, but, as we shall see in the next chapter, it is not as simple as that. Meanwhile, much of the research regarding the link between sugar and heart disease has been sidelined and suppressed through the efforts of the food processing industry. Animal fats are of no real use to the industry, so those within the industry have no concerns about how much bad press is given to them. The building blocks of food processing are sugar, wheat flour and vegetable oils, so the industry is keen to protect the reputation of these three at all costs. Sugar, as well as wheat flour and vegetable oil, is cheap and easy to produce. In helping to disguise the blandness of processed food, sugar is very effective, and it even acts as a useful preservative, using up the water in which bacteria might otherwise grow, and thereby helping to extend the shelf life of the finished product.

According to Sally Fallon and the many research papers she has investigated, sugar consumption has also been linked to kidney and liver disease, atherosclerosis and cancer. It would appear that tumours thrive on sugar, and research has shown positive indications that sugar is associated with cancer in humans as well as laboratory animals.

It is a widely accepted fact that sugar is also associated with tooth decay. The prevalent urban myth says that 'sugar will rot your teeth'. Less well publicised is the fact that over-consumption of sugar causes bone loss. Thus the connection between eating too many sweets and having fillings in your teeth is not quite as simple as it seems. What is happening, in bones and teeth alike, is that too much sugar is playing havoc, not just with blood sugar levels but also with the delicate balance between calcium and phosphorus. Tooth decay is not simply the result of bacterial activity in the mouth, it is precipitated by an imbalance of body chemistry. It is an exterior sign that something is wrong *internally*, in much the same way that thrush is likely to be an indicator of Candida overgrowth in the gut.

Such exterior manifestations are really an early warning system, giving us a visual sign that all is not well with the body's equilibrium and that the underlying cause of the symptoms needs to be found. It is not just a question of having a specific problem that requires fixing. Unfortunately, modern day medical practice seems to have come to this – a knee-jerk reaction to a particular problem. This is fine when it comes to emergency surgery. If a leg is broken, or a hand is lacerated, it is not just appropriate, but essential, to tackle the problem specifically. With general medicine, however, the emphasis should be on a preventative approach. But why bother, when there is a drug for every ailment?

Those with a vested interest in the production of industrialised food in general, and the sugar industry in particular, will deny all this, especially when they are being challenged by someone like me who is technically unqualified. Yet there is enough evidence out there to demonstrate how protective the sugar industry is of its products. They will deny that sugar is likely to lead on to disease of any sort, especially degenerative diseases like diabetes. So-called experts are wheeled out to speak on behalf of the sugar industry to refute such outrageous claims. But beware the hall of mirrors that is the domain of experts. Many an 'expert' is being handsomely paid by the sugar industry, the food processing industry, the drug industry and all the other global corporations to do their bidding and persuade the public that what they say is true and that all other theories and assertions are not valid.

It is not within the scope of this book to explore this area in detail but, for anyone who wants to find out more about how big business and its experts pull the strings on the media puppet, I can recommend an excellent book by Sheldon Rampton and John Stauber, *Trust Us, We're Experts!* This exposé deals mainly with practices within the US, but much of what is said applies equally to Britain and the EU. In this increasingly global world, of course, it will soon apply everywhere. It is alarming indeed to know that even such institutions as our oldest and most venerable centres of learning are not immune to the virus of food industry spin. It is said that money talks. Bob Dylan was probably closer to the truth when he said, "Money doesn't talk, it swears." The veracity of this becomes clear when we realise that the Department of Nutrition at Harvard University is mostly funded by the food processing industry.

We should understand that the quack doctor is not a thing of the past. He is alive and well and in the pay of the corporate food industry. We would do well to listen with scepticism to anything about food, nutrition or health that we are told through the media, and we would do better to trust our own common sense rather than any of the conflicting health messages in the media. If we are told that sugar is not harmful, we should wonder who stands to gain from this attempt to keep us eating it. By the same token, if we are told that animal fat is bad for our health, we should at the very least seek a second opinion.

THE FAT OF THE LAND

With just a couple of days to go before our brief stay in Perthshire comes to an end, we agree that it is time for a slap-up dinner. But we won't be going out to a restaurant. Instead we visit the local butcher in Aberfeldy. The first time we were in his shop, we noticed how wonderful his beef looked, and we are determined to sample it.

The steak looks gorgeous. Temptingly dark in colour with a layer of creamy yellow fat, this is the real thing. Supermarket beef looks bright red by comparison, with white fat, both sure signs that the beef has been intensively reared and has been given no time to mature. Not that there is any point in trying to mature industrial beef. Firstly, the animals have been intensively reared, and secondly they have been slaughtered in a highly stressful condition, an emotional state that tenses up the muscles and makes for very tough meat.

For the deep flavours of real steak, the animals must be reared by means of good husbandry, grazed on traditional pasture and treated with some compassion when it comes to slaughter. Before it is ready to eat, the beef must be hung for at least three weeks to soften the meat and tenderise the fibres. There is no way that a commercial profit-driven organisation would allow this to happen. Time is money, so we, the gullible public, have been drip-fed the message that bright red beef, as seen in your local friendly supermarket, is the way beef should be. Worse than that, the addendum to this message, and no doubt the foundation to the well-known urban myth, is that dark beef should be avoided because it is not fresh. As to the problem of rapidly processed beef being tough, the industry has solved this problem in the only way they know how – by finding another process for the meat to undergo. In this case, the beef is 'tenderised' by being incised by a tenderising machine which passes thin blades through the meat fibres and connective tissue to produce beef that is 'of acceptable tenderness'.

While he cuts our steaks for us, the Aberfeldy butcher confirms that the only customers who will buy this mature beef are people of a certain age who know the difference. His younger patrons steer clear of it. A depressing indictment of our modern world.

That night, back in the kitchen of our rented cottage, we marinate the steaks for an hour in a dressing of olive oil, vinegar and mustard. Actually, let's be more precise. We use extra virgin olive oil, a combination of true red wine vinegar and real balsamic (not the stuff that has had colour and sweetener added to it) a traditional Dijon mustard, and a seasoning of unbleached sea salt and some freshly ground black pepper. I make no apologies for sounding like a faddy foodie, because I am not, and nor is Sally. We just believe in quality not quantity and, when the steak is as good as you can get, there is no point in tainting it with a cheap dressing.

We serve the steak with some gorgeous buttered organic potatoes and fresh vegetables which we found in a super little greengrocer in the town. A meal that is simple to prepare and simply delicious to eat. The steak is so tender that it can be cut with an ordinary table knife. Its taste has an almost addictive succulence to it, a sensuousness that elevates the joy of eating far above that needed to merely refuel the body. The fat on the meat has taken on a slightly charred note in the pan and adds a new dimension to the steak as it lubricates the meat. It has a light melting quality to it and actually is another taste sensation all on its own, in the same spectrum as the lean meat but with a different emphasis.

Preparing this meal and sitting down to eat it is a pleasure that is hard to replicate in a restaurant unless one is willing to pay a high price for the privilege. Even then, in this country, a high price will not necessarily guarantee quality. It is a sad fact of life that whatever culinary skills we might have possessed in Britain have disappeared as quickly as hail in summer. Were it not for the new breed of chefs that is currently trying to reverse this trend and bring some respect back to the culinary arts of this country, we would be doomed completely. Unhappily, we have not yet reached the relaxed situation in which any given eating place will serve a meal that is wholesome, nutritious, fresh, local and a pleasure to eat. Caution must still be the watchword in Britain. One would probably have to be in Italy to enjoy the kind of hassle-free eating out where any eating establishment, humble or grand, takes enough pride in what they are doing to ensure the experience for the diners is everything it should be.

Our meal in the cottage is eaten slowly, each mouthful being savoured in a don't-want-it-to-stop way. Sitting at a kitchen table lit by flickering candles, we sip a Chilean Merlot from a fiercely independent vineyard that refuses to buy into the corporate sales pitch, preferring to produce its wines much as they have always been produced through several generations of the same family. Quality is what motivates them, and the complex flavours in our glasses belie the modest price we paid for this bottle. In a world dominated by the big producers, our ethos will not allow us to buy anything from the ubiquitous global brands that process millions of tons of grapes each year and shortcut the lead time to profits by adding oak flavour to their wines instead of allowing them to mature naturally. For us, it is the small artisan producer every time.

Clouds that had been gathering as we sat down to eat have now turned into a brief storm that reminds us that we are in the Highlands of Scotland and it is not yet summer. It gives the place a sense of wildness that adds to the atmosphere of course, and gives an extra dimension of cosiness to this kitchen in which we enjoy our simple repast. We could have gone to a restaurant, I suppose. No doubt the local residents would have been able to recommend one in the area somewhere. But there is much to be said for a meal like this, and for not having to drag on our coats at the end of it to drive through this storm back to our cottage. Instead, we are on the inside looking out.

In eating a bit of beef fat, the question we have to ask ourselves is whether we have committed some kind of dietary cardinal sin. There are those who would not just answer in the affirmative, but who would proclaim loudly that we are in fact doing ourselves harm. These are the people that Sally Fallon calls the Diet Dictocrats. They are the self-appointed guardians of our eating habits and the purveyors of what she calls Politically Correct Nutrition, and the premise of her book, *Nourishing Traditions*, is that the advice of the Diet Dictocrats is plainly wrong.

One of the main mantras of PC Nutrition is, "Less animal fats, less red meat." So we would be damned on two counts after our steak meal. According to the Diet Dictocrats, we are risking raised cholesterol levels in our blood and therefore practically signing warrants for our own death from heart attack. So who are they, Sally Fallon's so-called Diet Dictocrats? They are doctors, scientists, researchers and nutritionists, as well as government and non-government organisations. All tend to make sweeping generalisations about people and what they eat, coming to conclusions based on data that is not sufficient to set out guidelines for our health, guidelines that can be ill-conceived, erroneous and, at times, downright dangerous. Every one of us is an individual, yet PC Nutrition treats us as if we are all the same. We are not identical laboratory rats living in sterilised conditions, drip fed a controlled diet. We are living in an infinite variety of cultures in every climate on the planet and eating everything from insects to large mammals, creating and maintaining many ethnic indigenous culinary traditions that have sustained the different peoples of this earth for thousands of years. And then along comes PC Nutrition and tells us all how we must eat for the sake of our health, and that we must not eat red meat and animal fats because we will be risking death. Common sense tells me that this is total nonsense.

When I was growing up in Uganda, I became aware that what we ate at home was not the same as the food eaten by the indigenous people of the country. I also became aware that different tribal cultures supported different culinary traditions. Some, in the higher cooler areas above the rift valley had access to the fruits of the forest and enjoyed something of a vegetarian diet supplemented by an occasional small furry animal or an abundance of various insects, locusts being a favourite. Those who dwelt on the shores of Lake Victoria supplemented a basic vegetarian diet with an occasional catfish, whilst the nomadic cattle herders of the plains and more arid northern lands, the Acholi, Karamjong and Muhima, lived off their cattle. Their diet was mostly blood and milk, with some meat when occasion demanded the slaughter of a cow. Other than that, they ate a few grains, fruits and maize when they could find them. But their diet was essentially based on what they could get from their cattle. No one ever told them that such a high-fat, high-protein diet was putting them in mortal danger. In any case, they would have laughed at the idea. These people were not sickly or prone to disease, even from malaria or the bite of the tsetse fly. Far from looking as if their diet was doing them any harm, they were well-proportioned, tall, long-lived, athletic and literally fighting fit.

Around the world, many cultures subsist on an equally high-fat diet, for example those who inhabit northern India, certain parts of China, Soviet Georgia, Okinawa and the Mediterranean, to say nothing of the Swiss, the Austrians and the French. Another famous example is the traditional Inuit, who lived for the most part on fish, whale blubber and seal meat, but who are now, with the influx of American culture and its dietary fads, succumbing to all of the degenerative diseases so common in the Western world. The Japanese, who can boast the longest lifespan on the planet, are often said to enjoy this status through the benefits of a low fat diet, but this is not so. Their diet contains much animal fat and they consume greater quantities of cholesterol-carrying foods than the US, but what they *do not* have in their diet is refined vegetable oil, white flour or what we have come to know as processed food. However, in those parts of Japan where a Western culture is taking hold, as with the Inuit, the instances of degenerative diseases is going up. Perhaps the greatest enigma is the French, whose diet traditionally consists of large amounts of butter, cream, eggs, meat pâtés and generally rich foods. The so-called 'French Paradox' is that, despite this, the incidence of heart disease amongst the French is so much lower than in the USA, for example. In the latter, heart disease is running at a rate of 315 per 100,000, whilst in France it can be as low as 80 per 100,000, and this is in Gascony, where the locals have a penchant for rich fatty duck and goose liver recipes.

To me, someone with a common sense approach, and to many others who have conducted painstaking research, the French Paradox is not an enigma, any more than the other cultures mentioned. It all comes back to the same basic premise: there cannot be much wrong with food that has sustained Man for thousands of years, and there is no good reason why factory-made substitutes for this real food should be better for us. Yet PC Nutrition would have us believe that what they are telling us is gospel, and given to us in our best interests.

In making their judgements, the PC Nutritionists begin with the assumption that all proteins, fats and carbohydrates have equal nutritional value whether or not they have been processed. To them, all foodstuffs can be broken down into basic calorific values. No distinction is made between, say, organic produce and that grown under a regime of chemical fertilisers and pesticides; or between whole unadulterated grains and refined, bleached and depleted grains; or between pure unprocessed dairy products and those that come from intensively reared, overworked, protein-pumped dairy herds; or between fresh, ripe, seasonal fruit and the unripe, chilled and treated version so often found in our supermarkets. To them, an egg is an egg, with no nutritional difference between one laid by a hen roaming free all day around a farmyard and one laid by a hen that never sees daylight and is forced to lay her eggs into a wire tray.

PC Nutrition purports to give us guidelines for health, but will not say a word against the food processing industry. They remain silent on the health risk of consuming too much sugar or too many sugar-based products, such as fizzy drinks and cheap snack bars. The problems associated with eating processed dairy foods, such as factory made cheese and pasteurised, homogenised skimmed milk derived from intensively farmed dairy herds, are never mentioned. We hear no complaint from them about our degraded wheat and wheat flour products, nor are we made aware of the links to poor health from an intake of refined vegetable oils, especially those that have been hydrogenated. By way of explanation, hydrogenation is the process of making unsaturated fats more saturated (so that they solidify) by bombarding them with hydrogen atoms. This type of vegetable oil is present in many of the low-fat spreads that have flooded the market as a replacement for butter. But the process of hydrogenation creates trans fats, which have been widely recognised to be dangerous, with links to the onset of heart disease.

In the face of much public protest regarding this worrying information, there is now a rearguard action taking place as the PC Nutritionists attempt to defend their position on refined vegetable oils whilst having to admit that trans fats are an issue. Yet they will never say outright that these unnatural fats are bad for us. They continue to demonise the natural fats that have sustained us for millennia. Condemnation of traditional foods is not limited to butter and lard. Eggs, red meat and unpasteurised milk and cheese are also in the firing line. In trying to decide who is right in this war of nutrition, one merely needs to stand back from the argument, apply a little common sense and look at what we used to eat until about halfway through the last century, and then look at the graphs that show the steeply rising incidences of degenerative diseases that have occurred since our diet became industrialised.

We are told, by the all-powerful PC Nutrition lobby, that a low fat diet based on vegetable fats and the avoidance of animal fats is the key to perfect health. They tell us that saturated animal fats are bad because they are high in cholesterol. This assertion is based on research done by one Ancel Keys back in the 1950s, research that has since been demonstrated to be at best misinterpreted and at worst inconsistent and flawed. Anyone interested in seeing a more detailed examination of this issue than is appropriate here should read what Lynne McTaggart has to say about cholesterol. In her book, *What Doctors Don't Tell You*, she describes cholesterol as 'Medicine's Red Herring', and she comprehensively describes how cholesterol research since the time of Ancel Keys has moved on. With her thorough exploration of the research available, she discusses the issue from both sides and shows how the relationship between saturated fats, cholesterol in the blood and the potential for heart disease is not as clear-cut as we are led to believe.

Current thinking is that cholesterol is unlikely to cause the problems it has been blamed for over the last 50 years and that the differentiation between HDL and LDL cholesterol is misleading, as the body needs both. For the record, LDL is low-density lipoprotein, or so-called 'bad' cholesterol, and HDL is high density lipoprotein, or 'good' cholesterol. The *Journal of American Physicians and Surgeons* (10 no 3, 2005) says that the 'good' and 'bad' cholesterol story is 'overly simplistic and not supported by the evidence.' The evidence actually suggests that LDL and HDL are not even forms of cholesterol at all, but 'vehicles' for the transportation of cholesterol. Thus LDL carries cholesterol to the blood and the tissues, whereas HDL carries cholesterol from the tissues back to the liver. These lipoproteins simply help cholesterol to go about its business. Rather than being a promoter of atherosclerosis, cholesterol is actually beneficial to the body. Its many vital functions include digesting fats, making hormones and repairing membrane and tissue. The association with heart disease has been misconstrued, it seems. Many of those who suffer from heart disease have damaged arteries, and the body's response to this is to ferry cholesterol to the site of the damager via LDL, which would explain why high LDL is sometimes linked to heart disease. Nina Planck, in *Real Food*, has a vivid way of illustrating how the mistake might be made. She says that the presence of fire fighters at a burning building does not mean that they started the fire.

There is an overwhelming amount of evidence out there in support of this new research on cholesterol, and many articles and books, notably *The Great Cholesterol Con* by Dr Malcolm Kendrick, a clear and lucid account of why our current obsession with cholesterol as a health hazard may be thoroughly unjustified.

The truth is that saturated animal fats are not the demons they are made out to be, but this truth is difficult to see beneath the mountain of propaganda put out by the food industry in support of the industrialised alternative new fats, which of course have proved hugely profitable. As an example of how food industry spin gives the new fats a glowing profile can be seen in the sponsorship of the London Marathon by Flora. Here the health banner flies high and proud in the wind of promotion. No opportunity is lost to associate this brand name with the alleged health-giving properties of its products, despite the fact that there is little or no evidence that a diet low in saturated fats and cholesterol actually reduces the instances of death from heart disease or helps anyone to live any longer.

Consider the following random but salient facts:
- Heart disease was practically unheard of before 1920, but has gone up steadily since then and now accounts for around 40% of all deaths in the United States. In that same time period the consumption of saturated fats in that country has gone down

by 20%, whilst the consumption of vegetable fats has increased by 400% and the consumption of sugar by 60%.

- During the 1980s and 1990s, study after study (e.g. in *The Lancet*, 1983; the *Journal of the American Medical Association*, September 1982, 1984, April 1985; the *Journal of Nutrition*, November 1990; *Nutrition Week*, March 1991, to name a few) showed no correlation between cholesterol and heart disease, but clearly demonstrated the harmful effects of 'low-fat' diets.

- Mothers' milk is higher in cholesterol than any food, with 50% of its calories coming from fat, much of it saturated, because saturated fat is essential for healthy growth in babies, especially with regard to the brain.

- As mentioned earlier in this chapter, many cultures around the world thrive on a high-fat diet and are amongst the healthiest people in the world.

It seems clear, especially if one takes the trouble to look at all the research on the subject, that the notion that saturated fats can lead to heart disease is quite erroneous. The argument that demonises saturated animal fats is largely supported by the powerful food industry, through the published opinions of chemists, doctors, scientists and research departments being paid or funded by the food industry itself. I have seen a reference to a certain university head of department who altered his stance on nutrition following a change in the source of funding for his department. From highlighting the health problems caused by white flour in the diet, and positively demonstrating that too high an intake of vegetable oil, rather than animal fats, created a serious risk of heart disease, he allegedly did an about-turn, declaring that actually there was nothing wrong with white flour and refined sugar, even praising Coca-Cola as a snack. He also recommended *one cup of vegetable oil per day* as a means of warding off heart disease.

What are we to make of this? Call me cynical, but my own opinion is that it demonstrates two things. Firstly, it shows how powerful money is. Secondly, it shows that you should not believe everything you read, hear or see in the media. We live in a news-hungry world that has grown apace in the last fifty years. Newspapers and magazines abound in every newsagent, in supermarkets, railway stations, airports and sea ports. They take up an increasing amount of space on the shelves each year. Every radio station has news on the hour, at the very least. Terrestrial television also has regular news bulletins throughout its air time, and satellite and cable TV have dedicated 24-hour news stations. Put all these together and you have an insatiable, and arguably abnormal, appetite for news and stories. Thus it is not too difficult these days to put out a story in the media. If the story looks newsworthy and sounds convincing enough, it will be given air time. Although there are many journalists whose integrity is admirable, there are many others that are ruled by expediency and the need to get a story out. If that story appears to have a pedigree or to display the right credentials, it will slip easily into an editor's in-tray.

This accounts at least in part for all the conflicting health stories that we are bombarded with. One day we are told something is not good for us and then, just when we are getting used to the idea, along comes another story completely contradicting the first one. Then another one might come along in contradiction to the second one. We have only to stop and think about what is going on to realise that all of these stories start out as press releases aimed at particular editors at specific media destinations, carefully worded to catch the editor's eye. Once we understand that most news happens like this, rather than being tracked down by zealous journalists, then we begin to realise how the media can be manipulated for private gain.

Add to that the awesome power of marketing and advertising, which takes up another huge amount of space in the media, and we can see how we are indeed being manipulated. As a demonstration of this power, take the example of Coca-Cola. Suffering recently from a bad press, it resolved to set aside in the following year $2 billion for advertising, in order to repair the damage and reinforce the family-friendly image it prefers to be identified with. If you can't get your head around such a huge sum, try dividing it by 365. It works out at $5.4 million per day. That buys you an awful lot of advertising . . . but I digress. Such is the magnetic pull of psychological advertising and our willingness to listen to a good story and believe what we are being told, that it is extremely difficult to break away from the influence and actually start thinking for ourselves again. But, if we are to make sense of our modern world, and especially our modern food industry, thinking for ourselves is imperative.

To that end, we need to understand something of the language of food. Our new world is dominated by the media, by scientific explanation, statistical analysis and endless discussions through too many for-ums, inquiries, investigations, clinical trials and government reports. Without understanding the terminology used in all of these, we have no hope of assessing the information that is so blithely presented to us as irrefutable fact. Terms such as 'saturated fats', 'animal fats' and 'polyunsaturated fats' are thrown around like so much lexical confetti, but what do they all mean, and how can we tell which fats are bad for us?

At a basic level, fats are organic compounds not soluble in water which form part of that group of compounds known as lipids. They consist of individual fatty acids, which may be 'saturated', 'monounsaturated' or 'polyunsaturated', three terms used to describe the chemical structure of different fats. All fatty acids are chains of carbon atoms bonded with hydrogen atoms, and most fat in our bodies is in the form of triglycerides, which are a combination of three fatty acid chains and a glycerol molecule. Glycerol is a soluble carbohydrate which is converted to glucose by the liver. You may see fats described as 'esters of fatty acids and glycerol.' 'Ester' is a general term for any organic molecule produced by combining an acid and an alcohol – in this case fatty acids and glycerol.

All fats we eat are a blend of saturated, monounsaturated and polyunsaturated fatty acids. Each fat is classified according to its dominant fatty acid. Butter, though it has unsaturated fats in it, is mostly saturated fat, so it is classed as a saturated fat. Olive oil on the other hand, is mostly monounsaturated and is classified thus, whilst corn oil is mostly polyunsaturated and classed as such. That useful all-round fat, lard, is difficult to classify because it depends on the diet of the pig. Generally, however, and despite the fact that it is condemned because it is an animal fat, it is seen as an unsaturated fat because it is 60% mono- and polyunsaturated. Keeping it in the fridge will demonstrate quite clearly the extent to which unsaturated fats are present, as it will not become rock hard once chilled.

To understand the terminology more fully, we need to look at the structure of the different groups, starting with saturated fats. Speaking technically, saturated fats occur when all available carbon bonds are occupied by (saturated with) hydrogen. What that means in practice is that these fats are stable. They do not go rancid very easily, they are solid when cold and their stable nature means they are good for cooking. They are obtained mostly from animal sources, beef suet and butter being two prime examples, but they can also come from tropical plant sources, with coconut oil being the best known example. It is also found in chocolate, or more specifically in the cocoa butter.

Monounsaturated fats, in terms of their chemistry, have two carbon atoms double bonded and therefore lacking two hydrogen atoms. Such fats are liquid at room temperature and semi-solid when chilled. They are still relatively stable and they don't go rancid easily. Thus they can be used in cooking. Olive oil and nut oils are the most common available in this group. Also, the body itself makes its own monounsaturated fats by breaking down saturated fats.

Moving on to polyunsaturated fats, their chemical composition is based on two or more carbon double bonds, which means therefore that there are four missing hydrogen atoms. These fats remain liquid, even when refrigerated. The most common examples are corn oil and sunflower oil. They are highly reactive and therefore somewhat unstable. They also go rancid quickly, especially if heated. This means, despite what the food industry might say to the contrary, that they should never be used for cooking. Often referred to as linoleic acids, they most commonly appear as Omega-6 (double unsaturated linoleic acid) or Omega-3 (triple unsaturated linoleic acid). These cannot be synthesised by the body from other fats, but are still required for good health, and are thus known as 'essential fatty acids' (EFAs). Because the body cannot make them, they must be 'imported' directly from certain foods that we eat.

A huge amount of food industry propaganda, medical pontification and general media hype surrounds the issue of fats. The loudest mantra is, 'unsaturated fats are good, saturated fats are bad.' But, once again, life is not that simple, and it is worth spending some time looking more closely at the whole issue. Some fats are indeed bad, but which ones?

Let us start with the EFAs, Omega-3 and Omega-6. For optimum health benefits, these should be present in foods in a ratio of approximately 1:1 (some say 5:2). Omega-3 works as an anti-inflammatory, and Omega-6 as an inflammatory, hence the need for a balance. Because of what we have been told by the food industry, popular belief is that Omega-3 is what we should be looking for and the best source is oily fish such as salmon, mackerel, herring or sardines. Whilst this is true, it is not the whole story, and there are some other important points to consider.

Firstly, Omega-6 rarely gets a mention in all the publicity about Omega-3. This is evidently something to do with the fact that modern food production methods alter the balance between the two to the detriment of Omega-3. The consequent increase in the level of Omega-6, because of its inflammatory nature, is not good for us. Secondly, salmon is more popular as a fish than any of the others. Thus stocks of salmon have dwindled, especially since the supermarket trade decided that fresh salmon, smoked salmon and salmon-based ready meals were all must-have items in every branch of every major chain. Because of this, most salmon these days is intensively farmed. Like all such farming, this compromises the nutritional value of the fish as a human food source. Farmed salmon is exposed to a cocktail of chemicals, many of which are ingested by the fish and subsequently by those who eat it.

Intensively farmed salmon are sick creatures whose substandard constitutions are bolstered by antibiotics. Much like their land-based counterparts, the poor battery hens, farmed salmon live in cramped squalid conditions in which they are constantly under attack from sea lice and other parasites. They are fed a diet designed to fatten them up quickly, which includes growth promoters, and so the real value of farmed salmon as a source of Omega-3 is questionable. The toxic conditions in which the fish are reared means that the proportion of Omega-6 to Omega-3 is radically altered, anything up to 20:1. It is wise, therefore, to treat with some scepticism the hype on salmon as a source of Omega-3. Well it might be described as a 'source', but it is a better source of Omega-6 and a whole cocktail of toxic chemicals. It is best avoided by those who wish to protect their health.

Thirdly, we are not told that other good sources of Omega-3 are beef, butter and eggs. In a climate in which these ancient foodstuffs have been demonised, it is politically incorrect to laud them as a source of Omega-3. More importantly, beef and butter are practically the only source of a very important Omega-6 derivative known as conjugated linoleic acid, or CLA. This is an Omega-6 fat that behaves more like an

Omega-3. CLA is important in building lean muscle and also in fighting cancer. A word of caution, however. There is one major proviso when it comes to these three, beef, butter and eggs. It is essential that they are sourced from animals that have been reared on traditional pasture. Intensively reared grain-fed beef, butter from dairy cows similarly reared and eggs from battery hens all have an Omega-6/Omega-3 ratio that is completely out of balance (again, up to 20:1) which ultimately does us more harm than good.

In any discussion about good fats and bad fats, it cannot be stated categorically that saturated fats are bad and unsaturated fats are good, even though this is the basis of received wisdom from the food industry and the medical profession. As we have seen, all fats are composite. What can be stated emphatically, however, is that quality is important, and one of the most important qualities of fat is its ability to withstand heat. If fat breaks down in the presence of heat, it will oxidise, and oxidised fat has a detrimental effect on the body's metabolism. It can leave the body more prone to cancer and heart disease.

Over 20 years ago, *Science* (221, No 4617, 1983) was reporting on this particular issue. The article in question pointed out that unsaturated fatty acids are easily oxidised and that oxidation yields 'a variety of mutagens . . . and carcinogens.' Cooking with unsaturated oils is not recommended. Refined polyunsaturated oils, such as corn oil and sunflower oil are particularly vulnerable. It is disturbing to think that chips from a chip shop and fries from fast food establishments are generally cooked in this type of oil. Worse than that, the 'vegetable oils' that are supplied to the fast food industry through the wholesalers are not only refined but generally of inferior quality, cost always being an issue when it comes to business.

I remember, not so long ago, buying chips from a chip shop in Yorkshire. They had been cooked in beef fat. I have to say that for me this was an outstanding culinary moment in my lifelong involvement with food. These chips were a fabulous deep golden brown, crisp on the outside and soft in the middle. With a mouth-watering aroma and a taste reminiscent of Granny's roast potatoes, they were absolutely delicious. I hear on the grapevine that such chips are still available in Yorkshire. Long may this continue, because elsewhere in the UK we are faced with that uniformly soggy consistency and unappetising smell that afflicts 99% of the chip-shop chips in this country (the chip van on the harbour at Tobermory on the Isle of Mull being a notable exception). And every customer buying a bag of chips cooked the modern way is risking far more than I ever did with those beef-cooked ones.

Using refined vegetable oils for cooking is of course doubly risky. Such oils are heated during the refining process and so are already subject to oxidation and rancidity. This is exacerbated by heating them again to a temperature that will brown chips. If vegetable oils are to have a place in the kitchen at all they should be cold-pressed and always used cold. A further issue with these refined oils is that, although they are our main source of Omega-6 fatty acids, they have been subjected to processes which tip the balance of Omega fats in favour of Omega-6, as with farmed salmon and intensively produced beef, eggs and dairy produce. Thus we are again unwittingly increasing our intake of Omega-6 to levels that are unnaturally high.

Despite this, the PC Nutrition message is still loud and clear: cut out saturated fats and switch to polyunsaturated vegetable oils. The foundation of this thinking was laid in the 1940s, when some research was done on the correlation between cancer and the consumption of fats. According to a report in *Nutrition Quarterly* in 1993, the research failed to differentiate between genuine saturated fats and those that had taken on the appearance of saturated fats through hydrogenation. It was erroneously assumed at the time that all 'saturated' fats were alike. It is only more recently that the problems of hydrogenation, including the dangers of trans fats, have been revealed. Thus the fats on which the research had been conducted, and which had been condemned by the results as being linked to cancer, were hydrogenated vegetable oils rather than traditional animal fats. The truth is only just beginning to be made clear. Meanwhile, many companies have grown rich on the profits of selling us refined vegetable oils, margarines, low-fat spreads and products containing hydrogenated oils. These companies are not going to give all this up in a hurry. So, despite the adverse publicity surrounding trans fats, these products continue to fill supermarket shelves. Trans fats should be avoided, that much is irrefutable. They are highly toxic to the body. The problem is that they are absorbed and stored much like traditional fats but, once they are in the cell membranes, they disrupt normal cell metabolism. This in turn blocks the absorption of essential fatty acids. The harmful effects that this precipitates include potential paralysis of the immune system, leaving the body vulnerable to attack.

In trying to determine which fats are bad for us, we find we are dealing with a complex issue around which many conflicting arguments rage. In my short dissertation I have tried to steer a course through these rocky waters, and I have found what I believe is a safe passage that I would happily recommend to others, though I am of course a mere layman. In the end, it comes down to common sense once again. Accept the fact that the body needs some fat in the diet in order to function efficiently, so don't make fat a demon. Avoid fats and oils that are the products of industrial processing. These include refined vegetable oils and spreads, even the so-called low fat spreads, or those that claim to be devoid of hydrogenated oils – they have still been made with oxidised (i.e. rancid) oils. The fats that are healthy are the fats we have been consuming for thousands of years in their natural form: animal fats (including butter) coconut oil, cold-pressed olive oil, cold-pressed nut oils, sesame oil and hemp oil. Take care with animal fats and butter, however. Avoid the products of the intensive meat and dairy industry – they are not to be trusted. Seek out the products of pasture-fed herds. It will be worth the effort. And worth the price too. Remember the adage, 'you get what you pay for.' Mass market refined vegetable oils are indeed very cheap. Cold-pressed extra virgin olive oil looks expensive by comparison, but the former will probably damage your body and the latter will contribute to the nutrition it needs to stay healthy. The choice is yours.

REVELATIONS

Our time in Scotland is nearly up, but we cannot return to England without a brief visit to the Edradour Distillery, tucked away up in the hills above Pitlochry. Those who are tempted to do the tourist whisky trail will undoubtedly want to include Edradour in their itinerary, it being the smallest distillery in Scotland. There seems to be, amongst some whisky fans, a peculiar fascination with wanting to visit the smallest, the highest, the most northerly et al. A bit like trainspotters, those people who are so inclined seem to have been bitten by the collector bug and just need to tick boxes or underline names. Some no doubt actually like the whisky being produced in these places.

I can't speak for Sally, but I would certainly be happy to include Edradour in my top ten favourite whiskies, because I am partial to the golden colour, its smoothness, the hint of smoke and sherry on the tongue and the honey finish, but this is not the only reason why we want to visit. For us, this distillery represents something fundamental about the kind of life that we are rapidly losing. Though I may again stand accused of being on a nostalgia trip, I remain unshaken in my belief that we have 'gone global' at our peril. And I believe that this tiny distillery of Edradour is a symbol of a gentler, slower-paced way of life where human values and an understanding of our place in the world are still important.

It can of course be argued that building a distillery in the middle of a pretty valley is nothing more than intrusive industrialisation, but I can tell you that the distillery buildings look more in keeping with the landscape than any given modern housing development in the UK, with their everywhere-and-nowhere look. In general architectural terms, it is attractive, photogenic even, and certainly easier on the eye than, say, the giant Tomatin distillery near Inverness, with its 23 stills and its annual production capacity of 5 million litres. By contrast, the distillery at Edradour produces only 12 casks of whisky a week. Edradour's total annual production could be matched by Tomatin in seven days.

The whole operation is run in a traditional way by just three people, John Reid and his two assistants, who hand craft this whisky without automated processes. They simply rely on skills handed down through generations. It speaks of a time gone by, when commerce was more community orientated and those within any given local community understood the concept of 'enough'. I hear the arguments that say I am living in dreamland, that life in the past was harsh, that it wasn't all beer and skittles, that domineering landlords and greedy factory owners strutted their stuff and made everyone's life hell. Well, yes – life has always had people like that, the mill owners and the great land barons before them. But today the ethos of acquisitiveness has taken hold and created a desperately debilitating 'must-have' culture. Most ordinary people are no longer content. Everyone wants to be a celebrity. Everyone wants what they don't have. In many ways, it's a case of 'no change there, then', but society is now afflicted by a new perniciousness that pervades modern life and undermines human values, something which I believe is extremely unhealthy. Up here, at Edradour, it is easy to forget all this for a little while as we stroll around the distillery, admiring the original equipment, the two ancient pine washbacks and the two tiny wash and spirit stills.

How different is the attitude in this glen to that demonstrated by corporations whose only goal is 'more'. On the way up here, a few of the 40-tonne trucks we saw on the motorway were emblazoned with the Interbrew logo and the strapline, 'Making Beer Great'. Well, sorry, but Interbrew is doing no such thing. It does not make beer great. It is making beer cheap and nasty. It is adopting the usual corporate stance of 'the same everywhere.' Interbrew is now the biggest seller of brewery products in the world, having taken over a large number of smaller companies, subsequently doing what all corporations do – taking advantage of economies of scale to cut their costs and increase their already enormous profits. Interbrew sells billions of litres of beer through hundreds of labels worldwide, cheapened and tampered with to create cost effectiveness for the company. High pressure advertising keeps the sales up, but plays down the fact that, in the hands of Interbrew, great breweries like Boddingtons and Hoegaarden get closed down and the beers survive in name only as pale shadows of their originals.

Anyone is entitled to set up in business, and profitability is essential to the success of any enterprise. Growth and expansion come with the territory of a successful venture, but unfettered growth can be dangerous. Laws, some of them made centuries ago, have been put in place to curtail the growth of over-enthusiastic corporations. Such barriers were designed to prevent the dominance of potential monopolies, the existence of which was seen as unhealthy, especially for the consumer. Lobbying on behalf of these aggressive firms has gradually eroded the power of anti-monopoly laws over the years, and in the 1980s these firms almost literally stormed what was left of the barriers, persuading Ronald Reagan and Margaret Thatcher to make life easier for the big players, thus leaving the commercial world open to what we now see as globalisation. This is great news for the companies that have prospered as a result, but is not good news for anyone else. Many corporations are now more powerful than governments, and indeed in the USA and to a lesser extent in the UK, it is the corporations that work the strings and the governments that dance on the end of them.

I make no apologies for pointing this out. I am not, however, just a blinkered activist and I don't limit my protests to joining the marchers, toting a banner that says, 'Down With Corporations' or 'Close The Supermarkets.' Such protests are a vital part of the proceedings, in that they make the issues visible to a wider audience, but they are not an end in themselves. The huge power that we have as individuals must not be ignored, and joining a protest march is sometimes part of what we need to do, but it is not the only effective way of making a point. Sally and I make our point by not shopping at supermarkets. In fact, we go further than that. We won't buy a coffee from Starbuck's either, or a sandwich from Subway, or any goods from any other global brands if we can help it. We may not be 100% successful in this venture, but the point is that we have done something to remove our custom from global corporations and transfer it, wherever possible, to local independent traders, and each week we get better at it. By simply thinking that we can do something, we do. Once that first step is taken, the next one is easier.

Am I trying to motivate you? Yes, I am. That is because I am alarmed by the imbalance in the marketplace, the power wielded by the few to the detriment of the many and the abuse of power that is the inevitable corollary of monopoly. The principle applies to any commercial activity conducted on a global basis, from oil prospecting to the manufacture of clothes, but it is our food that I am particularly concerned with. When it comes to our food, the issue is not simply that our choice is reduced. At a fundamental level, it is also our health that is compromised. Corporate activity and industrialisation give us bad food and, worse than that, they give us bad food that is sold to us as the healthy option to all those traditional foods so recently demonised by those who would profit from selling the alternative.

That is why we came to Edradour. Not because whisky is food, although that is a moot point, but because the three people that make the whisky here are honest. What you see is what you get, and you can talk directly to the producer, in the same way that Sally and I can talk to all of the people we now buy our own provisions from. Real food is also honest food. The man who supplies the bacon that we cook for guests at Aspen House is not going to rip us off. If he does, we would be able to challenge him face to face. So he is going to do the best he can for us, because his livelihood depends on it. Bad news travels fast and he wants none of it.

Before the world became a smaller place, the whisky at Edradour would probably have been sold and consumed within a very small local area. The adjoining areas that surround this distillery would each have had one of their own. Today, as we sample a dram in the recently built visitor centre, we share the place with three Welshmen, a couple of Americans and a Japanese couple, as well as a small cross section of English people. The girl relieving these tourists of their money is German. It is a cosmopolitan world, so much so that the huge Tomatin distillery is solely owned by the Japanese Suntory Corporation. In many ways, it is exciting that the world has shrunk – we are all part of the same species, after all. But it seems that the price we are paying for this is loss of choice, suppression of cultural diversity and the enforcement of an alien, fast-food, throwaway consumer culture that seems to have originated somewhere on the North American continent. Quirkiness and cultural eccentricity drown in this tide and local cuisines become pasteurised and homogenised along with the milk. Places like the Edradour distillery, if they survive at all, become almost museum pieces to be gawped at by people who have no feelings for the place other than the desire to buy a bottle of what they are selling. It is as if they are consumers from another planet.

We have mixed feelings as we leave Edradour and head for the A924 east from Pitlochry to take us through the hills. Are we also no more than consumers from another planet? Did we look any different from the others on the tour around the distillery? Pleased that we had called in, yet strangely saddened that in the end we are no more than onlookers, we are now on our way to visit a place held in high regard by Dr Yellowlees.

High up on the moors, the Seer Centre lies tucked into the lea of the hills at around a thousand feet above sea level. 'SEER' stands for Sustainable Ecological Earth Regeneration and it was established in 1997 by two people, Cameron and Moira Thomson, dedicated to the idea of helping the planet to recover from what is widely perceived as a state of malaise. What they have set up in this remote part of the Highlands, in an area that may have only two frost-free months in the year, is a model garden created to show what can be achieved when the soil is healthy.

This is also their home, and we are invited in for a cup of tea. In their modest kitchen, we talk of real food, industrialisation and the erosion of real choice. Cameron, looking every inch the former art lecturer that he is, talks about how he became instead a kind of eco-warrior. Cameron and Moira are serious about finding practical solutions to our problems. What they see as our main challenge is that our soils have become depleted. Although the effects of climate will naturally leach mineral goodness from the soil, it seems likely that the human inhabitants of the Earth have contributed to the effect through the exploitation of natural resources and mismanagement of agriculture. Though arguments still rage over how much damage Man has actually done to this planet, I am sure no one will disagree that, over the centuries, we have helped ourselves to the Earth's resources in a thoughtlessly avaricious way. We have taken, but we have given nothing in return. The argument that we have contributed to the de-mineralization of the soil is a very persuasive one, especially in the light of the onset of chemical farming in the last half a century.

Moira and Cameron talk to us enthusiastically about the depletion of minerals in the soil, but even more animatedly about the fact that there is a solution to the problem. A carrot is produced by way of illustration. It is a huge carrot – about the size of an average parsnip. It is slightly split at the top, but otherwise it is in perfect condition and blemish-free. Cameron explains that the split was caused during a period of rain that had followed a dry spell. He is almost apologetic, but he doesn't need to be. The carrot is a wonderful specimen. We are amazed by its condition, considering that it must have been out of the ground for weeks, if not months.

Jokingly, I say, "If that's the size of your carrots, what are your parsnips like?"

Cameron slips out of the kitchen and returns a few moments later with something wrapped in a newspaper. Carefully, he peels the newspaper back and reveals a parsnip about two feet long. The diameter at the lower end is about an inch, so the whole vegetable might easily have been twice as long if it had been extracted with the whole root. On its crown, new green foliage is sprouting.

"That's because it's springtime, and it thinks it is time to grow again," Cameron explains, "But see how it hasn't withered at all, even though it was harvested in October."

As he says, the parsnip is solid and, like the carrot, blemish-free.

"Have a sniff," he invites us. This remarkable vegetable, harvested in October and then stored out in the shed wrapped in newspaper, smells very obviously of parsnip. You might think that's perfectly normal. Next time you pick up a parsnip from the local supermarket, try the sniff test. You will be lucky to get a smell at all, not without at least cutting into the skin first. And if you leave it lying around it will look soft and withered within the week.

Also in storage in the shed are some swedes. Like the carrots and parsnips, these are huge, unblemished and temptingly aromatic. The one that Cameron is inviting us to handle is the size of a football, but I believe him when he says that it will be succulent right through and not woody at all, despite its size. I believe him because I have seen something like these vegetables before.

The house in the country bought by my parents when I was in my teens was, as I mentioned in Chapter 1, surrounded by prime horticultural land, with deep loamy soils. What eventually became my father's pride and joy, his vegetable garden, was land that had been untouched for years. Its rich blackness smelt pungently of humus and dark healthy earth as my Dad toiled, tilled, drilled and sowed. The first crops that came from this garden were phenomenal. My Dad put me in charge of the spring balance as we checked the weight of the first cauliflower to be cut. It weighed in not far short of four pounds – two kilos in Eurospeak. Everything was big, flawless and free from parasites, much like the vegetables one sees at village shows, and much like the vegetables grown at the Seer Centre.

Obviously all such vegetables have something in common apart from their size and general appearance, and that something is healthy soil. Prize vegetable growers will make sure that their vegetables have only the best growing medium that can be provided. My Dad's vegetables benefited from an inherently rich soil that had not been cultivated for a few years. The giant vegetables he harvested that first year were exceptional. Although the garden produced excellent crops in subsequent years, that first year remained a one-off. In the case of the Seer Centre, however, such success is the norm. According to Cameron and Moira, this is simply because the soil here has been re-mineralized. Together with the right proportion of good organic matter, the minerals in the soil have brought it back to life.

As Cameron takes us around the garden plots, he describes the effort he and Moira put in to start up this idea. We are talking about just two people, with a little help from family and friends, making a decision to take on approximately seven acres of land fit for little more than heather and turn it into show gardens, a free range enclosure and field trial research project. That takes dedication. But the Thomsons are indeed dedicated, driven by an almost zealous desire to tell the world about re-mineralizing the soil.

That zeal has a long history. The Thomsons have always been inclined towards self-sufficiency and, back in the 1980s, were already growing their own vegetables. Results, in their cottage garden on a farm near Dundee, were moderate but not inspiring. By chance, they heard a book review on the radio. The book, by John Hamaker and Don Weaver, was called *The Survival of Civilisation*. Its central theme was a proposal that our farmland should be re-mineralized with fine rock dust, the kind of stuff that was creating mountains of waste in quarries all over the world. Because of the mineral content in the rock dust, including trace elements, new fertility would be brought to the soil and new biological activity would ensue. Silicates in the rock dust would weather, carbon dioxide would be taken from the atmosphere and 'locked up' through the formation of calcium and magnesium carbonates. An added bonus would be better crop yields from this newly enriched ground.

To Cameron and Moira this was something of a revelation. Thinking that this was perhaps what their garden was lacking, they set about finding a quarry that would supply them with some rock dust to add to the compost they were spreading on their garden. It worked. An exceptional crop of healthy vegetables soon had the neighbours talking and the Thomsons thinking that this experiment needed to be carried out where conditions were harder. Their chance came when a local landowner gave them the opportunity to work on a seven-acre plot he had available at Ceanghline, Straloch Farm, on the Pitlochry to Glenshee road through the mountains. From this was born the Seer Centre.

Our tour of the gardens ends in a small polytunnel, essential at this elevation as a sheltered environment for the more delicate crops, such as herbs, tomatoes, courgettes, cucumbers, and sweet corn. In the polytunnel, Cameron is telling us all there is to know about rock dust and the re-mineralization of soil. He asks us what we think about global warming.

"I think the term is misused," I reply, "I think that 'climate change' is a better way of putting it."

Cameron nods his approval and asks us if we would like to hear his 'lecture'. We are all for it. Cameron sits us down on a garden bench, then finds himself a round slatted garden table which he sets up as a kind of circular lectern. From behind this makeshift lectern, he begins.

"Imagine this is the Earth," he says, indicting the table, "And these slats represent the different climate zones. So we have the equator here, tropic of Capricorn here and the tropic of Cancer here."

He begins with a brief summary of why climate change is a reality and 'global warming' is misleading, and goes on to talk about the weather in geological terms. Looking at the bigger picture, we can see that the world's weather over the millennia follows a graph of peaks and troughs. The troughs represent periods of cold climate, or glaciations, and the peaks indicate the relatively hot periods in between, i.e. interglacial periods. The planet has had 25 glaciations in the last 2.5 million years, each lasting about 90,000 years, with interglacials of roughly 10,000 years in between. At present, the geological evidence suggests that the current interglacial might be nearing its end. Cameron talks of the growing catalogue of extreme weather conditions around the world, record lows of temperature as well as highs, floods, hurricanes, earthquakes, forest fires, drought and soil erosion. All of these are indicators of the planet moving towards the next ice age, it seems.

An interglacial period has four separate phases. For the technically minded, these are the protocratic (approx 3000 years) the mesocratic (approx 2500 years) the oligocratic (approx 4500 years) and the telocratic phases. With a span of about 170 years, give or take 40 years, the telocratic phase is the shortest of all, and it is the phase in which we are at present, if climatic indicators are accurate.

Using his table top as a model, our host demonstrates how the sun's rays deliver more of a direct heat impact around the equatorial latitudes and less at the poles. This represents prevailing conditions that apply as a result of our planet's position relative to the sun, but Man's activity has increased this effect. More water is now evaporating from the hot equatorial latitudes and being transported to the higher latitudes, where it is causing more rain, floods and landslides than normal. The Earth is also experiencing a heightened 'albedo effect', which essentially describes the planet's reflectivity, used as a cooling mechanism. As we increase the heat of the planet, more light is reflected back into space from the enlarging equatorial deserts and from the cloud, snow and ice of the higher latitudes. As more light, and therefore heat, is reflected back into space, so the planet cools.

Taking Man's activity out of the equation for the moment, we can catalogue the normal changes that take place through an interglacial period. At the beginning of the cycle, as the ice from the previous period of glaciation retreats, trees and new vegetation spring up. Leaf drop combines with the crushed rocks left behind by the glaciers and new soils begin to form. At the peak of our current interglacial, during the mesocratic phase, soils on the planet were up to 7.5 feet deep and trees were up to eight times the size of any left today. Rain and wind action gradually (over thousands of years) erode this highly fertile covering. As the oligocratic phase progresses, this erosion continues, leading to demineralization and acidification of the soil. By the time the telocratic phase has been reached, most of the soil has been eroded and the whole planet is in need of mineralization once more. Thus the present average depth of soil is a mere 6 inches or so The natural cycle of glacial and interglacial periods suggests that changes are now taking place which will precipitate a return to glaciation.

"But we could do something about that," says Cameron, "We could re-mineralize the soils and save the Earth from having to worry about it."

He goes on to explain that the natural cycle of an interglacial period, with or without Man, sees the planet's soils depleted to the point of exhaustion. A new ice age acts as a mechanism to crush rocks and deposit minerals on the planet's surface, thus beginning the next era of re-mineralised soils. Following the research done by John Hamaker and Don Weaver, the principles of which are being demonstrated here in Perthshire, the theory is that we have the understanding, the resources and the means to use rock dust to bring all our soils back to life and save the planet from descending into another ice age.

To Sally and me, this is the stuff of revelation. We came to the Seer Centre to talk about food and nutrition, but this serious gardener is talking to us about something much bigger. This is in the realms of fantasy, and yet it makes perfect sense. To some, it might sound like the ravings of a mad professor, but it sounds so simple that it could just be true. We might be able to heal our damaged planet and finally become responsible custodians. Cameron himself acknowledges that he and Moira have been treated as 'cranks and loonies' for years. They regularly get challenged by those who want to know how it could be possible to change the world simply by 'spreading a bit of rock dust on the ground'. But, as Cameron says, it is nature's way. It works at the Seer Centre and there is no reason why it should not work everywhere.

If Cameron and Moira were voices in the wilderness, it would be easy to dismiss these theories. But they are not. They are merely two more voices to add to those who have come before, like John Hamaker, Don Weaver and others. Before them, going back as far as the 1930s and 1940s, a number of people were engaged in various projects on the relationship between health and nutrition, crops and the soils they grow in.

In the USA, a doctor from Alabama by the name of Charles Northern was raising concerns about the poor quality foods then being consumed by Americans. He specifically highlighted minerals as being essential to human health. He in fact gave up his career as a doctor to concentrate on ways in which the mineral balance of exhausted soils could be restored and thus provide healthy produce for human consumption. Influential in his work, he even attracted the interest of the American Senate in 1936, when Dr Northern's research became the subject of debate.

His argument was that minerals were even more important than vitamins. Accepting that vitamins are complex chemical substances vital to nutrition, he pointed out something that was not common knowledge – that 'vitamins control the body's appropriation of minerals, and that in the absence of minerals they have no function to perform.' To put it more succinctly, without vitamins, the body can make use of minerals, but without minerals, vitamins are useless. As a clear example of how one thing leads to another, Northern himself had based his observations on the work of Nobel-prize-winning author, Alexus Carrel, 25 years previously, whose main premise had been that minerals in the soil control the metabolism in plants, animals and Man. Thus, he maintained, life would be healthy or unhealthy, according to the fertility of the soil.

In Britain, Sir Robert McCarrison, Dr G T Wrench, Sir Albert Howard and Lord Lymington (later Lord Portsmouth) were independent researchers who all came to the same conclusion – good health depended on good nutrition. All of these people in their turn influenced Lady Eve Balfour, who swam against the rising tide of chemical farming to conduct her own experiments at her farm at Haughley Green in Suffolk. The results were published in 1943 in her book, *The Living Soil*, which also gives details of the work of the above-mentioned researchers, amongst others, and how it influenced her own thinking. Out of all of this, in 1945, was born the Soil Association.

Over 60 years have passed since then, and it could be said that we are no further forward. The Soil Association still exists, and indeed it has become the recognised authority on all matters of organic farming. Its logo is a badge that many consider worth having. However, there are rumblings of discontent amongst many of its members, who feel that the Soil Association, under pressure from supermarkets to compromise its very strict principles, will bend to that particular wind and relax its rules. This demonstrates how little real progress we have made and how powerful are the forces that would dismiss or sacrifice that progress on the altar of corporate profitability. Yet the principles laid down by Lady Eve Balfour, her predecessors and by the new prophets of sustainable living, are as sound now as when first mooted.

Whatever we might be told to the contrary, the picture is quite clear. Good health can be achieved only through good nutrition, and good nutrition comes only from 'clean' nutritious food, which in turn comes from healthy plants and animals. Moreover, the only way to ensure healthy plants, and the animals and humans who feed off them, is to grow them in healthy soil. Healthy soil requires no chemicals. To bring the wheel full circle, we come back to the Thomsons' definition of healthy soil, that is to say soil that benefits from a high organic content and is fully mineralized. Simply adding minerals to the compost that goes into the soil guarantees that microbial activity will return and the soil's ecology will be rebalanced.

This simple relationship – healthy soil = healthy plants = healthy animals = healthy people – projects a powerful and persuasive message. It is beyond the scope of this book to conduct an investigation into the viability of the Thomsons' argument that it would be possible to re-mineralize all of the planet's agricultural soil, and thereby stabilise the planet for future generations, but the need for something along these lines is obvious, and it is hard to see how the proposed solution can do anything but good. At the very least, a move towards re-mineralizing our soils, and thus bringing them back to life, makes absolute sense. The alternative – to stay as we are – makes no sense at all. Staving off the next ice age is an appealing idea, but might be a case of setting our sights too high at the moment. Our priority is to fix our soils and make them healthy once more. That would be a great start, and who knows where it might lead?

Our time at the Seer Centre comes to an end, as has our brief visit to Perthshire. Tomorrow morning, we will be heading home.

We drive back to Pitlochry alternating between silence and animated discussion. We are moved by the obvious dedication of Cameron and Moira Thomson, but we feel that they are destined to join that long list of prophets, like Eve Balfour, Robert McCarrison and Walter Yellowlees who, over the years, have subscribed to a clear and visionary survival strategy for mankind, but whose vision is clouded by the obfuscatory tactics of those with louder voices. One question preoccupies us: what is it in the character of mankind that allows us to be dominated by those whose selfishness and greed robs us of our own common sense? It is a mystery, certainly, unless we are simply programmed to self-destruct.

Nevertheless, we take hope from our trip to Scotland. Voices crying in the wilderness they might be, but Walter Yellowlees, Cameron and Moira Thomson, the owners of The Watermill and even the Aberfeldy butcher are voices in unison. They know, as we know, that something is rotten, not just in the state of Denmark, but in the rest of the world too.

We add our voices to this chorus, and we invite you to join us. Our planet is sick, the produce that comes from it poisoned by chemicals, and the factory food made from this produce is nutritionally depleted. A very small number of people are making large sums of money from this situation, and the rest of us are suffering. The good news is that all is not completely lost. The Aberfeldy butcher is not quite the last of his kind. There are still enough butchers, bakers, greengrocers, dairymen and organic farmers to bring our food back from the brink. Enough, but only just.

If we want to reverse the swing of the pendulum, we must do something ourselves. Not just add our voices, although this will certainly help. What is required is change. Those who profit from the existing situation will never change. Thus the onus is on us, unfair as this might seem. But every independent butcher, baker and grocer, every organic vegetable grower, every farm shop and bottler of home made jams needs our support. Every pound spent in this dwindling independent sector of the market is one more pound towards supporting a local economy, and a vote against the global domination of giant corporations. We must understand that this is not someone else's problem. It is ours. Yours and mine. So it is up to all of us to do something. Make a change today. Now is not the time to propose excuses for inactivity. Now is the time for action. To borrow a phrase from somewhere else, every little helps.

With the vision of the Thomsons, we may one day even get as far as re-mineralizing our planet, but first things first. One step at a time. Our priority is to change the way we shop, reclaim our food and take charge of our own wellbeing. I can hear the objections already, that making these changes will be too difficult, too expensive, too impractical, too inconvenient for a population that has got used to the one-stop shopping experience. But nothing is difficult if the desire is there. Changing the way we shop, and seeking out real nutritious food is not the uphill struggle it is often perceived to be. Neither is it, in real terms, expensive. To continue as we are now will cost the Earth. To change will give us a clearer vision of our world, the only one we have, a tiny living speck of blue floating in the vast sea of the known universe.

part three

FINDING OUR WAY OUT

Reclaiming your right to real food
and optimum health

TAKING BACK CONTROL

We take the slow way home, leaving Scotland and meandering down through the Lake District, before taking off on the old A6 for a leisurely drive through Carnforth, Lancaster and Garstang. Picking up the A49 south of Warrington, we follow our noses to Whitchurch, Shrewsbury, Ludlow and all the way home.

It is said that it always takes longer to come back, but that's only if your mind is on your destination rather than your journey. We find that, once we get off the drag strip of the motorway, there is so much to interest us along the way that we always seem to be home sooner than we expected. I am sure there is a lesson to be learned from that.

As we unpack the car, there is no sign of post-holiday blues. We are still full of excitement, and our conversation is non-stop as we reflect on our meetings with Dr Yellowless and the Thomsons. All of our misgivings about modern food have been vindicated, and we have no doubt that the way out of the food maze is through real food. The maze is well constructed, intricate and established enough to confuse our senses and block our view. But it is not much more than 50 years old. Not quite established enough to hide the real food prize at its centre. We must claim that prize while we still can.

Every journey has the potential to veer off in the wrong direction. It is helpful to know where you are going, and sensible travellers will have at least some idea of their destination. A map might be considered vital for any journey with which the traveller is unfamiliar. A navigator could also be useful (though not a satellite navigator, please). But what if the traveller puts his trust in someone else? A self-styled tour guide perhaps. And what if the guide has never done the journey either, and is relying on someone else to read the map for him? What will happen to our traveller? Will he get to where he needs to go? Not likely, says the voice of common sense.

When it comes to sourcing our food, this is exactly what we have done in the last couple of generations. We have opted to travel in someone else's vehicle and we have put our trust in the bus company, the government. A succession of company bus drivers has taken us on a mystery tour around the lunatic fringe of food technology. Along the way, the bus has also been hijacked by other drivers, employed by chemical companies and industrialists to use the bus for their own purposes.

The result is that we are lost. Even those of us who have decided to get off the bus are now stranded in a maze of disinformation, conflicting data, propaganda and a mass of bewildering new terms. Food has lost its appeal. Many people now live in fear of food. It seems to have stopped being about eating, nutrition and vitality. It has been reduced to a mathematical exercise involving the counting of calories, the analysis of the Glycaemic Index (GI) and the assessment of RDA, or Recommended Daily Allowance (not to be confused of course with

GDA, the Guideline Daily Amount). With 'nutritional information' adorning every packaged food including sweets that are 98% sugar, we are bombarded with percentages, weights and proportions. People talk of nothing but 'five-a-day', 'fat-free', 'low cholesterol', 'balanced diet', 'added vitamins' and a whole lot more phrases that have entered the language in the last few decades.

Most of this is total nonsense. The food to which we are asked to apply all of this statistical analysis is not real food, but processed, industrialised ersatz foodstuffs, the ingestion of which can, in an uncomfortably large number of cases, do us more harm than good. Though it may be polluted by chemicals and nutritionally depleted, we are being asked to believe it is as healthy as something you might buy direct from a farm. This propaganda even goes as far as to say that many of our traditional foods, such as unpasteurised milk, butter, eggs, animal fat and meat, are dangerous to our health. It is quite clear from a significant number of studies that modern poor quality food is the prime suspect in the dramatic increase in degenerative diseases, yet those with vested financial interests in the food industry continue to try to persuade us that all such food is healthy and that the so-called diseases of civilisation are caused by other factors.

This is like the scientist and the jumping flea, a little schoolboy joke that demonstrates how easily the 'scientific' approach to empirical double-blind testing can still throw up the wrong answer. In this story, a scientist wishes to test the athletic capabilities of a performing flea. He commands the flea to jump and, when it does so successfully, he removes one of its legs and commands it once more to jump. It does so, and so he removes another leg. The process continues until finally, after having removed all of the flea's legs and commanded it to jump, the flea does not respond. The scientist writes in his report, "Once one has removed all of the flea's legs, it goes deaf."

It is equally erroneous for science to tell us that obesity, heart disease, arthritis, chronic fatigue, respiratory problems and sundry other ailments are all to do with eating too much and not exercising enough. Pointing the finger at the consumer takes pressure off government and the food industry and draws the eye away from the sleight of hand that is being performed. But it does not obviate the need for a complete rethink regarding how our food is produced, distributed and sold. However, although this need is pressing, we can be certain of one thing. Nothing will change. An industry that is already blaming consumers for these problems is not going to suddenly change tack, hold its hand up and say, "Actually, we have been compromising your health all this time by selling you nutritionally depleted food." So long as there are enough people out there who believe that the corporations that run the food industry can do no wrong (and that is what the majority of supermarket shoppers think) there will be no pressure for those corporations to change the way they do things. We must also remember that the food industry funds scientific research that is expected to come up with 'scientific proof' that processed food and chemical additives are safe to eat.

If you are interested in making a positive change to your health and well-being, you are going to have to do something about it yourself. Your only chance of success is to take back control of your own life and the food that should sustain that life. You will not be able to rely on those who currently provide your food to help you find something better or to change the way *they* do things just so that they can supply you, and others like you, with more nutritious food. Governments and big corporations can be lobbied and persuaded to change, but they are so big that it is like bringing a supertanker to a halt. Lobby if you feel so inclined, but if you want an immediate result, simply make the decision to change the way you think about food.

At this point I can again hear those objections in the background – "I live in the centre of a city. What chance have I got of finding real food when my only choice is the supermarket?" And then there is the other oft-quotes reason, "I'm too busy to go out looking for all these other places." We have already been told by our friends, especially those with young families, "Busy mums have to shop at the supermarket." Fair enough. We have used the same argument ourselves – busy B&B owners have to shop at the supermarket. But in the end it depends on how important it is to look after your own health and that of other members of the family. It is all a question of priority, but we can tell you from experience that it is ultimately an easier transition than most people might imagine to change from doing the supermarket run to shopping from independents, as we shall see in Chapter 22. Even in city centres, the choice is huge. It's all a question of looking around, seeing what is available and then deciding how to get hold of it. If you really are hard pressed, you can make a start even at the supermarket. Quite a few basic real foods are available in the big stores. Organic grains and pulses, for example, are readily available and often of the same quality as those in the wholefood shops. Make this a short-term solution if you can, though. The independent wholefood shops need your support.

Five years ago, when we moved to Aspen House and opened our doors for business, we were just like everyone else in that we were always dashing to the supermarket to buy our household goods and most of our food, with one or two exceptions. Firstly, there was the bacon. Having worked for a butcher who cured his own bacon, using the meat from rare breed pigs, I needed no persuasion that this was the kind of bacon we would be using. This butcher's bacon was gorgeous, and in a completely different league from the water-injected, super-salinated, chemical-tasting thin sad slices from the supermarket. So we had to find some traditional dry-cured bacon, as well as some proper sausages, for our guests. Then there were the eggs. If we were going into the B&B business, we needed really good eggs to go with our home-cured bacon. There was no way I was going to serve up eggs from a supermarket. I have tasted such eggs and they are pale, watery, uninteresting and tasteless compared to a real egg from a hen in a farmyard. We were in the country now, so there was no excuse (even when I lived in town in a previous life, I always managed to find a good supplier of eggs). So we made it a priority to find a source of real eggs.

Thus breakfast at Aspen House had at least some good parts to it. In addition, we were making bread and preserves at home, but not simply because of our stance. It was simply to show potential guests that they could be sure of a good breakfast. We offered dinner as well as bed and breakfast, because we love cooking and this seemed the perfect way to generate more turnover. The fresh vegetables for those first dinners came from the supermarket, but we had no idea that there was anything wrong with that. After all, a carrot is a carrot, or so we thought. Had it not been for the fact that I was suffering from chronic fatigue, we might never have found out the truth.

Concerned by my alarming tendency to fall asleep as soon as I stopped moving, in the middle of the day and every time I sat in front of the computer, Sally called on a friend of hers to come over and talk to me about food intolerances. I was told that intolerances to certain foods were affecting a large proportion of the population, and that an intolerance could manifest itself through a variety of symptoms, from asthma to headaches, from eczema and other skin conditions to difficulty in sleeping to what I appeared to be suffering from, chronic fatigue. Sally's friend also told me that the foods to which people were mainly intolerant were wheat and dairy products. She offered to test me, to discover if I too was intolerant to these foods. I was. From that first testing session, the two of us found ourselves on the proverbial voyage of discovery, learning more and more about food, its nutritional value and the importance of provenance. The supermarket began to look like an alien environment as we gradually began to piece together the food jigsaw.

THAT EUREKA MOMENT

Sally's friend is a kinesiologist, and I feel a certain amount of trepidation in mentioning the fact. Kinesiology is what is known as a complementary therapy, although some people prefer to use the phrase 'alternative therapy.' Complementary therapists are much maligned by certain sectors of the general public, and they are regularly put down by 'experts' and 'scientists', many of whom are employed by the pharmaceutical industry to denigrate the activities of anyone who makes a stand against the onslaught of these drug barons.

The main criticism of complementary therapists is that what they do is unproven. In other words, there are no double-blind empirical tests to prove what they are saying. However, most complementary therapists do not, indeed cannot, work like this. Their approach is generally holistic. In other words, they do not look at symptoms in isolation, believing that it is infinitely more meaningful to look at symptoms in conjunction with what the body is experiencing as a whole. There is a lot to be said for this approach. It cannot be denied that the body is an interlocking collection of systems, each designed to work in harmony and in balance with all the others. Homeostasis, the state of equilibrium, is where our bodies need to be. Thus it is quite logical, in taking this holistic viewpoint, to assume that if one system is out of kilter, it is likely to impinge on one or more of the others. Even in the mechanical world – the internal combustion engine, for example – this interdependence of systems is recognised, as is the need to fine tune each individual system in order to get maximum efficiency from the whole.

By contrast, the scientific approach to healing the body is not like this. Possibly in homage to Louis Pasteur's germ theory, science looks at the parts of the body and the different operating systems in isolation, to examine symptoms clinically and aim the solution at this small target. Elimination of all other influences is considered desirable in order to arrive at an irrefutable conclusion as to cause. Such an empirical approach to the understanding of how our bodies work is the bedrock of scientific investigation. The danger is that we end up with someone who, say, understands a lot about the way proteins work, or fats or carbohydrates, but who understands little of how the body deals with all these substances all at once. Complementary therapy at least makes some attempt to see all symptoms in the context of the bigger bodily picture. That is how we all expect a mechanic to tune our cars – is it not reasonable to expect the same approach when tuning our bodies?

This method is not foolproof, any more than the scientific approach, but it is as valid. The main danger with complementary therapy and its holistic approach is that it opens the door to all manner of charlatans and quacks, some of whom are not qualified in any way at all. These tricksters have a tendency to interpret the holistic ethos by doing little more than burning some incense in a dimly lit room, waving their hands about in a pseudo-mystic way whilst wearing an expression of beatific omniscience, and then relieving you of some hard-earned cash. With therapists, as with accountants, solicitors and estate agents, a good rule of thumb is to go to someone who comes with a personal recommendation from someone who you can trust.

In my case, I certainly trusted Sally's friend, and her use of kinesiology to test for intolerance to certain foods seems to me to produce unequivocal results. This method uses muscle resistance as its indicator, working on the principle that if the body is confronted with a food to which it is intolerant, the ability of the muscles to offer resistance against a force disappears. To some, this might sound like mumbo-jumbo but, once it has been experienced, it cannot be denied that the results are dramatic and quite precise.

Though there is no scientific data to explain why this should work in this way, there is no denying that, in my case, my muscle tension collapsed completely in the presence of some foods whilst remaining immovably rigid in the presence of others. It is impossible to intellectualise something like this. Either you accept that it works, or you walk away from it. Personally, I would recommend it as a starting point for anyone who is seriously concerned about weight gain, fatigue, skin problems, respiratory difficulties or in fact any general ailments that cannot be explained away by the medical profession. As a bonus, it is also non-invasive and drug-free, so nothing is to be lost through trying it, other than the fee you will have to pay the therapist.

My experience was that my body reacted badly to certain foods. It turned out that, as suspected, wheat and dairy products were harmful to me. There were also other foods I was told I should avoid if at all possible, mainly coffee, sugar, yeast and mushrooms, plus some that I should be wary of, including oranges, peanuts and dried fruits. Though the last one came as a surprise, all became clear once it was explained to me that my eating habits in the past had precipitated an overgrowth of candida albicans in my gut. Thus anything that was yeast based, fungal in origin or with a mould on it was to be avoided because it was feeding the Candida. So Marmite (yeast extract) was out, as were fresh and dried mushrooms and dried fruit. Sugar was a complete no-no, because it is the one thing that Candida loves above all else.

Like complementary therapy itself, the idea of Candida is not welcome as a topic of conversation within the medical establishment. Candida is difficult to diagnose when it is running riot in the gut, but that does not mean that it does not exist. The medical profession accept its existence – they just don't like to talk about it. Complementary therapists are different. They are happy to accept not only that such conditions occur but also that, although they can cause havoc, such imbalances can be rectified.

Having been diagnosed with runaway Candida, I was put onto an 'anti-Candida diet', although it was not a diet as such, more a question of being selective. Designed to act as a sort of detox, it meant avoiding all of the foods that were likely to exacerbate the condition until the Candida was back in balance. Once that had been achieved, the theory was that I would be allowed gradually to re-introduce these foods into my diet. Whilst this was in place, I was tested on a regular basis to see what progress was being made. Some interesting developments took place. At one point, I was pronounced okay with peanuts and then, on the next session, it was discovered that I was not okay with organic peanut butter. Then it was the soya milk I was using instead of cow's milk, followed by Olivio and Pure spreads with which I had replaced butter. My body showed an intolerance to all of these.

Overall, I was getting better. My chronic fatigue had dissipated, and I was able to spend much longer in front of the computer. Before testing, I would last about eight or ten minutes before going to sleep. I felt well in myself, quite a few aches and pains (that I had previously accepted as the inevitable legacy of getting older) had disappeared and I had lost some weight. In fact, my weight had gone down to what I sometimes refer to as my 'fighting weight' and stabilised at that point. Effectively, that meant that I had lost well over a stone in weight over a few months and gone down to the weight I was in my twenties. More importantly, I have remained at that weight, give or take a few pounds, ever since then, a period of nearly four years.

However, we were all concerned about my intolerance to the alternatives I was being offered for dairy products. The theory was mooted that I may be intolerant to certain ingredients in products like Pure spread. In fact, describing it as 'pure' began to look a little disingenuous, because it is not pure, it is processed, and therefore contains ingredients that may be affecting me adversely. When it came to the peanut butter, which allegedly contains nothing but peanuts, salt and sunflower oil, we began to wonder whether there was something in the processing that was upsetting me. After reading some publications on what happens to sunflower oil when it is heated and processed, I became convinced that this was the problem. As we have seen, sunflower oil is polyunsaturated and is thereby unstable, breaking down into something potentially toxic during heating.

These discoveries made us both more inquisitive, and we began reading anything we could get our hands on that gave us information on modern-day food and the industry that supports it. Becoming increasingly alarmed at what we discovered, we began to theorise that avoiding processed food altogether would improve my health considerably. This has turned out to be the case, and the eureka moment came on a day when I was due to be tested again by way of a progress check.

Dairy, it seemed was an ongoing problem, so testing me on milk had become a routine part of each session. I 'failed' every time. Prior to this latest testing session, it just so happened that Sally had been reading Gina Mallett's, *Last Chance to Eat*. More particularly, she had been reading about milk. Gina Mallet's praise for real milk is unstinting, and it prompted Sally to suggest that it would be interesting to get me tested on raw milk. The hunt was on, and we did manage to find some in time for the testing session.

On that occasion, I was going to be tested on some organic milk. It was pasteurised, of course – all milk is these days. But it was whole milk and it had not been homogenised, plus it was from a local dairy, and I had high hopes for it. Being local and organic is deemed to be a good thing of course, but the main criterion for organic eligibility is that the cows should be fed on organic feeds and not subjected to antibiotics. There is nothing to say that organic milk should come only from traditional pasture-fed herds. The milk from this local dairy, though organic, was from a herd of overworked milkers, and the milk was pasteurised, so two negative points there but, in terms of what is generally available commercially, it was the best we could find. Once again, not surprisingly, the test revealed intolerance. No change there then. Next came the raw milk (from a grass-fed organic Jersey herd). My muscles remained rock solid. In fact, it was one of the strongest reactions I have had to anything on which I had been tested.

That did it for me. From that moment, I avoided anything processed, even something as 'gently' processed as pasteurised whole milk. Today, we both eat what might be called traditional foods in that we prepare our food from scratch, using the best we can find – vegetables from the market garden down the road, meat from grass-fed herds, eggs from pastured hens, fruit from local orchards (we rarely eat oranges these days) dairy products from a local dairy. We still treat ourselves to chocolate, but only the best organic, plain, Free Trade chocolate we can find. I have been tested on a regular basis since my eureka moment and I still have no problem with real milk, farmhouse butter, unpasteurised cheese or indeed anything, so long as it is not factory produced, adulterated, tampered with or in any way the product of an industrial process. And, yes – I can hear those words of protest again. "We can't shop like this – we only have the supermarket." We have already seen that even the supermarket will have some of the things you need. The rest will come with a little re-organisation of your time and the adoption of a different mind set. Let's change that half empty glass into a half full one.

As well as undergoing testing for intolerances, I also visited my GP, as an academic exercise to have certain things checked. I was especially interested in my cholesterol levels, but only because the medical profession makes such a fuss about it. I pointed out to the GP that my level of consumption of animal fats, especially butter, lard and beef fat, had gone up dramatically since my last cholesterol test three years previously. I mentioned that I was eating at least two eggs a day, although there were some days when that consumption went up to around six if I had poached eggs for breakfast and then a big omelette in the evening. And what had happened to my cholesterol level? It had dropped, from 5.9 mmol/l to 3.6. Similarly, my blood pressure and pulse rate had dropped from what would be expected of someone of middle years back down to the levels of my youth. All the GP could say was, "Whatever you are doing, there appears to be no reason why you should not carry on doing it." Well, thanks, Doc, that's good to know. And I am more than happy to carry on doing it. Anecdotal? Of course. Unsubstantiated? Well, I suppose I could ask the GP for the examination notes. Too good to be true? Overstated? You have two choices in assessing the validity of this story; you can accept that I am giving you the facts, or you can assume that I am exaggerating for effect. But ask yourself this, why would I be lying?

A MATTER OF TASTE

When Sally first introduced me to her friend, all I was concerned with was that I felt so dreadful so much of the time. It was a struggle to do what I had to do each day. Here we were, running a busy B&B, and my agenda for each day was along the lines of, "Get through it." I needed help, because I couldn't see how I was going to stand the pace. So my main preoccupation was to get better, and I was prepared to talk to anyone who might be able to help. That did not include my GP of course, because I did not want to be sent away with a prescription for happy pills or some other kind of pharmaceutical pick-me-up, so talking to a kinesiologist was fine by me. Any drug-free remedy was worth trying, in my opinion. The experience of being tested for intolerances was positive beyond my expectations, though it provoked more questions and opened up new avenues of investigation. Without doubt, it turned out to be a real voyage of discovery.

The eureka moment with the milk was the point on that journey when I hit a fork in the path and went off in another direction. But what a magical world I found around the next corner. It was a world of food with taste. I had forgotten that such food existed. The flavours and aromas took me back to a time of childhood, when I would accompany my Grandpa to the vegetable garden in the snow to cut some sprouts for the pot.

As I regained my health, we would seek out farm shops and go to the Farmers' Markets in Hereford, gradually building up a very long list of suppliers for all the food we needed. Though most of the people we were now dealing with were following organic principles of husbandry or production, we were not specifically seeking out food that had an organic label hanging from it. We had discovered by then, for instance, that organic carrots from the supermarket often taste just as bland as the ordinary ones, so we knew that there must be more to it than simply claiming organic status.

In doing a side-by-side taste test between organic and non-organic vegetables from the supermarket, it was not difficult to sympathise with those who say that the only difference is the price. Buying from independent growers with low volume sales, however, was a different story. Through Farmers' Markets, these people were offering vegetables for sale that had still been in the ground the previous day, grown in healthy, chemical-free soils. They had real taste. More than that, they had a zing to them only found in vegetables that are fresh and grown in the kind of humus-rich soils that small operators are able to maintain. It is a sad fact of life that vegetables quickly lose their just-picked taste, but buying from Farmers' Markets gave us access to vegetables not long out of the ground, and thereby the chance to experience the true taste of everything, or something very close to it.

When it comes to this level of taste and freshness, supermarkets just cannot deliver. At first, we wondered why, but finding the answer is not difficult. To put it plainly, they are just not geared up for it, due to bulk buying and their central distribution systems. Moreover, when it comes to organic, the commitment to bulk buying is unshakeable, because they must keep their systems efficient. Thus, organic or not, they shop around for bigger suppliers and buy from whoever is prepared to deliver the quantities demanded. They will buy from anywhere in the world and they do not always buy from ethical organic producers, or they buy from countries where the rules are less strict than they are in the UK. So, for the two of us, 'organic' and 'supermarket' were terms that were mutually exclusive, as we were losing out on both taste and freshness. Organic supermarket produce just did not hit the spot for us. Our advice is to treat *everything* from the supermarket with suspicion. This is not hysteria, but simply recognition of the fact that supermarkets avoid the logistical and profit-damaging exercise of sourcing the kind of fruit and vegetables that we are talking about. The same proviso applies to all fresh produce, including, meat, eggs and dairy items. Buying 'supermarket organic' is better than buying non-organic, and it is one step in the right direction. But it is no more than that. Look upon it as a temporary stopgap that gives you time to find something better.

At the high-volume end of retailing, labels, such as 'organic', have to be defined and, once the definition is in place, unscrupulous operators are then able to bend the rules, or at the very least to employ some creative interpretation – chickens can still be crammed by the thousand into huge sheds, but fattened with 'organic' feed. Is this organic, or is it just another form of exploitation bearing a more attractive label? In consideration of this, we wanted to go beyond all labelling systems and get to the heart of real food production. What was important for us was being able to talk to the people who were raising the animals or growing the vegetables or milling the flour, because these were the people whose dedication was obvious, whose products spoke loudly of their passion for what they were doing.

Because I had now been presented with a list of 'banned substances' such as sugar, milk and wheat, I also had to rethink my approach to breakfast, including tea and coffee. I suppose I am lucky that I don't really have a sweet tooth, but I did like a bit of sugar on my cereal, a spoonful in my coffee and the occasional spoonful in my tea, and of course milk with everything. My weakness was a penchant for cheap chocolate snacks such as Cadbury's flake, KitKat and Galaxy, with the odd Mars bar thrown in when I fancied a change.

Even without a particularly sweet tooth, it was quite hard weaning myself off my favourite treats. What kept me going was the fact that I was feeling better by the day keeping off the things that had been identified as bad for my body and my health. But, as I eliminated sugary snacks, something remarkable happened. My taste came back. Remarkable indeed, because I didn't think I had lost it. Nevertheless, as sugar was expunged from my diet and its memory cleansed from my system, my tastebuds came back to life. I could now taste sweetness where there had been none before. I began to understand what 'sweet' meant in terms of the taste spectrum. It was like taking a favourite CD and playing it on some high spec equipment – all of a sudden you hear the horn section that was always there but you never picked up, or that second guitar in the background, and the two backing singers that you hadn't been aware of on your tatty old portable Matsui.

That Bramley apple that I had always considered to be a 'cooker' now took on an interesting taste eaten raw, and other apples were just different shades of apple flavour, from tart to honey-sweet, but they were all sweet. I could taste the sweetness in cabbage and a different sweetness in potatoes. Coupled with the fresh, top quality produce we were buying, my eating experience was moving into a different dimension. And all those chocolate snacks? Finally, I could recognise them for what they are. The taste was cloying, sugary, sickly sweet and unpleasantly artificial. I still love chocolate, but it has to be real *chocolate*, not some pale processed imitation. The predilection I used to have for industrial chocolate had gone. No longer was a KitKat one step closer to heaven. Now it just tasted of cheap fats and sugar, and it was far too sweet.

Having undergone this change in eating habits, I now understand that I was, in my own small way, addicted to sugar. When I look back at what was happening to me at a psychological level, I am sure that I was displaying some of the early signs of addiction. I see it now with people I know, when they say to me in that emphatic, half joking, half serious way, "I can't give up Cadbury's Dairy Milk – I'm addicted to chocolate!" Yes, you are addicted, but not to chocolate. Chocolate is gorgeous, sensuous, sexy stuff, but it is not made in giant factories using cheap vegetable fat and a boxful of additives, emulsifiers and three different kinds of sugar. Chocolate is not this syrup-sweet confection that sticks to your teeth, gives you a brief high and then drops you on the floor. Chocolate is made by people who care, master chocolatiers or nascent new-wave companies like Booja-Booja, Divine, Montezuma or Plamil.

I talk to people about giving up sugar and I see the panic in their eyes. They cannot imagine a world without sugar. They think that they will always need sugar, but I know they won't. I could say, "I was that person, but I have changed." But I don't want to sound like some zealous evangelist. I do, however, want to suggest that sugar is not necessary in our diet. Sugar is a killer. It kills not just tastebuds, but some of the internal systems that keep you healthy. We cannot see much of the sugar that we consume, but it is there in alarmingly high quantities. It is hidden in your breakfast cereal, your mass-market pot of honey and your neatly packaged ready meal. All of this is too big a hit for your system. It is literally a body blow every time your system has to cope with another dose of refined or processed sugar. It messes up your blood sugar levels, depletes your vitamins and leads you inexorably down a path that you would not go if you could see the chasm at the end of it. You may not tumble into the chasm until later in life, or you may be one of the lucky ones who manages to avoid it, but it is there nevertheless. Everyone has a different immune system, so some succumb quickly to adverse symptoms, others get away with it for longer. But sooner or later most people will suffer from some form of degenerative ailment that could be avoided with a little more awareness.

If there is one thing that should be at the top of your Agenda for a New Life, it is to remove refined sugar from your diet. Once you do this and thereby regain your ability to taste food as it should taste, you will wonder how you could ever have eaten some of the industrial foods that have come to dominate our lives. And then you will understand why the supermarket system will never be able to deliver the kind of food we need in the way that we need it, with the possible exception of companies like Innocent. But watch these innovative companies closely, for once they hit the big time, changes occur. Along comes an offer they can't refuse and they get swallowed up by a big corporation. Then, sooner or later, you are likely to find the product has been diminished in some way.

It is virtually impossible, given a global distribution system and shareholder pressure, for a giant retailer to deal in quantities small enough to capture the essence of taste. This is really available only in produce that has been grown traditionally, in organically rich, chemical-free, mineralised soil by dedicated people who put quality before quantity. In the end, the only way to find real food that is bouncing with nutritional value is to think local, think seasonal and find the producers who think the same.

STRAWBERRIES IN JUNE

I know that June is not the only month in which strawberries are available, and that even outdoor strawberries can grow from May to October if the weather is right, but for many people June traditionally signals the start of the strawberry season. Perhaps it is the long association with Wimbledon. Or perhaps it is simply the fact that June is the peak of the season and thus strawberries taste better in that month. Whatever the reason, seasonality is a key point. Certain crops, asparagus for example, are still traditionally seen as being seasonal. Not too long ago, however, a great many fruits, vegetables and even meat and dairy products were available only on a seasonal basis. One might almost say that our lives were governed by the seasons.

Now all that has changed. Our industrialised culture and the supermarket concept of Permanent Global Summertime has taken away the need to think seasonally, as well as virtually eradicating our former skills of coping with gluts and devising ways of storing up for the leaner winter months. The rot set in with the first rumblings of the Industrial Revolution and gradually over the years we have lost touch with the seasons. We now live 'in a world of cheap year-round abundance', as Paul Waddington puts it in his book, *Seasonal Food*.

The question that many people ask is whether there is any point in worrying about the seasons when everything we are likely to want is available whenever we want it. I say, yes, there is every point. If food and its health-giving potential are important at all, then thinking seasonally is equally important. Most foods have a season and they are at their best at the height of that season, when they will deliver optimum nutrition to our bodies. Food in season is fresher, more nutritious and more succulent, making it a joy in the summer months to eat raw produce. It is infinitely more tasty that the out-of-season, chiller-stored sad vegetables that are put out on display at the wrong time of year. Many are forced to grow too quickly and too soon or they are flown halfway around the world – all done in the name of 'extending the season'.

Seasonal food gives us more variety. It keeps our interest going as fruits and vegetables come into their own for a brief period before giving up their place to the next ones in the spotlight. This is infinitely more stimulating than going into a typical aircraft hangar superstore and seeing the same old things in the same old place. There is something deeply depressing about the far-too-glossy Granny Smith apples and the uniformly sized traffic light capsicums, same size and shape this week as they were last week. Not to mention the pots of suspiciously green herbs that have so little flavour in them that they taste like grass once they are chopped. And then of course the Great British Strawberry, taking up shelf space from April to November. This is the ubiquitous Elsanta variety, renowned for its keeping qualities but very little else. Bright red and carefully selected in the field to be of uniform size, it always appears to be sold at a reduced price to tempt you into buying another bargain. Break them out of the pack and what do you find? They are pale fleshed, insipid and slightly tart. They taste a bit like strawberries, but they have absolutely no zing to them. If you are lucky enough to have a pick-your-own field anywhere near you, I recommend you get down there with your basket. Buy some true outdoor strawberries grown in season and picked at the right time and you will have fruit with a lush deep pink interior and a taste explosion in your mouth. You will be able to smell the fruit as you walk down the rows, and by the time you have got them home, your car will be filled with their wonderful aroma. You will need to be strong-willed to keep your hands off them until you get home.

We buy our strawberries from three local growers who, between them, can supply about ten varieties of strawberry, designed to come on stream at different times of the summer, just like other crops. Thus we get seasons within a season, with hardy early strawberries appearing in late May if the weather is right, and moving through to late varieties that are still available into September. That is quite a lengthy season, without having to resort to polytunnel culture. By the time September comes, though, our interest in strawberries has waned. We are looking forward to apples, plums and blackberries, then pears, more apples and maybe some quinces in November just before the ground goes to sleep for another winter. February, and the anticipation of the early rhubarb crop, signals new life. Though the fruit bonanza of summer is still at least three months away at this point, there is always something uplifting about that early rhubarb, harbinger of the time of plenty.

Working with the seasons nurtures respect and understanding for nature and its potential bounty. Of all the people that trawl the supermarket aisles looking at the same stilted variety of fruit and vegetables, how many have any perception of the relationship between this produce and the soil in which it was grown? Very few, I imagine. Losing that perception means losing the instinct for what is good, what is bad and what is indifferent. Detached from the process of growing and harvesting food leaves us uninterested in the food itself. We descend into food apathy, willing to accept the basest products the industrialised food industry cares to cast before us.

Rekindling our recognition of the seasonality of produce will help to revive our interest in food and the pleasure of eating it. Once this spark of interest ignites our desire for the taste of real food, we develop a sense of purpose in tracking down the best of what is available in season. This in turn leads us to those farmers, growers and farm shop proprietors who stand in defiance of the homogenising influence of global retailing. These are the people who really care about food, and you are quite likely to find some of them right on your doorstep – yes, even in the heart of a city. For others, you might have to travel further afield, but it will be worth it. Once food takes on the important role that it rightly deserves, its new priority status ensures that we look around us with keener eyes, seeing places and producers who were always there, but beyond our previously narrow horizon.

Seasonal almost by definition means local, because the most effective way to buy seasonal produce in optimum condition is to buy it locally. Streamlined retailing systems are not, and never will be, geared to this kind of supply and demand situation. There is really no point in buying, say, new season's potatoes from a big retailer, because the potatoes will have been harvested long before you get to buy them. They will have been sent to a distribution depot to be bagged up into 500g packs and then they will be trickled out through the retailer's stores over a period of time in order to keep the price up for as long as possible.

Jersey Royal potatoes are typical of this kind of value-added retailing. The big retailers try to corner the market in a commodity like this because they understand that there are sufficient customers willing to pay the price for the first Jersey Royals of the season. By buying up the stocks, the supermarkets try to create a situation where Jersey Royals are available nowhere but in their own stores, and then they can keep the supply trickling out for as long as they need to. But go to your local farm shop and see what is available there. You may be lucky and find Jersey Royals but, if not, you might still be able to buy fresh new potatoes that will be just as good, and probably better than anything on offer at the supermarket. If your farm shop is genuinely supplied from the locality, the chances are that you will be buying potatoes that were dug up that morning. If they all sell out by lunchtime, there may be another batch in by the afternoon. Otherwise, the next lot will be fresh in tomorrow. It's the next best thing to growing your own, and they will taste wonderful. Just be aware, though, that even farm shops are capable of cutting corners. If you think the produce on offer looks as if it has been bought from a wholesaler, just ask questions: Are these your own potatoes? What variety are they? Where were they grown?

Sourcing seasonal food at a local level is exciting. Okay, maybe it is not all that exciting for someone whose interest in food has gone into terminal decline, but for those of us who still enjoy the pleasure of eating, seasonal local food has another quality so often overlooked. It shows us local variation. There is something very appealing about finding a different variety of potato in Cumbria from those you might find in Cornwall, and it is a pleasure to travel from the homeland of brown and white Hereford cattle to see shaggy Highland cattle up in Scotland. Beyond this, there are also annual seasonal differences to keep us on our toes. One year might be a good year for plums, but a bad year for apples. Vegetables might be prolific one year and poor croppers in the following year, and so on. When it comes to wine, we think this is perfectly normal, even desirable. It adds an extra dimension to wine buying when one has to track down the good vintages from specific vineyards. But many people find it difficult to think like this when it comes to fruit and vegetables. Nevertheless, this is exactly how it is.

Because the work of running a B&B revolves around the buying, cooking and serving of food, we are keenly aware of these variations. Jams never come out the same way twice. Everything seems to depend on where we bought the fruit, what the weather was like at the time and what the weather had been doing from the time the fruit began to form. Different varieties of strawberry produce different consistencies of jam, and different varieties of gooseberry produce different colours, from olive green to bright red.

Sally once questioned whether it was a good thing that each batch of preserves she makes will be a one-off. But ultimately, it must be. Like any hand made product, wine or cheese for example, variations will occur, and we think this is quite natural. It is more like real life. How dull would life be without its ups and downs? Life must have that element of doubt, that degree of unpredictability, and food should be the same. Global retailing eliminates the uncertainty, cutting a horizontal line through the peaks and troughs of our normal food experiences. If you buy your food in a supermarket, you know that those boring traffic light peppers, three to a bag, will be exactly the same every time you visit the store, exactly the same, year in year out, and exactly the same in the rival supermarket down the road. Go to somewhere like Abergavenny Food Festival, however, and you will see peppers of all shapes and colours. They will be glossy, fresh, bright, aromatic. Their sensuous shapes will seduce you, and the smell of them will transport you to the Mediterranean or the Mexican border. You will go home and feel inspired to cook. This high spot of culinary adventure may well shine out as a beacon of creativity amongst humbler efforts, but this is the stuff of memories. What memories come from bland uniformity? The giant food retailers need uniformity to make them function efficiently. But food is not about this kind of efficiency, it is about living, and the way to live is to seek out locally produced seasonal food, buy it from the people that grow it, then take it home and cook it yourself, eat and be transported.

By buying in this way, we are also supporting those brave farmers, growers, horticulturalists and producers who understand that the future of food production must be sustainable. In addition, moving away from year-round availability towards seasonal and local food has a positive effect on our methods of production, giving us improved soils, a recovery of depleted biodiversity and less pollution. Chemical agriculture and intensive stock farming are ultimately doomed because they create more problems than they solve. Using synthetic nitrogen fertiliser, that is entirely dependent on fossil fuels for its creation, means that two calories of energy are used to produce one calorie of food. This just has to be stupidity on a grand scale. Intensive systems take from the land without giving anything back. Moreover, they create disastrous ecological imbalances. Such one-sided exploitation is economically myopic and has no long-term future. That this type of farming is called 'conventional' is a demonstration of the power of spin. It is hard to believe that something completely unnatural, which has overturned 10,000 years of tradition can, in a few short decades, become known as 'conventional,' but that is indeed what has happened. Logic dictates, however, that these unnatural systems must eventually implode.

Meanwhile, we should encourage the alternative. With support, an increasing number of people will be willing to farm using sustainable methods. With farmers currently going out of business at a frightening rate, we need a new incentive to make farming attractive once more. It is in everyone's interest to stop this decline before it becomes terminal. Already the hands on the clock stand at five minutes to midnight, but it is still not too late. We can reverse the trend, but it is down to each one of us. It must happen from the bottom up, because no one at the top is going to do anything much about it. And those corporations that believe that they hold all the power can be made to understand that it is actually the consumers who hold all the power. We, the consumers, can bring about change, so long as we work positively together. It is imperative that this happens, in order to have a new foundation on which to build, once the house of cards that is conventional farming collapses.

THE FOOD CHAIN

Traditionally, we all used to have a very clear idea of where our food came from. For the most part, in rural areas certainly, food was produced within any given community for local consumption. Despite the onslaught of the Industrial Revolution and the huge urban sprawls that it created, most people still had some sense of provenance regarding the foods they ate. Following food shortages precipitated by World War II, it took very little persuasion for the British to 'dig for victory'. Cultivating a private vegetable plot or allotment became second nature as the war came to an end and the country slowly recovered from the years of austerity.

As the culture changed, clever marketing persuaded us that we no longer needed to spend precious time in the garden weeding between the rows of carrots. Interest in horticulture waned as the new post-war generation became bedazzled by the growing light of consumerism. Why bother with the garden when there were new shops to explore in town, and why bother to grow your own carrots when you could buy them ready washed at the local convenience store? Gardens and their associated vegetable plots became redundant and then neglected. By the end of the 1960s, only a few stalwarts who remembered digging for victory were digging anything at all. Their offspring were digging the scene, but not the garden. Within a decade or so, designer gardens and makeovers were all the rage, and vegetable plots disappeared altogether in favour of relaxation areas with raised decking and water features.

We lost interest in food, preferring to spend our time and money on the new gadgets that flowed from the factories. Responsibility for the procurement of food was given up and taken over by the big retailers. Our food chain began to stretch. As the retailers grew in size, so the methods of procurement changed, demanding ever more sophisticated supply systems in order to keep the shelves stacked in what were now becoming known as supermarkets. The food chain stretched further as expansion of these retail companies accelerated. Expansion was achieved through opening more branches, at a rate that quickened considerably from 1980 onwards. By the late '80s, Tesco alone was opening a new out-of-town superstore every three weeks or so. Soon all the major retail companies were represented in every major town and city in the country. It would be accurate to say that by 1990, the majority of shoppers in this country had become completely divorced from the source of most of their food. The supply chain from producer to consumer had grown long enough to take in many middlemen along the way, each of whom wanted their slice of the profit. This was dangerous. Squeezing more profit out of the supply system impinged directly on the quality of the food being supplied.

Having no direct contact with the people who actually produce our food means that we have no control over how the food is produced and what happens to it by the time it reaches us. We really have no idea what we are being sold. Worse than that, if we put our trust in someone else to source food for us, and that person or company has no scruples about compromising the quality of the food in pursuit of greater profits, then we are being unwittingly duped. If we trust those who source our food and we also trust their sales patter, then perhaps we deserve to be duped.

It is beyond the scope of this book to conduct a detailed examination of how much we are being deceived by those who profess to have our interests at heart when sourcing our food, but it is fair to say that there is a staggering amount of misinformation and deception within the publicity that supports the big retailers. That may sound like a sweeping statement, but is it so surprising? We have been conned by unscrupulous salesmen since the proverbial dawn of time, and there is no evidence to suggest that sharp practice has suddenly become a thing of the past. To begin to understand the scale of this problem, all one needs to do is to stand back, take a detached view and question everything we are told. Extricate yourself from all the hype, look at it in an impersonal way, and ask questions like, "What's in it for them?" or, "Can they verify that statement?" or simply, "Is that really true?" This effortless little test will reveal that there are gaping holes in the publicity fabric with which these companies clothe themselves.

Good nutritious food is fundamental to our health. We cannot exist without it. Despite the fact that its importance has been relegated to the lower rungs of our priority ladder, we are all tied to the preoccupation of finding and eating food every day. Whether we are die-hard traditionalists who insist on eating three meals a day at the proper time, or whether we are modern-day grazers snacking on fast foods whenever we feel the urge for a little something, food is still central to our survival. Surely it makes sense to take care over what we are eating. We can no longer trust the big retailers to source good nutritious food for us, so we have to bite the bullet and accept responsibility for sourcing our own food. That doesn't mean driving round the corner to the local BP garage to top up with a few ready made sandwiches and a couple of chocolate bars. It means finding real food that will subdue our craving for cheap chocolate and factory made snacks. It means getting to the source of production. Ideally it means talking to the man who has dug the vegetables or reared the pigs or made the cheese. This might appear to be difficult in the centre of a city, but it is not impossible. The internet abounds with mail order companies just itching to get an order from you for fresh produce. You may well have to email or phone in the order, but you will effectively be talking directly to the producer.

Each one of us that makes a conscious effort to reduce the length of the chain between the producers and ourselves will be helping to redress the balance in the retail market. Though I do not wish to labour the point about the power of the supermarkets, it cannot be denied that they now dominate the retail food trade. They control 80% of our food supply. Will they be satisfied with that? No, how can they be? They are committed to growth. Next year's growth will have to come from somewhere and, if there is 20% of the market still being supplied by others, that is as good a place as any to start. The only people who can make a difference to that situation are the people who shop in those supermarkets. As powerful as the retail giants are, their customers are more powerful. If the customers were to decide to shop elsewhere, supermarket turnover would drop accordingly.

I am not saying that we should get rid of supermarkets, although personally I would not be disappointed if they were to go. What I am saying is that we should try to redress the balance. By taking at least some of our custom elsewhere, we are reducing the dominance of the giants and reviving the livelihoods of the smaller shop. With the subsequent increase in smaller shops, our choice increases. A number of other fringe benefits also occur as a result of this move towards diversified shopping.

Firstly, we renew human contact. It is very difficult to go into an independent shop for your groceries and not talk to someone, even if it is only the person who takes your money. Go in more than once, and that same person will no doubt greet you, having recognised you from your previous visit. Go there on a regular basis and you will find you have built a relationship, albeit of a conversational nature, with at least one other human being. This is very important. I know that the predictable reaction to this scenario is to say, "I'm a very busy person – I don't have time for idle banter." But how many people who think like this also envy the French, the Italians or the Irish, to say nothing of most other European countries, for their laid-back approach to life? Why not think like them for a change? Slow down a bit, talk to someone about nothing in particular, relax, take in your surroundings. You may find that you are not as busy as you thought you were. It is important to stop long enough to smell the roses. Living life at an increasingly manic pace is senseless. Like the man that overtakes you on a dangerous bend and races over the horizon, it gets you nowhere – you will catch him up at the next set of lights. Taking life easier and finding the time to talk to people is essential to our well-being, as is the human bond that it creates. To live life as a discrete being in a world of strangers is not good for the soul. Human contact is vital. Extend that contact to people outside your immediate circle of family and friends and you will feel the benefit.

The second benefit of shopping around for your food is that you increase your chances of picking up something nutritious. Supermarkets deal with enormous quantities of produce every day. Small shops and producers have had to devise ways of staying in business and circumvent the buying power of the retail giants. They have done this by seeking out smaller suppliers and by working directly with their customers via Farmers' Markets and other similar venues.

Our local greengrocer, for example, buys some of his produce from small wholesalers, but much of what he sells is garden surplus from individual suppliers. If Mrs Jones from the farm down the road has a few dozen eggs to spare, she will bring them in, or if Jack the Jolly Gardener has a glut of runner beans, he may well pass them on to the local shop to sell. There may be no organic labels in evidence with people like this, but you are practically guaranteed a better product than you would find in the local superstore. You can almost smell the nutrition. You will certainly smell the produce and it won't be wrapped in clingfilm.

At the Farmers' Market, you will be dealing with the farmer himself, or the vegetable grower, cheesemaker or baker. These people, like the produce they are selling, are honest. Let's put it this way, it has never been our experience to find one who is not. You are talking directly to the person who made that cheese or those sausages. They will tell you anything you want to know about their products. They have nothing to hide. From our experience, the products are also the best you can get, far superior to anything you can find in a supermarket, guaranteed fresh, obviously nutritious and not as expensive as you might think.

There seems to be a popular myth that Farmers' Markets are expensive, but this is unfounded if you compare like for like. The chicken you buy at the Farmers' Market is not the same as the one you might buy in a supermarket. Even if your supermarket chicken is plastered with organic labels and other insignia, it will have come from a large supplier. In reality, there is no comparison between this top of the range supermarket chicken and the one from the Farmers' Market. The latter is so superior in terms of taste, tenderness, nutritional value and careful husbandry that it is in a different league altogether. It is quite simply a chicken that is too good for any supermarket. Attempting a price comparison is futile. The only maxim that applies here is, 'you get what you pay for.' At the Farmers' Market, you are paying for the best you can get. Considering this, you are getting it remarkably cheap.

Shopping in this way reduces the food chain to one or two links. At the Farmers' Market, it is just you and the producer. I cannot envisage any serious argument that will convince me that this is worse than shopping in a supermarket. All a supermarket can offer me is convenience and cheapness. In my opinion, the convenience is specious, based on persuasive marketing that tells me it is better to swap the bustle of a colourful, individual, eccentric and delightfully 'inefficient' town centre shopping expedition for the cold, frustrating experience of shopping amongst strangers in a ruthlessly efficient neon-lit emporium. As for the cheapness, that too comes back to the maxim of 'you get what you pay for.' Supermarket food is cheap, but much of it is nutritionally depleted, despite the fact that it is so prettily packaged. In many cases, you would be better off not buying it at all. What price are you actually paying for all this cheap food? And how much money are you taking out of the pockets of the people who supply the supermarkets with all this cheap food?

Buying direct from the producer or from small independent shops generates honest transactions. You buy at a price that the producer can afford to sell at. In return, he will sell you something that is in prime condition. You will be able to buy fruit that is ready to eat, not something that has been picked too early and will never ripen. You will be able to buy vegetables that have not been out of the ground for more than 24 hours. You will be able to buy meat from animals that have had a good life and the best of caring husbandry. And, above all, you will be able to have fun.

Talking to real people about real food is fun. Food is so fundamental to our survival that once we take our eye off the ball, as it were, and relegate it to some minor status, we risk not just our health but our happiness. I am convinced that reducing the buying, cooking and eating of food to just three more items on the day's agenda generates negativity at some subliminal level. Food, and more particularly nutritious food, is so essential to life that there is no shame in giving it priority status. Once this is understood, our desire for healthy food engenders new interest in what we are buying. Innate instincts begin to stir as the hunter-gatherer in us sets out to track down something for the pot. Eating becomes a delight once more, especially in the company of others. To sit and eat a good meal with family and friends is a pleasure that should not be underestimated. It is fine to do this in a restaurant from time to time, but there really is no substitute for the full experience of finding, cooking and then sharing what you have cooked with others. It is an essentially human activity that is worth reviving.

JOINING THE DOTS

Breaking out of the supermarket mindset gives us back control over what we eat. More importantly, as we have seen, it takes away some of the control currently exerted by the big retailers. I know that in the pages of this book I have had no kind words to say on the rise of corporate control, but I make no apology for it. I am in good company. Even the great J K Galbraith was a lifelong critic of the unbridled power of corporations. So there it is. The emperor is quite naked, and that is an end to it. Without getting bogged down in the political, economical and commercial reasons for the spectacular growth of UK retail corporations, it is a fact that more than three-quarters of the UK retail food trade is in the hands of four extremely powerful corporations. During my years at university, the economics textbooks that I was reading (at least one of which was written by J K Galbraith) were all agreed on one thing – monopoly, or its close cousin oligopoly, was a Bad Thing. But here we are with the bulk of our food retailing in the hands of an oligopoly of four.

The corporations that form this oligopoly are immensely powerful. Two of them, Tesco and Asda, have a global presence, as well as 46.5% of the supermarket turnover in the UK. This is a massive problem, so large that no government has the will, or indeed the power, to solve it. There is really only one thing that can curb the relentless growth of such corporations – the customer. The customer, wooed and flattered by those that need his custom, is the Achilles heel of all corporations, because without customers the corporation is dead. The strength of a corporation depends on persuading more and more people to become its customers, which it does with consummate ease through its well oiled publicity machine.

It seems unlikely that the giant retailers are going to do anything other than grow even larger. They have no alternative. As corporations dependent on their shareholders, they are compelled to maximise profits, minimise costs and to grow year on year. But we don't have to help them. We can take our custom elsewhere. Once we turn a deaf ear to all the entreaties that it is more convenient, or cheaper or more satisfying to shop in an out-of-town warehouse, we are free to shop elsewhere. As we have seen, this has many advantages. We get fresher, more nutritious food, we get more choice, we meet new and interesting people and we have lots of fun. Best of all, we have freedom. Those who have shaken the clinging demon of corporate hype from their backs can once more stand upright, see the vista before them and make their own decisions about which direction they will take today.

Choosing to shop in independent shops or to support Farmers' Markets will make the picture clearer, but joining all of the dots can be more difficult. We know people who are highly active in condemning the proliferation of polytunnels for the growing of soft fruit in Herefordshire, yet they have not made the connection between the polytunnels and the supermarkets, so they quite happily do their weekly shop in the local superstore, adding another £100 a week to the store's turnover. Supermarket propaganda is so slick that most people think that there is a proliferation of polytunnels in Herefordshire solely because the customers are demanding English strawberries in November. This is a long way from the truth.

Firstly, customer demand is a fickle thing and, as such, represents something of an unknown quantity to the corporations. This had to be brought under control through well-directed marketing. Since the end of the Second World War, we have been coaxed, cajoled and persuaded into believing that we no longer want to buy our groceries from a number of different High Street shops, but that we would rather buy everything under one roof. We have been further persuaded that we would like to drive to somewhere really convenient on the outskirts of town, where we can enjoy free parking and the opportunity to buy even more things under an even bigger roof. Our town centres have all become clones of each other and the souls has gone right out of them. Again, through clever marketing, the finger of blame has been pointed at us by the supermarkets, who say that all they are doing is responding to customer demand.

Customer demand, apparently, is ruthless. Customer demand allegedly has forced down the price of milk to the extent that dairy farmers can barely make a living, and one farmer a week is committing suicide. Nothing to do with the price the supermarkets are prepared to pay for a litre of milk, it seems. They would have us believe that they have been forced by customer demand to pay the dairy farmers less per litre than it costs to produce the milk. Strange that the supermarkets are able to make a handsome profit on each litre they sell to the public. Something does not quite add up here. The supermarket makes a profit, the giant dairy wholesaler makes a profit, the company that supplies the milk cartons makes a profit, and the poor old farmer goes to the wall. And all because of consumer demand for cheap milk? I don't think so.

The truth is that, as the supermarkets began their takeover of our High Streets in the post-austerity years of the 1950s, the one weapon they were able to wield effectively was the cut-price offer. In post-war Britain, the cost of living was a serious social issue. In any case, everyone loves a bargain, so the cut-price sword slashed away at the traditional High Street shops, the proprietors of which were probably as strapped for cash as their customers, and the price war was upon us. Thriftiness has always been an admirable characteristic of the stoical Brits, and the new retailers took full advantage of it, competing with each other for customers by offering a better deal than the rivals. High Street shops could not compete and began to fall by the wayside. The big retailers just got bigger.

Today, this price war still rages, but it has driven down prices to unrealistically low levels. It is imperative for the supermarket to ensure that it still makes a profit, so the discount on the selling price has had to come from other areas. It has been taken from the price that is paid to producers, from the cost of animal feed, from the wages of those employed in the food production industry, from the cost of the ingredients used in food manufacturing and out of the pockets of the farmers and growers who work at the sharp end of food production. The only ones to have benefited from this are the big retailers. Their profits can now be counted in billions, and the CEOs of these corporations, who look down on us from their towering glass palaces, choose not to see the trail of destruction left in the wake of this mad scramble for dominance of the retail food market.

Strangely, this destruction appears to be invisible to most of the public too. They cannot see what competition between giant retailers is doing to our world. Happy to rail against polytunnels, they are unable to see that the polytunnels are there only because the supermarkets are competing with each other to be the top seller of English strawberries over a longer season. Supermarket price wars killed the pick-your-own industry that used to be such a pleasurable activity for so many people on any given summer weekend. Having done that, pressure was put on the few growers left to supply supermarkets on demand with such huge quantities of strawberries that only the most tenacious and ruthless growers could stay in the game. Then came the demands to extend the English season that resulted in the adoption of Spanish-style polytunnels. The argument put out by the big retailers that they are responding to public demand is spurious and disingenuous. The only thing they are responding to is the threat that their rivals might have English strawberries for longer on their shelves.

Bemoaning the fact that cod is now an endangered species, those who shop at supermarkets cannot make the connection between that and the huge demands the supermarkets put on the fishing industry to supply fresh fish to their hundreds of stores. As we saw in Chapter 6, a fresh fish counter in a supermarket is not like a traditional fish shop. In the traditional fish shop, the catch of the day, landed by a small fishing fleet in the nearest fishing port, was displayed first thing in the morning, with the hope that all would be sold by the end of the day. Not so in a supermarket. A supermarket, because it is terrified of what its rivals might be doing, has to have a complete range of fish, from sardines to skate, from tuna to salmon, and from lobster to squid. The counter has to look good all day – the customer must be greeted with a display of abundance. But in order to keep this up, demand is forcing the cruel over-fishing of our seas by giant factory trawlers that take everything there is to take without a thought for the consequences. For those who wish to study this problem in detail, Charles Clover's book, *The End of the Line*, pulls no punches in its condemnation of modern fishing methods.

Sadly, supermarkets are unscrupulous in their attempts to keep their shelves filled with produce all the time. I have worked in a supermarket and I have seen what happens at the other end of this greedy intake. Not all the fresh produce is sold at the end of every day, but each day has to start with the whole store fully stocked once more.

Anything that hasn't been sold, that looks tired or has reached some arbitrary sell-by date ends up in the skip, to be carted off by waste disposal contractors to a landfill site. In the supermarket in which I worked, no attempt was made to sort this waste into different categories. Everything was thrown into the same skip – eggs, fruit, vegetables, plastic wrapping from the pallets, broken bottles, dented tins of beans, anything and everything. Even the plastic bags that had accumulated in the store's bag recycling bin. This was taken to the skip when full and its contents tipped in with the rest of the detritus.

Even with everything that I have said about supermarkets and their corporate ethos, there is so much more that can be said. There is no room in this book to explore fully the impact that this culture has had, and continues to have, on our planet, and in any case it has been amply covered elsewhere. There is much that could be said about plastic bags, unnecessary packaging, warehouse distribution, food miles and general environmental malpractice, but I merely wish to give an indication of the true picture that emerges once we begin to join the dots. Because, as I have already pointed out, the retail corporations will do nothing about any of this unless forced to do so, and the way to force a change is to take your custom away from them. Your custom and my custom is their life blood. Without it they will die. Once lifeblood begins to drain away, a change of practice might well be conceded. The biggest danger for the supermarkets is that they will lose us forever. Adopting a different approach to our food buying makes it impossible for us to go back to something that is so clearly an inferior option.

We all must take the trouble to join the dots if we are to see the true picture. Joining the dots shows us how the different elements of our food industry work, how our food is stripped of nutrients and how our health is compromised. It also shows us something more alarming, and that is the inaction of government. Bad practice in the agricultural industry, followed by the growth of multi-national retailers, has left most governments in the developed world impotent in the face of awesome corporate power. Asking the government to do something about the state of the nation and its health is like arranging a cock fight between a sparrow and an eagle. Governments today pass the buck so quickly that it is difficult to see it move. Issues are dealt with by committees, study groups and research organisations, whose findings are brought to our attention via daily news bulletins.

"A recent study reveals," says the news reader, "That only one child in 200 does any significant exercise, and the study concludes that, if we are to contain the increase in obesity, we must encourage our children to do more exercise." Nothing in there about the dreadful food they are eating.

Such news items are typical. Any major issue, be it the health of the nation or climate change, is dealt with in this way, and the result is always the same – the finger is pointed at us. Climate change is our fault because we drive around too much and leave the TV on standby. Obesity is our fault because we eat too much and don't exercise enough. There is just enough truth in such statements to make them plausible, but they avoid the real truth. The elephant in the room is allowed to walk around freely. Climate change, for instance, will most likely turn out to be a natural phenomenon, the speed of which is being accelerated by human activity. But it will not be put right by everyone remembering to switch off the TV standby. The activity which is so damaging to climate is based on a self-destructive global economic system that relies on the relentless consumption of resources in order to generate fabulous quantities of wealth for a tiny proportion of the whole population. As to the health of the nation and the degenerative diseases from which so many of us suffer, this is quite clearly the result of agricultural exploitation, chemical pollution of our soils, depletion of nutritional balance in soil, plants, animals and, by implication, in humans too. On top of that, we have a proliferation of unnatural foodstuffs which have mostly replaced the natural foods that have sustained us for thousands of years.

What is wrong with our food today is so wrong, and has been going wrong for so many decades, that any government is now completely powerless to do anything about it. To unravel the problem is too complicated a task for any political party to have the guts to tackle, especially within a five-year term in office. The problem is exacerbated by public resistance to change. Most people want the government to take care of all their problems, but they still want to buy cheap chicken and junk food. So even if we had a party in power that recognises what must be done, it would still resort to the lame 'study report' to give us a watered-down version of the real situation. If we are to rely on our government to tackle the issue of food and health, then we must expect that government to declare that all chemically dependent agriculture must stop, that large farms must be broken down into smaller units and all intensive production systems ditched, that factory production of food must stop, that food manufacturers must never again add anything artificial to what they are making, that supermarkets must be dismantled and the retailing of food put back into the hands of small retailers who operate on a local basis. This is clearly never going to happen.

Although this is not our mess, it appears that it is down to us to clear it up. It falls upon each one of us to make decisions about how we are going to go forward from this point. No one is going to help us except the farmers, growers, producers and small independent retailers that are hanging on by their fingernails waiting for us to come along and help them in return by buying the real, fresh, nutritious food they have to sell. They may be few and far between, but they are there. It is up to us to find them and support them. Without that support, they will disappear, and it will then be another case of 'when it's gone, it's gone.'

FINDING REAL FOOD

Finding real food is not difficult. What is difficult is changing our mindset. We have grown so accustomed to being able to pop into the supermarket and buy everything we want under one roof – change can be difficult. It is too easy to say, "I just *have* to shop at the supermarket, there is nowhere else." A change of mindset moves us from 'the glass is half empty' to 'the glass is half full'. And it can be done, believe me.

One day, many years ago, I was enjoying myself immensely at the Puck Fair in Killorglin, County Kerry. Towards the end of the weekend, I found myself somewhat short of money, and thus threatened by the horns of a dilemma, as you might say. My available funds at that late hour on the last day of the festival would buy me either half an ounce of tobacco or another pint of Guinness. Grappling with this problem for a few minutes brought me to a point where a decision had to be made. I concluded that tobacco tastes the same anywhere, but Guinness tastes better in Ireland. So I happily spent the last of my money on a pint of Guinness, conceding quite readily that I could do without the tobacco. I haven't smoked since.

I use this story to illustrate a point. We all receive information about the world in which we live and from that information create our own notion of ourselves. We tell ourselves that we like to have a cigarette with a drink, or we tell ourselves that we can't get going in the morning without two cups of coffee. Or perhaps we are convinced that we do not have the time to source real food. These are all beliefs that we construct for ourselves in order to build stability. We like to know who we are. But it is important to differentiate between a fundamental characteristic and an attitude. An attitude can be changed, just like I changed my attitude to smoking.

It can be useful to do a little soul-searching to discover just what you think are the most important priorities in your life and what you really think about food. As far as the food is concerned, this little 10-point plan might help.

1. **Stop for a moment and think about where you are today**. It is difficult to know where you are going unless you know where you are starting from. Are you happy with what you eat? Are there things you would like to change about the food that comes into your household? What you do today and how you eat today can be different tomorrow if you understand what differences you would like to put into place.

2. **Think about how you obtain your food**. Every one of us has to eat, but how we get our hands on food might differ depending on what is available in terms of shops. Whether we live in a rural or an urban area, we might consider our choice limited. But ask yourself, is it just a question of going for the easiest option? Have you really explored all the possibilities?

3. **Decide what changes you would like to make to the food you buy**. Are you happy with what you buy? Do you think it is fresh, nutritious and healthy, or are there aspects of your food that you are concerned about? With a new attitude, you can start to make those changes straightaway. From the very next time you shop for food, you could be shopping in a more rewarding way.

4. **Decide how you are going to source your food**. Once you have decided what changes you want to make, you must think about where your food is going to come from in the future. Your new positive attitude will help you overcome objections about the inconvenience of creating a new shopping regime. Because you have adopted a new attitude, sourcing of food stops being a chore and becomes fun.

5. **Consider the ethical implications of food buying**. When you make positive changes to your food buying, you will see food differently. You will begin to understand the precious resource that real food is, and how it has been exploited and debased for commercial gain. Raised awareness of food brings with it a conscience. There is no such thing as a free lunch, and everything comes with a price that may not be immediately obvious. That chicken you used to buy for the price of a pint? Its true cost is reflected in the misery that the bird endures in its short life, in the cheap feed it has been raised on, in the damage that this sick meat will do to you if you eat it. A bird raised in freedom, pecking and scratching the ground and allowed to roam freely might cost you four times the price of the rock-bottom supermarket broiler, but it is real, tasty and nutritious – and you will be paying the farmer that raised it a fair price. And then there are the other questions raised with standard supermarket food – what is its provenance; how many miles has it been transported; how is it packaged? Ultimately, our food choices affect the whole planet. Awareness of the significance of this leads on to better food choices – ethical as well as nutritional. Better ethical choice equals better health equals better justice. Where do we go from there? As justice increases, so civilisation finds peace. And all this could come about if we make the right choices about our food. . .

6. **Think fresh and seasonal**. It is a natural consequence of becoming involved in the sourcing of real food that you will find yourself shopping locally, even if 'locally' means the guy down the road, or in the next county, who organises a weekly veg box scheme. Thinking locally raises your awareness of the change of season, because local, fresh and seasonal are all part of the same thing. You will soon be put off by the supermarket policy of 'everything all the time' because you

will understand that such a policy, paying no homage to the seasons, is by definition not local, and therefore carries the stigma of food miles, agri-business and the taint of pesticides. Seasonality, and the locally produced fresh real food that defines it, stimulates the palate as well as the imagination, and puts the excitement back into food.

7. **Sharpen your cooking skills**. Whatever your skills in the kitchen, you will find a new desire to use them. The excitement of working with real food tends to whet your culinary ability as well as your appetite. Like going through an invisible door to a parallel universe, you will find that you really want to do this food justice. You will be hungry for knowledge as well as for those saltmarsh lamb chops you found at the Farmers' Market. At the risk of sounding like an evangelist, I can tell you that the feeling of having seen the light will make you a little euphoric, and you will want more of it.

8. **Develop your interpersonal skills**. Sourcing real food takes you out of the supermarket and into the town, the farm shop or the Farmers' Market. As your taste buds and health respond to good nutrition, so your interest in food is recharged. You will want to ask questions, so you will end up in conversations with producers, growers, farmers and the owners of independent shops. The energy of human interaction is a powerful stimulant, especially when the talk is of real food, cooking eating and sharing. The latter is what you will want to be doing with all this wonderful food you are finding. If you have children, get them involved. Make real food a real experience. Take your kids to the market – make it an adventure. You might be surprised by how well they react to it. Before you know, family meals will be top of the agenda again. Real food brings people together like nothing else I know.

9. **Get off the treadmill**. Now would be a good time to reassess your priorities. The alternative to the treadmill is personal freedom. You may well find that, in common with an alarming number of people, you have been getting busier and busier, filling your life with all of those things that we are told by big players, major advertisers and lifestyle magazines are absolutely essential to our happiness and wellbeing. This crazy merry-go-round is not going to stop, but you can get off without breaking a leg. Try it. Turn your back on the hype for a few days. Disappear into the wilds, seek out some real food in an area you have not explored, sit on a cliff top and watch the sun go down. Let your mind be still. And then ask yourself what is really important in life. Is it really the latest technological gadget, the review section of the Sunday paper

or another flight to an exotic location? If it is, go back to Point 1 and start again.

10. **Make life fun.** Food is fundamental to our survival. Cheap and nasty won't do it though. Nutritionally depleted, pesticide-laced, industrial food does not hit the spot. All it does is make us sick, whether that sickness manifests itself as a headache, asthma or cancer. Turning your back on this rubbish and treating your body to real food changes your whole perspective. You will see things differently. Step through the looking glass and enter the real world. Shake off the cloying grip of those who see you only as a consumer. To the insatiable corporations, you are no more than the primary route to profit. Put yourself out of their reach – at least the ones that try to sell you debased food. Don't let them have your soul. Go off-grid and regain your life. You have the power to say 'no' to the world that has been created for you. And all that is required is a decision to reject imitation food in favour of the real thing. Believe me, that's when life becomes real fun.

Once we can see the big picture of how our whole food industry works, it is easy to understand that real food is rarely, if ever, found in a supermarket. A bold statement, I hear you cry. But not unfounded, I respond. In the pages of this book, I have tried to throw at least some light on this situation. Much more has been written elsewhere about supermarket practices, notably in *Not on the Label*, by Felicity Lawrence and in *Shopped*, Joanna Blythman's grim exposé of the darker side of supermarket operation.

I am not the dedicated investigative journalist that Ms Blythman is. I am just an ordinary person trying to stay healthy whilst attempting to make sense of it all and find the threads of truth that run through the fabric of propaganda that clothes all corporate activity. Though I understand perfectly well that anecdotal reference is frowned upon in works of non-fiction, I believe that human stories carry their own relevance, so I am going to tell you one now.

Recently, a young couple near us have taken the brave step of renting a couple of fields from a local farmer so that they can set up a small business growing vegetables and keeping a few chickens for eggs. Resourceful and enterprising, they looked around for some customers in the retail trade in order to secure regular weekly orders. Hearing that Waitrose were making noises about their 'buy local' policy ('local' being defined as 'within a 30-mile radius') and publicising this heavily in the media, they decided to approach Waitrose with a view to selling eggs from their 200 chickens. Waitrose has a branch in Monmouth and another in Malvern, both within 30 miles of this farm, so it was with some confidence that the approach was made. The answer was a shock. Waitrose were not prepared to deal with them because their flock of hens is too small. In fact, Waitrose stipulated that they would buy eggs only from a supplier that has a 'free range' flock of

3000 birds or more, because their central distribution system was not geared to cope with anything smaller. When challenged on their 'buy local' promotion, the response from Waitrose was that this did not apply across the board but to certain items only, and generally not to fresh produce. At least that saved our intrepid pair from having to ask Waitrose if they would be interested in taking some vegetables . . .

What this illustrates, apart from the fact that this young couple still have much to learn about the way supermarkets work, is precisely the fact that these retailers are too big to operate on a truly local basis. The comment about fresh produce in fact proves the point. A retailer who works via a central distribution system finds it very difficult to keep fresh produce looking good because, quite frankly, it does not last. 'Fresh' should mean fresh out of the ground. If you grow your own vegetables at home, you will know that once you have taken something out of the ground it will begin to wilt and deteriorate almost immediately.

In finding real food, therefore, this is the first rule of thumb – keep it local. How local is 'local'? Well, ideally, your own back garden, but obviously only for fruit and vegetables. For those of you lucky enough to have enough space for a couple of sheep and a dairy cow, life could get really exciting, but let's assume that most of us will be limiting our back garden efforts to the growing of fruit and veg. It is surprising just how much can be grown in a relatively small space. There was of course a time when many people had a small vegetable patch somewhere in the garden, but vegetable gardening diminished in popularity as food generally became cheaper. Now that 'cheap' food is being recognised for what it is, vegetable gardening is enjoying a tentative renaissance. Urban dwellers as well as their rural cousins are showing an interest and, to meet this growing demand, there are a number of very good books out there that deal with vegetable gardening in small spaces, including patios, roof gardens and even window boxes. When I lived in a flat in Malvern, I had no garden at all, but I had a fire escape outside one of my windows. It was a bit limited, but I still managed to grow a good selection of herbs out there. Better than nothing.

Much can be made of container growing. Most people will be familiar with the idea of growing herbs in a pot, but this can be extended to salad plants and other green leaf vegetables such as spinach. Container gardening is not limited to leafy plants. To name a few more, broad beans, peas, courgettes, chilli peppers, onions and radishes are all happy in containers. Also, root vegetables, such as carrots, beetroot and turnips, can be grown successfully in pots with a depth and width of at least 30cms (any smaller and there is a danger of drying out too quickly). Even potatoes can be grown in an old tub on the patio, with tomatoes and soft fruit, such as strawberries, in hanging baskets. A wigwam of canes on top of a large pot will let you grow climbing plants such as runner beans. This is not a book on gardening, so I will not go into no further detail, but do browse your local bookshop or the internet for more information about container or small space gardening.

If creating your own vegetable plot is not an option, you will need to find a local supplier for fruit and vegetables. You may be surprised at how easy this can be. In Malvern, I was lucky enough to have a very good independent greengrocer just up the street. There were also two independent butcher's shops within the same walking distance. In other towns and cities, this is not always the case, but sometimes we don't really see what is right under our noses. When we first set up business at Aspen House, Sally and I regularly passed the door of a little veg shop in Ross-on-Wye on our way to the local supermarket. We hardly gave the place a second glance, blinkered as we were into believing that everything we needed was in the supermarket. Then one day, we stopped long enough to look in through the window of this greengrocer's shop. It looked well stocked. We went in, and were greeted by the owner, a lovely aroma of sweet fruit and the kind of earthy smell that is given off by bags of fresh potatoes – something I hadn't smelt since my Grandpa used to harvest his main crop potatoes to store in an earth clamp to last him through the winter.

Much of the standard supermarket range was available in this shop, but there was more besides. Fresh hen and duck eggs from local individual suppliers, for instance, plus turkey eggs and goose eggs in season – not something you are ever going to find in Tesco or Asda. The vegetables were interesting too. With a long list of local suppliers, from wholesalers to private individuals with surplus from their own gardens, this shop had many unusual varieties on show. Depending on the season, we have found kohl rabi, rainbow chard and yellow beetroot. As autumn rolls out, there might be a dozen varieties of English apples in here, at least three main crop potato varieties (King Edward, Caesar and Sante) as well as four kinds of squash – Turban, Queensland Blue, Crown Prince and Red Onion.

Unexpectedly, we had discovered a little goldmine. Though there is often a bag or so of fruit and vegetables breathing their last and tucked way in a corner somewhere, thus giving the place a kind of sad, untidy air, this is part of its charm. It has a sort of Aladdin's Cave feel to it, and we are careful to have a good look around when we go in, just to make sure we haven't missed anything. We soon built up a rapport with the owners of the shop, Colin and Margaret, and now when we pop in, Colin is quite likely to say, "I've got something special for you today." All he is doing of course is being aware of the needs of his customers when his suppliers tell him what's available. Such service is to be found only in this one-to-one situation.

Just up the road from Colin's greengrocery is our local organic shop. Apart from fruit and vegetables, the place is stocked with meat and dairy products, pulses, grains, tins and jars, as well as organic wines, spirits, beers and ciders. Other shops we frequent in town are the wholefood shop and the local delicatessen, each run as independent enterprises and each careful in their buying policies, so that we as customers can be assured that we are getting the best of what's available. A very high proportion of what is sold in the little deli is locally produced, including wonderful charcuterie, bacon, ham, pies, cakes and beverages. We are also fortunate in having a choice of two traditional butcher's shops in town.

We realise that not everyone is lucky enough to have this kind of choice, but we also know that the two of us were practically oblivious to this choice when we were doing all our shopping in the supermarket. Now that this is no longer the case, we can see just how mesmerising is the pull of the big retailers and their powerfully persuasive advertising, the kind of advertising the small independents cannot ever contemplate. My observation is that all is fair in love and war and business, yet there is no sense of fairness when the advertising might of the Big Four is compared to the puny efforts of the independents. Supermarkets have marketing budgets that run into millions – the local shop does not have a marketing budget at all, having to rely instead on being able to offer a good service and a good product to passing customers, who might then become regular visitors.

The small shops can survive only if we support them – they cannot afford to splash out on sophisticated advertising campaigns to 'create demand' like the big boys do. What is important is that they are there at all. All we have to do is to stop rushing for a moment, look around and we will see them. Sometimes they are well hidden, but they are there. In Hereford city centre, for example, which is currently served by two Tesco stores (one in the centre and a huge one two miles out) a huge Morrison's, a huge Sainsbury's and a huge Asda, as well as a Lidl and an Aldi, there are still four independent butcher's shops operating. In addition, there are at least three greengrocer's shops within the same radius, as well as two very good delis, not including the Polski Delikatesy that opened last year. Plus there are two wholefood shops in the city where most of the produce is organic, and this includes fruit, vegetables, meat, dairy and the usual pulses, nuts, grains and seeds. This may not be the case where you live, but it is certain that, in any given town or city, there will be more independent shops than are immediately apparent. All we have to do is to seek them out. Becoming aware of exactly what is around your locality is the first step in adopting a new approach to food shopping. You will begin to see things differently, to focus your attention on the alternatives and on how best to re-adjust your daily schedule in such a way that sourcing real food becomes a pleasure. If the French and Italians can do it, so can we.

Having said that, locating independent greengrocer's shops can be a chore in some places. It can also be a disappointment. So often, the independent greengrocer is no more than a dingy corner shop, run by someone who is hanging on to business by the fingernails. Sadly, it is so often the case that these small retail outlets are often no more than the shop of last resort and, as such, can be a pale imitation of the supermarket up the road, but more expensive and rather poorly stocked with cheap goods from the cash-and-carry. The challenge is to find the few gems that are left in this sea of sad shops. They are there, but often hard to spot. If there isn't one in your neighbourhood, don't despair. Just move on to the next item on your checklist.

Generally easier to find than the local upbeat greengrocer is the Farmers' Market. Again you may be lucky in that your city, town or village will have one. If it does, chances are you will know where it is, although you may have to do a bit of research to find out when it is. If it does not have one, there may be one not too far away that you can investigate. Going to a Farmers' Market is well worth the trouble, but you have to understand what these markets are all about. Go with an open mind and be part of a more rewarding shopping experience. Granted, you will not be able to just pick something off the shelf and take it to the checkout, but you will be able to talk directly to the person who grew the vegetables, made the cheese or reared the pigs that provided the bacon that is on show for you to buy.

I am not being patronising when I say that this can be a little difficult for some people. Sadly, many of us have got out of the habit of talking to people in shops. This applies particularly to food shops. We have become so used to taking things off the shelf, putting it in the basket or trolley and taking it to the checkout, that we no longer need the facility of actually discussing with anyone the food we are buying. Talking to other people, however, is an essential human activity, and talking to other people about real food is very rewarding, even educating.

A Farmers' Market is a key source of real food. It may not necessarily carry an organic label, but the produce will be prime quality. If for no other reason, it will be because the person selling the produce is selling directly to you, so he is not going to con you. If you want to know something about the product, you will be given a straight answer. There is no point in being anything but totally honest and transparent. In a one-to-one dialogue, integrity is essential, because human instinct in this situation is generally acute enough to detect anything that does not feel right. Look at it from the producer's point of view. He is, say, a pig breeder outside the streamlined retail system. Why? Probably because his pigs are special and he wants to treat them in a special way. They may well be rare breed pigs, but even if they were standard British bacon pigs, the chances are that anyone selling at a Farmers' Market is doing so because he does not want to be part of that intensive industry in which he has to abuse his animals, treat them inhumanely, sell them like a commodity cash crop and then end up being paid virtually nothing for them when they go to slaughter. He is at the Farmers' Market because he believes in the principles of good husbandry and because he wants to get the best possible return on his investment of time, money and care. And the best way he can do that is to sell directly to you and cut out all the middlemen.

What a fantastic opportunity that gives you, me and all the people who buy from farmers like this. The food chain is as short as it can be. We don't have to worry about traceability because we are talking directly to the farmer. We can ask him anything. We can discuss what the animals have been eating, where they live, how many to the acre, how many times the vet calls. Whatever we want to know about the product, the person selling it to you will be pleased to tell us. From our experience, they will go as far as to show you around their farms, delighted that you are interested enough to want to make the visit.

Something odd seems to happen when you take to the real food route. Although it seemingly costs more than the factory equivalent, nutritious real food is more satisfying, so ultimately we spend less. Figures are available for average weekly food expenditure in this country through organisations such as Defra and the Office for National Statistics but, because they are based on averages right across the UK buying public, it is difficult to establish a true figure for, say, a family of four. However, the indications are that a typical family of four will be spending between £65 and £120 per week on food. What Sally and I spend at Aspen House compares favourably to this. Buying the very best of all local produce, the total amount we spend on food, for our own consumption and the needs of the B&B, varies between 15% and 20% of our total outgoings. In 2006, this figure was still below £150 per week, and that includes all the food needs of a B&B that caters for dinner parties as well as breakfasts. This may not be the last word in accurate statistical reporting, but we see the figures in our account book, so it is good enough for us. And when our accountant says to us, "Your food expenditure is remarkably low – is it all here?" then we are both convinced that not shopping in supermarkets is a money saving exercise.

If you do not have a Farmers' Market that you can get to, don't despair. Try seeking out a Food Festival. You may be lucky enough to find one near you, and of course there are new ones springing up year by year. A Food Festival is really no more than a giant Farmers' Market, with no doubt many stalls there that are local. Other stalls may be run by experienced festival retailers who, although they may not be local, will almost certainly have some kind of mail order system in place so that you can buy what they are selling once you get back home. So try a Food Festival. You will get a lot of fun out of it and you will meet some really passionate people.

Also, there are veg box schemes everywhere, with new ones seemingly springing up every week. A new one started up in our area less than twelve months ago and now, despite the fact that this was in competition with other established schemes, their business has grown to the extent that they believe it warrants the purchase of a second delivery van. Veg box suppliers are keen to get fresh vegetables to you and, like the producers at the Farmers' Markets, they are very willing to help in any way they can. There is a myth out there that all you get in a veg box is a few gritty carrots and a limp cabbage infested with caterpillars. This of course is not necessarily true. The whole point of a veg box is to get over the problem of vegetables going limp once they have been pulled from the ground. Those who operate box schemes today are generally pretty efficient in getting vegetables to their destination in prime condition. Anyone not doing this will lose customers, so it has been a matter of some urgency to eliminate logistical problems.

Veg boxes are, by definition, seasonal, so anyone using a veg box scheme will face the same problems as someone who grows vegetables at home – what to do with yet another batch of courgettes. On the face of it, this might look like a problem, but it quickly becomes part of the fun. For those whose appetite for cooking has been jaded by the predictable range of same-old fruit and veg languishing in the supermarket, the challenge of coping with a veg box can be very stimulating. Or indeed downright scary. But think positive. Sometimes, the supplier will give you ideas about what to do with the contents of the box (and, no, it won't include the option of chucking the lot in the river). Failing that, there are some excellent seasonally based cookery books in the shops or there is information the internet. One of the best sites we have come across is the one that goes by the maxim of 'a veg box is for life, not just for Christmas'. Check out www.vegboxdiary.wordpress.com for yourself. You will not be disappointed. Even if you have never seen a veg box and are never likely to be the proud recipient of one, this site is worth a look. It might even change your mind if you are still experiencing some reluctance in embracing the idea of vegetables being delivered to your door. This is not the only site dedicated to the challenge of cooking the contents of a veg box. More information can be found in the Appendix at the end of this book.

Some veg box schemes, our local one for instance, offer more than just vegetables. Ours brings us unpasteurised milk and Ecover refills for the kitchen. Others offer farm eggs. Those with refrigerated vans might even offer you meat from the local farm. Generally speaking, though, for this level of choice and more, the Farm Shop is where you need to be. The true farm shop has grown out of a need for farmers to find a way of selling that actually makes them a bit of money. Faced with only one other option, that of selling their produce through a wholesaler into the retail trade, they needed to revive the idea of a farm shop or just give up. Many of them do – dozens a month – and Britain is heading for a huge disaster as a result of it. Neglect for farming and the rural foundation to our society is part of the future chaos we face unless we arrest its downward progress now. So it is good to see the farm shop offering us a choice of shopping venue.

Granted, not everywhere has a farm shop, especially right there in the heart of the urban jungle, and once more it is up to us to find them and support them. If your town or city does not have a farm shop, or indeed a Farmers' Market, close investigation might reveal a wholefood shop that is selling a good range of the kind of products normally found in either. Our local organic grocer's shop has freezers full of top quality meats from Graig Farm in Wales, as well as a very good selection of fruit, vegetables and dairy products. In Cheltenham, to quote one more example, the Natural Grocery Store in Bath Street sells all things organic and even runs a mail order service. And that brings me to the internet, a growing source of all things, good and bad alike, but a great source of superb real food. There is no need to dwell on this. Anyone who is interested in sourcing the best food around but has a problem finding any serious shops in their own locality, will find the whole world just waiting for an online order. To take some of the graft out of this particular exercise, the Appendix at the end of the book lists the major sources of real food as well as a number of other sites that are worth exploring for their wealth of useful information, material and links for further investigation.

REAL FOOD – THE ULTIMATE SUPERFOOD

When it comes to superfoods, we should be clear on one thing. In this heavily hyped, contradictory and confusing world of ours, 'superfood' has become a bit of a buzz word. It can be found in the same box of random phrases as 'low-fat', 'low calorie', 'cholesterol-free', and 'no added sugar'. All four of these phrases, along with others like them, are virtually meaningless. In the context in which they are generally used, that is to say with reference to the factory food we eat, they are at best irrelevant, and at worst misleading or even dangerous.

The word 'superfood', though diluted through the same misuse, does at least refer to actual foodstuffs. But what constitutes a superfood? In a Daily Mail article, written on 22nd December 2005, a top ten of superfoods lists the following: apples, baked beans, broccoli, olive oil, wholegrain seeded bread, salmon, tea, yoghurt, bananas and brazil nuts. But the article makes no differentiation between items off that list bought in the supermarket or bought from the local farmer. Apples are top of the list, but which apples? Under-ripe, pesticide-tainted, colour-graded, over-waxed Granny Smiths from South Africa, or new season's English varietal apples picked in prime condition from an organic orchard and sold at the local farm shop?

Then we have baked beans. Does the author mean any old baked beans, even Tesco value beans, dosed up with too much sugar and practically devoid of nutrition, or some home cooked organic haricot beans? And what about the bananas and the salmon? There is no discussion in the article about whether or not you should avoid bananas sold through supermarkets by the dominant companies in the industry, yet such bananas are routinely subjected to highly toxic chemicals (even after picking, in order to keep them blemish-free in transportation). These include substances such as Aldicarb (potentially lethal to humans at alarmingly low levels) Chorpyrifos (described by the World Health Organisation as 'hazardous') and a pesticide that goes by the simple name of DBCP, an innocuous epithet for a chemical that can damage the reproductive systems of female plantation workers and cause mutagenic effects in their children. The banana industry is a very heavy user of chemicals, and bananas are particularly good at retaining residues of the chemical cocktail in which they are bathed. However, the article in the Daily Mail makes no comment on this, thus implying that all bananas are superfoods. I suggest that the author has done insufficient research into the different grades of foods available, and that avoiding the issue diminishes the value of what is being said about so-called superfoods.

Take salmon, for instance. It is indeed a fantastic food and a good source of essential oils, but not if it is farmed. The market, especially the volume retail market, is now flooded with low-grade farmed salmon. It has gone from the king of fish, scarce, prized and seasonal, to a commonplace commodity food with a ubiquitous presence all year round in practically every branch of every supermarket. You don't need me to tell you that, in order for this to happen, factory farming has had to take place on a massive scale. Any advantage as a source of Omega-3 is quickly wiped out by the dominance of Omaga-6 and by the presence of toxins and antibiotic growth hormones lurking in the flesh of what are effectively sick fish. Can this really be described as superfood? I think not.

Moving on to another branch of the media, television, we find that Amanda Hamilton on GMTV lists the following as superfoods: spirulina, bentonite clay, wheat grass and acai berries, all of which can be beneficial. Patrick Holford, the well-known nutritional guru, and a person for whom I have a good deal of admiration, also has his say on GMTV, adding aloe vera, garlic, shiitake mushrooms and soya to his list. Gillian McKeith, a different kind of guru, advocates the use of goji berries, preferably with her own packaging. All of these are examples of how we are guided into the realms of exotic extras that we can add to our diet in order to boost its efficacy. Generally speaking, there is nothing wrong with this idea, although it might well open up arguments about the food miles involved in putting these exotics within our reach. However, many of those who would advise us to supplement our diet with these so-called superfoods make no reference to the fact that their efficacy will be reduced if the basic elements of our diet – vegetables, fish, meat, etc. – are of poor quality in the first place.

Another thing that is often ignored by those who make pronouncements on what we should eat is that we are all individuals, so it is inadvisable to generalise. Taking soya as an example, many people are intolerant to soya. Instances of this intolerance are increasing, partially at least due to the production methods used in growing this bean. After maize, it is the one commercial crop that we should be extremely wary of. Mostly it is tainted with toxins and can even be contaminated with GM strains, in addition to which it is now a commercial additive, appearing in many guises in industrialised foodstuffs, particularly as the emulsifier, soya lechitin. Making sweeping statements such as, "Soya is a superfood," is misleading and potentially harmful to many people, including me.

One thing that is more certain about labelling something a 'superfood' is this – it will increase sales. The success story of the original 'superfood', blueberries, is legendary, and over recent years many foods have been given this accolade in a cynical attempt to boost revenue. The list runs to nearly 100 items and includes, as well as blueberries, spinach, avocado, sweet potatoes, tomatoes, oats, red wine, pomegranate juice, turkey, dark chocolate, brown rice, almonds, rhubarb, watercress and walnuts. The EU has recognised that much of the hype that surrounds this idea may be spurious, and new legislation has clamped down on the indiscriminate use of the word 'superfood'. From 1st July 2007, the word has been banned from all foods unless it can be proved beyond doubt that the food in question has qualities that clearly elevate it to this superior status. It can be predicted with some certainty that those who stand to gain most from the increased sales which the use of the term generates will quickly find a way around this new legislation, but nevertheless it is encouraging that some attempt has been made to curb what is undoubtedly an inappropriate use of the word. However, the fact remains that there is no official definition of the term 'superfood' and that big companies use it simply as a marketing tool. We can quickly see that we should not allow ourselves to be taken in by over-zealous marketing, but should look intelligently at the food available to us and decide for ourselves what we are going to eat.

Superfoods do not necessarily come in pricey little packets or in the shape of an exotic, rare and expensive fruit. No doubt some, or perhaps all, of these are good for us, but none of them works as an instant fix. One cannot simply live off poor quality food on a long term basis and counteract the effects of this by chewing a few goji berries from time to time. There is, however, one type of super food that is essential and will always do you good, and that is clean, honest, fresh and nutritious food, the stuff that I am calling real food. If the food you eat is like this and excludes or limits those products of the food industry that damage your carefully balanced internal systems, then you should have no need to seek out exotics like spirulina and acai berries.

The biggest challenge we all face today is to ensure that what we eat is in the main wholesome. I say 'in the main' because I believe that it would be virtually impossible to live a normal life without ingesting, either accidentally, or deliberately, something that is not entirely nutritious. No one wants to become a martyr to a cause. All any of us wants is to stay healthy, and we can stay healthy so long as our diet is fundamentally nutritious. The more nutritious it is, the healthier we should remain, leaving aside for the moment other issues about lifestyle and the way this impinges on our wellbeing. By the same argument, of course, we will fall into ill health if our diet is not nutritious. The main difficulty is in finding wholesome food through the mainstream outlets, with 80% of our food retailing in the hands of the supermarkets. I sometimes think it would be easier to walk through a minefield. The increasing level of intervention of industrialists in the production and subsequent processing of our food means that it is no longer possible to trust anything that we buy through any retail outlets other than certain small independent shops. That is a depressing but inescapable fact.

Even though legislation now calls for a paperchase of information that is supposed to ensure traceability and provenance of all our foods, this is a laughably inadequate system. It means nothing to the consumer, other than the fact that some sort of finger-pointing follow-up might be possible if someone should contract food poisoning. It seems to be designed principally to let government off the hook. How convenient for modern governments to remain in denial about the dreadful state of our agriculture and our food industry when they have provided legislation to ensure 'full traceability'. So, if you know that the meat in your chicken ready-meal has just come into the UK aboard a container ship that has brought it all the way from Thailand or South America, then you have no one else to blame but yourself if you contract the latest deadly strain of E-coli. But, under normal circumstances, how would you know that your meat has entered the country in a container ship? The problem is that understanding all there is to learn about the provenance of our foodstuffs is a complex issue. So it is difficult to know where any food comes from unless you can talk directly to the supplier. The fewer links there are in the chain between us and our producers, the easier it is to know what it is we are eating. Sad but true. However, if our health is important to us, we have to make the effort to source real food. Real super food.

Sourcing real food can be difficult at first, until we establish a new picture of what is available through independent retailers, and then we are able to re-draw the map and food sourcing becomes really enjoyable. But we must be prepared to think laterally, because we are up against an entrenched culture. The received wisdom of the last half a century is that anything to do with the finding, cooking and eating of food is at best a drudge and at worst a complete waste of the kind of precious time that could be available for the real pleasures of life, such as shopping, TV, exotic holidays and more shopping. This is a perversion of human nature, and it is a crime that the status of food has been reduced to no more than this, and that its perceived value is reflected in the rock bottom prices trumpeted by the supermarkets. To kick against such received wisdom brings back the thrill we all felt as adolescents when we stood up against the authority of our parents and teachers. So try it. Get that feeling back. Refuse to accept the claim that big business and weak-willed governments have all the answers. Be radical. Do something about taking charge of your own life. Don't let marketing hype tell you what to do, what to wear, what to drive and what to eat. You are not a number, even though big business wants you to be. Big business is all about numbers. Don't give them yours.

Real food is a wake-up call. Real food is real and very very powerful. Real food puts us in touch with ourselves and the world of nature around us. It is a source of essential nourishment but, more than this, it helps us to understand how we fit into the holistic picture of this tiny planet.

To eat real food, we have seen that it is necessary to think seasonal and local, and even grow our own. This brings us back into the rhythm of nature. It can show us that we are out of step with nature. We are arrogant where we should be humble, we are destructive where we should be constructive, we impose ourselves on the order of nature and have the temerity to suggest that we can do better, that we can create a more efficient order than that which we have inherited. We have, through this arrogance, created an unnatural world and made ourselves into unnatural beings, propped up by an unnatural diet. Like the soil in which we grow our plants, the animals that feed off the land and the crops we eat, we are terminally sick.

To eat real food is to regain some of what we have lost. It is one step in the direction of regaining a place in the natural scheme of things, a place that will soon be lost to us altogether if we continue on our present course.

Real food reminds us of who we are and how we should behave. Going back just a few generations shows us people who lived by nature, people who, like the birds and animals around them, took full advantage of the abundance of summer in order to sustain themselves through the winter. We would do well to remember that this is the true order of things, that getting through the winter months was something that involved a different outlook, a more peaceful approach, the ability to look upon life with a natural eye. As the birds, animals and the plants they feed on slow down with the approach of winter, so we would have done the same. With no fields to plough and no crops to sow, winter would have been a quieter time of the year. Go back a few hundred years and even the care of stock was wound down to a much lower level. Every living thing would have survived through the winter at a lower ebb, drawing on reserves built up in the summer in order to sustain the body until the first stirrings of spring.

Today, we have circumvented all this. We have put ourselves outside the system. We live every day the same, winter or summer. Yet nature will have her revenge, bring us down with colds, flu and other ailments as we battle through the winter trying to maintain levels of summer energy. The only way we can do this is to prop up our systems with drugs, while we go to work with coughs, streaming noses and an inappropriate bravado.

Change is vital, and it starts with each one of us. We are all in this together, and we have only this planet to sustain us all, but the change starts with you. It's your life, your health and your future – so make a change, however small. You might make a point of trying out the local grocer next time you are on your way to the supermarket, or popping into the local deli for some artisan cheese. Or buy yourself a breadmaker and some decent flour. Or put your name down for an allotment. Perhaps you might think big and decide to get off the wheel, move to the country and grow vegetables for a living. It doesn't really matter what you do, but do something. If every one of us does something, the tide will turn. If every one of us adds our voice, those distant murmurings that you can hear will become a roar of protest against the limitation of our choice and the adulteration of our food.

A return to real food might just remind us of who we are and what the true essence of life is really all about. It might put us back into rhythm with nature and allow us to feel comfortable with that idea. Knowing that we are, or should be, part of the natural order, might even put us in tune with nature once more. Thus humbled, we will cancel our contract with the devil and regain our soul. We will use our inimitable skills, our huge resources of knowledge and our great technological ability to work with nature, not against her, and help nurse her, as well as ourselves, back to health.

APPENDIX : FINDING REAL FOOD

Details of those suppliers and other organisations listed below are correct at the time of going to press, but please be aware that this is a rapidly changing industry, and more suppliers come on board as demand for real food grows. To find the most up-to-date information, the internet is invaluable. As information changes, many of these sites are updated accordingly, especially the directory sites. The internet is a very effective tool, so please use it.

Organic box schemes, local producers, etc
Big Barn, College Farm, Great Barford, Bedfordshire MK 44 3JJ, 01234 871005, www.bigbarn.co.uk
UK's No 1 local food website, helping people to find good, safe, accountable food from local sources.

Farmers' Market
National Farmers' Retail & Markets Association (FARMA), 12 Southgate Street, Winchester SO23 9EF, 0845 45 88 420, www.farma.org.uk
Also www.farmshopping.net and www.farmersmarkets.net
FARMA is a co-operative of farmers, producers selling on a local scale and Farmers' Markets organisers.

Slow Food UK
3 Alliance Court, Eco Park Road, Ludlow, Shropshire SY8 1FB, 01584 879599, www.slowfood.org.uk
Part of a growing international organisation dedicated to the principles of real food. Join up to meet like minded people.

Fruit and vegetables
Abel & Cole, 16 Waterside Way, Plough Lane, Wimbledon London SW17 0HB, 08452 62 62 62, www.abel-cole.co.uk

Farmaround Organics, The Old Bakery, Mercury Road, Richmond, North Yorkshire DL10 4TQ, 020 7627 8066, www.farmaround.co.uk

GoodnessDirect, South March, Daventry, Northamptonshire NN11 4PH, 0871 871 6611, www.GoodnessDirect.co.uk

Riverford Organic Vegetables, Wash Barn, Buckfastleigh, Devon TQ11 0LD, 0845 600 2311, www.riverford.co.uk

The Natural Grocery Store, 150-156 Bath Road, Cheltenham, Gloucestershire GL53 7NG, 01242 243737, www.naturalgrocery.co.uk

Meat and Game

Clare's Organics, Freepost, RLZE-KGKT-BJXX, Barney's Barn, Berrycroft, Ashbury, Swindon SN6 8LX, 01793 710810, www.claresorganics.co.uk

Daylesford Organic, Daylesford, Kingham, Gloucestershire GL56 0YG, 01608 731700, www.daylesfordorganic.com

Graig Farm, Dolau, Llandrindod Wells, Powys LD1 5TL, 01597 851655, www.graigfarm.co.uk

Higher Hacknell Farm, Burrington, Umberleigh, Devon EX37 9LX, 01769 560909, www.higherhacknell.co.uk

Sheepdrove Organic Farm, Warren Farm, Lambourn, Berkshire RG17 7UU, 01488 674747, www.sheepdrove.com

Swaddles Organic, Royal Oak, Daventry, Northamptonshire NN11 8QY, 0845 456 1768, www.swaddles.co.uk

The Well Hung Meat Company, Tordean Farm, Dean Prior, Buckfastleigh, Devon TQ11 0LY, 0845 230 3131, www.wellhungmeat.com

Fish & smoked products

Deverill Trout Farm, Longbridge Deverill, Warminster, Wiltshire, 01985 841093, www.purelyorganic.co.uk

Fish 4 Ever, 13 Old Humphrey Avenue, Hastings, East Sussex TN34 3BT, 01424 439352, www.fish-4-ever.org

Fish in a Box, 3 Nova Units, Audley Avenue, Newport, Shropshire TF10 7BX, 01952 820966, www.fishinabox.co.uk

Inverawe Smokehouse, Taynuilt, Argyll PA35 1HU, 01866 822446, www.smokedsalmon.co.uk

Loch Fyne, Clachan, Cairndow, Argyll PA26 8BL, 01499 600470, www.lochfyne.com

Organic Smokehouse, Clunbury Hall, Clunbury, Craven Arms, Shropshire SY7 0HG, 01588 660206, www.organicsmokehouse.com

Beers, ales, cider & wine

Black Isle Organic Beers, Old Allangrange, Munlochy, Ross-shire IV8 8NZ, 01463 811871, www.blackislebrewery.com

Orchard Hive and Vine, 50 Westgate, Leominster, Herefordshire HR6 8SA, 01568 613576, www.orchard-hive-and-vine.co.uk

Festival Wines, 13 Ship Street Gardens, Brighton N1 1AJ, 0800 0242 969, www.festivalwines.co.uk

Freedom Organic Beer, Brothers Brewing, Park Lodge House, Bagots Park Estate, Abbots Bromley, Staffordshire WS15 3ES, 020 8859 0606, www.freedombeer.com

Vintage Roots, Farley Farms, Reading Road, Arborfield, Berkshire RG2 9HT, 0800 980 4992, www.vintageroots.co.uk

Tea and coffee
A Lot of Coffee, Unit 55, Milford Road, Reading RG1 8LG, 0845 094 6498, www.alotofcoffee.co.uk
Café Direct, City Cloisters, 196 Old Street, London EC1V 9FR, 020 7490 9520, www.cafedirect.co.uk

Clipper Teas, Beaminster Business Park, Broadwindsor Road, Beaminster, Dorset DT8 3PR, 01308 863344, www.clipper-teas.com

Hampstead Tea and Coffee Co, P O Box 52474, London NW3 9DA, 020 7431 9393, www.hampsteadtea.com

The Bean Shop, 67 George Street, Perth, Scotland PH1 5LB, 01738 449955, www.thebeanshop.com

Bread
Hobbs House Bakery, Unit 6, Hatters Lane, Chipping Sodbury, Bristol BS37 6AA, 01454 321629, www.hobbshousebakery.co.uk

Joshua's Harvest Store, Gosford Road, Ottery St Mary, Devon EX11 1NU, 01404 815473, www.joshuasharveststore.co.uk

The Metfield Bakery, 23 Charles Wood Road, Dereham, Norfolk NR19 1SX, 01362 695340, www.metfieldbakery.com

The Village Bakery, Edenholme Bakery, Lazonby, Penrith CA10 1BG, 01768 898437, www.village-bakery.com

Storecupboard essentials

To supplement your main grocery items, why not have all your cooking 'essentials' delivered to your door once a month . . . have a look at these websites.

Buxton Foods – www.buxtonfoods.com

Community Foods – www.communityfoods.co.uk

Goodness Direct – www.goodnessdirect.co.uk

Hider – www.hider-foods.co.uk

Meridian Foods – www.meridianfoods.co.uk

Naturally Good Food Ltd – www.goodfooddelivery.co.uk

Real Food Direct – www.realfooddirect.co.uk

Daily Bread Co-operative – www.ecofair.co.uk

Food-buying groups

Here is another way of getting your storecupboard essentials; club together with a bunch of friends and buy from wholesalers . . .

Clearspring – www.clearspring.co.uk

Eostre – www.eostreorganics.co.uk

Essential Trading – www.essential-trading.coop

Organico – www.organico.co.uk

Suma – www.suma.co.uk

BIBLIOGRAPHY

Baillie-Hamilton, Paula, *The Detox Diet*, Michael Joseph, London, 2002

Bakan, Joel, *The Corporation*, Constable, London, 2004

Balfour, Eve, *The Living Soil*, Faber & Faber, London, 1943

Blythman, Joanna, *The Food We Eat*, Michael Joseph, London, 1996

Blythman, Joanna, *Shopped*, Fourth Estate, London, 2004

Blythman, Joanna, *Bad Food Britain*, Fourth Estate, London, 2006

Chaitow, Leon, *Candida Albicans*, Thorsons, London, 1985

Cleave, T L, *The Saccharine Disease*, J Wright & Sons, Bristol, 1974

Clover, Charles, *The End of the Line*, Ebury Press, London, 2004

Dibb, Sue, *What the Label Doesn't Tell You*, Thorsons, London, 1997

Dufty, William, *Sugar Blues*, Warner Books, New York, 1976

Fallon, Sally, *Nourishing Traditions*, New Trends Publishing, Washington DC, 1999

Galbraith, J K, *A History of Economics*, Penguin Group, 1991

Greenwood, Pippa, *Pippa's Organic Kitchen Garden*, Dorling Kindersley, London, 1999

Grohman, Joann, *Keeping a Family Cow*, Coburn Press, Dixfield ME, 2001

Hamaker, John, *The Survival of Civilisation*, Hamaker-Weaver Publishers, 1982

Hanson, J L, *A Textbook of Economics*, Macdonald & Evans, London, 1964

Harvey, Graham, *We Want Real Food*, Constable, London, 2006

Holford, Patrick, *100% Health*, Piatkus, London, 1998

Honoré, Carl, *In Praise of Slow*, Orion, London, 2004

Howard, Sir Albert, *Farming and Gardening for Health or Disease*, Faber & Faber, London, 1943

Hume, Ethel Douglas, *Béchamp or Pasteur*, Daniel, 1932

Humphrys, John, *The Great Food Gamble*, Coronet, London, 2001

Lawrence, Felicity, *Not on the Label*, Penguin, London, 2004

Kendrick, Dr Malcolm, *The Great Cholesterol Con*, John Blake, London, 2007

McCarrison, Sir Robert, *Nutrition and Health*, The McCarrison Society, London, 1982

McTaggart, Lynne, *What Doctors Don't Tell You*, Thorsons, London, 1996

Packard, Vance, *The Hidden Persuaders*, David McKay, New York, 1957

Planck, Nina, *Real Food*, Bloomsbury, New York, 2006

Pollan, Michael, *The Omnivore's Dilemma*, Bloomsbury, London, 2006

Price, Weston A, *Nutrition and Physical Degeneration*, (published by author) Los Angeles, 1939

Rampton, Sheldon and Stauber, John, *Trust Us We're Experts!*, Tarcher Putnam, New York, 2002

Sams, Craig, *The Little Food Book*, Alastair Sawday Publishing, Bristol 2003

Schlosser, Eric, *Fast Food Nation*, Harper Perennial, 2002

Tudge, Colin, *So Shall We Reap*, Penguin, London, 2003

Waddington, Paul, *Seasonal Food*, Eden Project Books, London, 2004

Yeatman, Marwood, *The Last Food of England*, Ebury Press, London, 2007

Yellowlees, Walter, *A Doctor in the Wilderness*, Janus, London, 1993

Yudkin, John, *Pure White and Deadly*, Viking, Harmondsworth, 1986

Websites mentioned in the text.

www.archive.corporatewatch.org Watchdog site for the activities of global corporations

www.farmgarden.org.uk
www.motorwayservices.info
www.pesticidescampaign.co.uk
www.seedsofhealth.co.uk
www.tescocorporate.com
www.tescopoly.org
www.vegboxdiary.wordpress.com
www.westonaprice.org

INDEX

f you enjoyed *The Food Maze*, perhaps you would like to recommend it to others. And we'll pay you to do it . . .

At the Real Life Book Company, we believe in human values, not the anonymity of the corporation. So you will not find this book in big retailers such as Waterstones, W H Smith or supermarkets. Our ethos is also to aim for quality not quantity. We print small runs, identify those who might be interested in the book, and then distribute it through independent shops and individual recommendation.

If you know of anyone who might be interested in buying a copy of this book, we will happily pay you a commission on every sale you generate. Just get in touch with us via any of the options below, and we will explain how it works. And there's no catch, by the way!

Contact details:

Sally Dean or Rob Elliott

Tel:
01432 840353

Post:
Aspen House, Hoarwithy, Herefordshire HR2 6QP

Email:
sallyandrob@reallifepublishing.co.uk